EXPONENTIAL ORGANIZATIONS EXO 2.0

The New Playbook for 10x Growth & Impact

Also by Salim Ismail

Exponential Organizations
Exponential Transformation

Also by Peter H. Diamandis

The Future is Faster than you Think
Bold
Abundance
Life Force

Also by Michael S. Malone

The Big Score
Exponential Organizations
Team Genius
The Autonomous Revolution

EXPONENTIAL ORGANIZATIONS EXO 2.0

The New Playbook for 10x Growth & Impact

**SALIM ISMAIL
PETER H. DIAMANDIS
AND MICHAEL S. MALONE**

FOREWORD BY RAY KURZWEIL
CURATED BY THE OPENEXO COMMUNITY

ethos
collective

Published by Ethos Collective™
PO Box 43, Powell, OH 43065
www.ethoscollective.vip

LCCN: 2023910571
Paperback: 978-1-63680-178-0
Hardcover: 978-1-63680-179-7
e-book ISBN: 978-1-63680-180-3

This is a "Living Book."
Join our OpenExO Community.
Together we're continuing
to write the story.

Dedication

Salim Ismail

This book is dedicated to my son Milan, who embodies adaptability, agility, and resilience, and to Lily Safrani, the rocket engine that makes my life scalable and exponential. In their collective attributes, we see the embodiment of an ExO, and thus, I am.

Peter H. Diamandis

I dedicated this book to the CEOs of the exponential organizations in my life: Anousheh Ansari (XPRIZE), Erik Anderson (Singularity University), Julie Van Amerongen (Abundance360), Mei Mei & Lou Reese (Vaxxinity), Robert Hariri (Celularity), Teymour Boutros-Ghali (BOLD Capital Partners), Dugal Bain (MyLifeForce), Joe Stolte (Futurescope), Tyler Donahue (PHD Media), Yianni Psaltis (PHD Advisory Services), and Kristen Diamandis (Diamandis Family).

Michael S. Malone

To all those willing to fight for their place in the future

Table of Contents

PART I: EVOLUTION

PART II: SCALE

PART III: IDEAS

"We've learned how to scale technology; now it's time to scale the organization."

Exponential Organizations, First Version, 2014

Note to the Reader

When we unveiled the first edition of *Exponential Organizations* back in 2014, we were stepping into the unknown.

Would the world embrace our ideas?

Would they implement our principles into their lives and careers?

Little did we know, our concepts would trigger a global transformation, impacting leaders, businesses, even entire nations across myriad industries.

Fast forward nearly a decade, our inbox overflows with tales of burgeoning Exponential Organizations (ExOs for short), creating an avalanche of value for clients, customers, and stakeholders each week.

So, here we are, humbly and gratefully, bringing you the second edition. The world is shifting under our feet, and the need for ExOs has never been more critical.

Are you geared up to embark on an exhilarating journey into the realm of ExOs? If your answer is a resounding 'Yes', then keep reading. We're thrilled to be your navigators. To get you started, we present the ExO Mind Map™, the master blueprint for this journey, and this book.

ExO Mind Map™

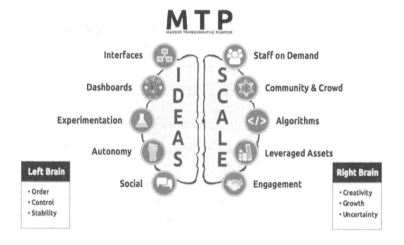

On the right side, you'll notice the first letter of each word spells SCALE. This section constitutes Part 2 of this book. Now look to the left side. The first letter of each word spells IDEAS. This section constitutes Part 3.

We wanted to provide this context—almost a You Are Here—so you can lock in the coordinates of where we begin and where we end in our journey together. Hence the name: ExO Mind Map™.

Foreword by Ray Kurzweil

It has been my unique privilege and pleasure to have worked alongside Peter H. Diamandis (my Singularity University Co-Founder) and Salim Ismail (SU's first Executive Director) since the inception of Singularity University (SU) nearly fifteen years ago.

Singularity's foundation was built on the shared conviction that the grand challenges of our world could be met with the lever of exponential technologies, and our purpose has been to educate, inspire, and empower leaders to apply these technologies to address humanity's challenges. In the past decade and a half, I've had the distinct joy of mentoring Peter and Salim and witnessing their remarkable impact in shaping the course of our collective future.

So when they approached me to write the foreword for this book I was immediately enchanted by the concept and honored to contribute to this extraordinary endeavor.

We find ourselves at a critical juncture in human history, a time when our world is evolving at an increasingly accelerated pace, characterized by wave upon wave of technological advancements that are both converging and growing exponentially. This transformative landscape, defined by diverse and potent technologies like artificial intelligence, robotics, 3D printing, augmented and virtual reality, sensors, and networks, represents an immense potential for creativity, innovation, and impact.

As a pioneering futurist and inventor, I have spent my life at the cutting edge of technological evolution. My relentless pursuit has always been to tap into the formidable power of technology to improve our lives and shape a future that is brimming with possibilities, opportunities, and human flourishing. It is precisely why the concept of the Exponential Organization (ExO) encapsulates my most ardent hopes for the future.

Exponential Organizations 2.0 brilliantly distills the core tenets that define an ExO. It elucidates the importance of having a Massive Transformative Purpose (or MTP) and the 10 distinct attributes that power these organizations to be not merely incrementally better but an order of magnitude— ten times—more impactful than their contemporaries. Ever since the inaugural book was released in 2014, the data has painted a striking picture. Organizations that use the attributes described in the ExO model have been found to yield a 40-fold increase in Total Shareholder Returns compared to those that don't.

Throughout this illuminating playbook, you will explore a plethora of case studies demonstrating the transformative potential of these attributes when ingeniously harnessed by startups and existing corporations alike. You will discover the unprecedented levels of growth, innovation, and scalability that the ExO model fosters.

However, this book is far more than just a blueprint for business excellence. It is, in essence, a manifesto for solving the world's most daunting problems. It shows how the principles that drive ExOs can be wielded to tackle systemic challenges, from eradicating poverty and reducing inequality to reversing environmental degradation and averting global pandemics. By leveraging technology to scale our impact, we can engender a future that is brighter, more prosperous, and more equitable than ever before.

In this increasingly volatile and complex world, the principles underpinning Exponential Organizations will become paramount. If every corporation were to behave as an ExO, operating at the nexus of technology, purpose, and impact, we would catalyze a profound shift in how we address global issues, fostering a more sustainable and inclusive future.

I urge you to dive into this book with an insatiable curiosity and a fervent openness to explore the vast expanse of possibilities that the ExO model presents. The contours of the future are not predestined; they are ours to shape. The ExO model equips us with the transformative tools and the visionary framework to mold that future into one that reverberates with prosperity, equity, and human potential.

This journey that you're about to embark upon with Peter and Salim is not just a journey into the heart of exponential growth but an odyssey into the very future of human enterprise and civilization. As you turn these pages, remember that every profound change begins with a singular step–that step is yours to take.

One more thing... The future of books... Introducing "RayK."

There is one more thing I'd like to address in this Foreword, something for which I'm both excited and honored.

Since 2012, I've been a director of engineering at Google and, in the past year, Google's Principal Researcher and AI Visionary. In that role, one of the projects I lead is called "Talk to Books," which was first introduced to the public in April 2018. "Talk to Books" demonstrates the potential of natural language processing, allowing a user to explore a large volume of books using a conversational, natural language interface. You simply pose a question or make a statement, and the system will search over 100,000 volumes to find sentences in books that respond to your input. Rather than relying on keyword matching, "Talk to Books" uses machine learning to understand the semantic content of the user's input and to generate responses that are relevant in meaning.

In a similar fashion, Salim and Peter have built a Generative AI that allows you to query their book *Exponential Organizations 2.0*, and soon over 600 case studies that the book is based upon. I love this idea that books are now evolving into living and interactive bodies of knowledge.

I am honored that Peter and Salim have named their Generative AI Interactive Book "**RayK**" in my honor.

As an example, you can ask RayK, "I'm a company offering these services, and I'm wondering how I can best implement interfaces or crowd/community?" Or a question like "I'm a shipping company in Europe, delivering grain around the world. What technology breakthroughs might disrupt my business?" Or a question like, "I'm an XYZ business,. What technology breakthroughs can I leverage to scale my business?" Or, "I'm a dentist. How do I turn my practice into an ExO?"

I hope you'll use RayK to make the most of this amazing body of work.

You can access RayK by visiting OpenExO.com/chat.

Best wishes for your Exponential Future.

—Ray Kurzweil
Chancellor & Co-Founder, Singularity University
Google's Principal Researcher and AI Visionary Author,
The Singularity Is Near

PART 1
EVOLUTION

Introduction

History will likely look back upon NASA's space shuttle program with a mixture of amazement and disbelief—and not in a good way.

Though the shuttle program was sold to the public as a major technological achievement, it is increasingly likely to look to our descendants like a staggering example of an organizational paradigm that was becoming obsolete before it got off the ground.

The shuttle program was born during a period of declining public interest following the incredible success of the 10-year Apollo program that landed human beings on the moon, one of the greatest achievements in the history of humankind. When the shuttle program was originally sold to Congress, it was expected to cost $50 million per flight and fly as many as 50 times per year. In the end, it cost on average $1 billion per flight and flew only four times per year.

Indeed, and sadly, what we are most likely to remember about the space shuttle, beyond its astronomical costs, are its tragedies. Those, too, were a measure of our growing complacency towards the program: shuttle flights had grown so predictable that NASA had resorted to promotional activities like putting a schoolteacher on board. The world watched in horror and disbelief in January 1986 and again in February 2003, as first the *Challenger* and then the *Columbia* fell burning from the sky.

That the *Challenger* disaster was largely the product of bureaucratic blunders was a further reminder that America's space program, specifically NASA itself, had lost its way. It no longer had an overarching vision—to put a human on the moon—to galvanize its employees and the public. Its operating systems were products of a previous and fading century. Its technology was antiquated. It used organizational structures and business models that dated from before World War II. The space shuttle program required a standing army of more than 20,000 employees—which itself cost NASA more than $4 billion a year. The result had been bureaucratic bloat.

It seems hardly surprising that, in the years since the *Challenger* and *Columbia* crashes, the shuttle program has been slowly reduced to conducting deliveries of astronauts and cargo to the International Space Station (ISS) (another compromised and overpriced initiative). The shuttle program was eventually shut down in 2011 when it was replaced by the much more affordable Russian Soyuz launch system for crew and cargo to the ISS. That shift left a massive void in America's ability to access the space frontier.

But then, something extraordinary happened. A large, traditional US aerospace giant—like Boeing, Lockheed, or Northrup Grumman—did *not* step in to resolve this crucial missing US capability. Instead, a group of upstart technology entrepreneurs stepped into the fray. Raised in the years following the Apollo Space Race, and with entertainment like *Star Trek* and *Star Wars*, they believed space was within their reach. Armed with their wealth and track records of success, they set out to build their own private space capabilities.

Thus began the private commercialization of space. And, once again, the general public grew wildly excited about their own future prospects of going into orbit, to the moon, and perhaps even to Mars.

Peter Diamandis, one of this book's co-authors, incentivized the new Space Race with the $10 million Ansari XPRIZE. Founded in 1994, XPRIZE is a non-profit organization created to design and host public competitions with the goal of benefiting humanity by encouraging radical breakthrough technological development. Since its inception, it has funded more than $300 million worth of incentive competitions, ranging from mapping the ocean floor and cleaning up oil spills to creating robotic avatars and replicating the *Star Trek* tricorder medical device.

But the XPRIZEs that have had the greatest impact to date have been those related to space: from the first— the $10 million Ansari XPRIZE for sub-orbital flight (1996–2004)—to the $30 million Google Lunar XPRIZE (2007–2018) for successfully launching, landing, and operating a rover on the moon's surface.

Some of these prizes were won by successful teams. Others—including the Google Lunar XPRIZE—have gone unclaimed, despite some impressive attempts. But all of them stimulated massive innovation and investment, harnessing the imaginations of millions of people to tackle big ideas with enormous potential. The potentially huge awards—rather than traditional government investment—further incentivized competitors. Even when prizes went unclaimed, the pursuit produced impressive advances in human knowledge.

The XPRIZEs set the stage for the next leap in space exploration: the arrival of entrepreneurs. Like financiers of the past, these individuals—most notably Amazon's Jeff Bezos with Blue Origin, Virgin Galactic's Richard Branson, and, most successfully, Elon Musk of SpaceX—saw a historic personal, scientific, and economic opportunity in space. Like all great entrepreneurs, they took off in pursuit of it.

Tellingly, each pursued an opportunity on the final frontier where they thought they could build a successful long-term business. Musk focused on building a new generation of rockets, capturing the market left vacant by the space shuttle. He set his longer-term sights toward Mars. Bezos built a thriving suborbital tourism business. He also pursued the development of larger commercial rockets but set his objectives on the moon. Branson, who purchased the rights to the winning technology demonstrated by the Ansari XPRIZE, focused exclusively on tourism.

The impact of these initiatives has already been stunning. SpaceX, in particular, has introduced two major innovations. First, it pioneered the reusability of rockets—long heralded as the key innovation for affordable space flight—by demonstrating the return and reflight of its Falcon-9 first-stage booster. (As we write this, SpaceX has reused a single, first-stage booster of nine engines more than 13 times.) It removed the massive human army of workers that, until now, has characterized space exploration. Today, SpaceX charges NASA approximately $100 million per launch of its astronauts to the ISS—at an estimated cost of half of that to SpaceX itself. In other words, SpaceX has not only achieved a tenfold improvement in the cost of launching astronauts to orbit, but it has also made a significant profit in the process.

And that's just the beginning. Several new entrants in the field are primed to compete with the likes of SpaceX with a newer generation of rockets. Tim Ellis is CEO of Relativity Space, which is 3D-printing as much as 95% of their rockets, enabling another tenfold cost drop. Ellis and his co-founder, Jordan Noone, were both 23 years old when they started the company. Both were interns, one at SpaceX and the other at Blue Origin. Meanwhile, an Indian startup, Agnikul Cosmos, has successfully test-fired a single-piece, 3D-printed rocket engine.

The New Rules

Why didn't the largest, most experienced, best-funded aerospace players in the field step into the void left open by the cancellation of the shuttle program? Why, instead, did passionate young entrepreneurs with no space experience transform America's assured access to space?

Because the rules have changed.

Ronald H. Coase won the Nobel prize for his rationale that, for big companies, internal transaction costs were lower than getting things done on the outside, thus creating economies of scale. This became known as Coase's Law.

Coase's Law has been broken by the enormous power of technology. Between mobile phones, the internet, and AI, the lines between a large organization and the outside world have blurred and fragmented. As a result, over the last two decades, large operating companies have given way to platforms, and platforms are transforming into ecosystems.

What's most incredible about this transformation is its sheer speed:

- TikTok reached a billion users in five years.
- ChatGPT reached 100 million users in just two months.
- Apple took from 1976 until 2018 to achieve a market capitalization of $1 trillion. It took just two years to hit $2 trillion.

- The number of "unicorn" businesses reaching a billion-dollar market cap is more than five times higher today than in 2014 when we first unveiled the ExO model.
- Cloud security startup Wiz reached $100 million of annualized revenues in just 18 months.

This chart shows the time it took for selected online services to reach one million users.

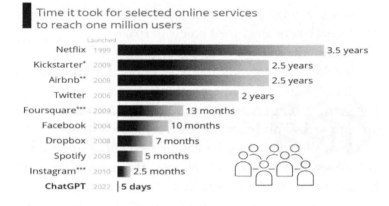

Time it took for selected online services to reach one million users

	Launched	
Netflix	1999	3.5 years
Kickstarter*	2009	2.5 years
Airbnb**	2008	2.5 years
Twitter	2006	2 years
Foursquare***	2009	13 months
Facebook	2004	10 months
Dropbox	2008	7 months
Spotify	2008	5 months
Instagram***	2010	2.5 months
ChatGPT	2022	5 days

And in terms of actual revenues, see the incredible acceleration in the chart below:

Fastest from $1M to $100M ARR

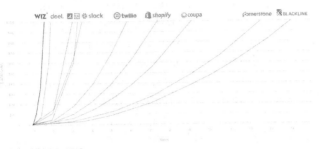

Image Credits: Wiz, Bessemer Ventures[1]

We are witnessing a new breed of organization that is scaling and generating value at an unprecedented pace. It's important to understand why this is happening and just how unprecedented this shift is.

A World of ExOs

Welcome to the Exponential world of business. It is a place where neither age nor size nor reputation nor even current sales guarantees that you will be around tomorrow. On the other hand, it is also a place where if you can build an organization that is sufficiently scalable, fast-moving, and smart, you may enjoy success—exponential success—to a degree never before imaginable. And all with far fewer resources and in far less time than the successful businesses of previous decades.

---

[1] Assaf Rappaport, "$100m ARR in 18 Months: Wiz Becomes the Fastest-Growing Software Company Ever: Wiz Blog," wiz.io, August 10, 2022, https://www.wiz.io/blog/100m-arr-in-18-months-wiz-becomes-the-fastest-growing-software-company-ever.

We have entered the age of billion-dollar startups and trillion-dollar corporations, where the best companies and institutions move at seemingly light speed. If you haven't transitioned into an Exponential Organization, it will not only seem as though your competition is racing away from you, but worse, that you are sliding backwards into oblivion.

Enormous waves of creative destruction have been unleashed. More than half of the companies that made up the Fortune 500 in 2000 have vanished.[2] Giants like Global Crossing, Chrysler, GM, Brookstone, The Limited, Sears, and Toys "R" Us have all fallen by the wayside via bankruptcy, acquisition, or shutdown.

A hundred years ago, the average lifespan of an S&P 500 company was 67 years. Today, it's about 15 years.[3] And it's going to get even shorter as these corporations aren't just forced to compete with but are annihilated—seemingly overnight—by a new breed of business that harnesses the power of exponential technologies, from AI and data mining to synthetic biology, blockchain, and robotics. The founders of those new companies will become the leaders of the world's economy for the foreseeable future. Even governments will come to them on bended knees.

---

[2]   "When Digital Disruption Strikes: How Can Incumbents Respond? - Capgemini," Capgemini Consulting, 2015, https://www.cap-gemini.com/consulting/wp-content/uploads/sites/30/2017/07/digital_disruption_1.pdf.

[3]   S. Patrick Viguerie, Ned Calder, and Brian Hindo, "2021 Corporate Longevity Forecast," Innosight, August 9, 2023, https://www.inno-sight.com/insight/creative-destruction/.

The Foundational Underpinnings for ExOs

Rather than armies of people or large physical plants, Exponential Organizations are built upon information technologies that take what was once physical and dematerialize it into apps, transforming bulky and expensive hardware into cheap and nimble digital, on-demand information flows. The transformation of music from cassettes and CDs to iTunes® and Spotify® is an obvious example. Three aspects of this transformation are completely unique to this era:

1. **A dozen accelerating technologies.** Today, more than a dozen technologies operate on patterns originally described in Moore's Law: doubling computational price/performance every 18 months. Ray Kurzweil calls this the Law of Accelerating Returns (LOAR), which posits that any technology that is information-based will see doubling patterns. Before now, perhaps one or two technologies accelerated simultaneously. Never before have we seen so many technologies accelerating at the same time.

2. **Technology convergence.** While each technology grows exponentially, the convergence of two, three, or four of these technologies is truly re-inventing industries and transforming business models. For example, we are using deep-learning AI, robotics, and genome sequencing to analyze cancer trials. The multiplier effects of several doubling technologies are staggering.

3. **Cost collapse.** Throughout human history, advanced technologies have typically cost more. But today, for the first time, advanced technologies are

demonetizing at an incredible rate. Solar energy is cheap, sensors are cheap, many online AI tools (GPT4, DALL-E 2) are free, and most Blockchain technologies are open source!

The torrid pace of today's technological innovation and product development is unprecedented. And it's only the beginning. We are seeing industry after industry—from glamorous fields such as space to mature industries like food processing and agriculture—light up and launch into exponential innovations. For example, drones are being used with infrared sensors to scan fields for infestation. The launch of GPT4 (and its many follow-ons) will transform dozens of industries.

The notion of "Exponential Organizations" is relatively new. At just under a decade old, it has already radically restructured and continues to restructure forward-thinking companies—from global giants to aggressive new start-ups—around the world. The COVID-19 pandemic and its associated technological and workplace shifts have dramatically accelerated the ExO paradigm.

As we will show in this book, Exponential success stories are quickly mounting. The data is streaming in. It suggests that if you haven't learned about Exponential Organization theory, you'd better learn quickly. If you're thinking about implementing it, you'd better get started. And if you've been forward-thinking enough to begin, you need to bring yourself up to date on the field's latest discoveries and innovations.

Wherever you are in the process, this book is designed to help you take the first step—and then the next step. The word "exponential" signifies not just a theory but also a warning: the business world is beginning to move so quickly and so purposefully that if you're not already changing your business model and thinking differently (and way bigger), you are going to be fatally left behind.

ExO: Second Generation

The original *Exponential Organizations* book was published in 2014. The impetus to create it was a growing recognition that something important—and as yet undocumented—was going on in the tech world. Salim Ismail, in particular, had been running Singularity University in Silicon Valley. He was regularly seeing exciting new companies that didn't look like the Valley's traditional startups—not just in the nature of their products and services (novelty is the heart of the Valley) but also in the way they were structured and operated. In 2011, Salim began giving talks and lectures about this phenomenon and started writing the book. In 2012, Yuri van Geest joined as a writing partner; he was instrumental in the development of the ExO model and the creation of the book. Michiel Schuurman performed extensive research for the case studies in the book. Meanwhile, Peter Diamandis, the primary founder and first chairman of Singularity University, had noticed the same trend and had also begun to write about this new phenomenon.

New organizational models in Silicon Valley and tech have a deep history, dating back to the HP Way in the 1950s, through Theory Z in the 1970s, and up to the present. Companies that successfully adopt new models suddenly accelerate, leaving the competition behind and becoming the dominant enterprises of their era. Witness how quickly eBay® and Craigslist® decimated the newspaper classifieds. With Peter advising, the team set out to formulate a definition of these "Exponential Organizations." This is what they came up with.

An Exponential Organization (ExO) is one whose impact (or output) is disproportionally large—at least 10x larger—compared to its peers because of the use of new organizational techniques that leverage accelerating technologies.

The team then needed to explain the new techniques and technologies these organizations used and to show how they produced these extraordinary outcomes. They analyzed 70 different business paradigms, from Michael Porter to Clay Christensen to Lean Startup to Jim Collins and many others, to see what they did differently. They then researched more than 200 "unicorns"—privately held startup companies valued at more than $1 billion US—that were scaling their organizations as fast as their technology. The team then enlisted Silicon Valley journalist and author Michael Malone, who had thought and written a lot about precisely these kinds of organizational revolutions, with Valley pioneer Bill Davidow, who had co-authored the seminal book *The Virtual Corporation* (1984) and a follow-up book on "protean corporations." He concurred with Salim, Peter, and Yuri: in Exponential Organizations, they had found the next evolutionary step for business and other enterprises.

In 2014, this team, along with a community of about 100 contributors, published *Exponential Organizations*, bringing together in a coherent narrative all they had learned about this compelling new phenomenon. They hoped to bring about a global conversation and perhaps to spark some test cases to see if their model worked as well as they predicted.

After ExO launched, Yuri went on to integrate his organizational thinking and frameworks into consciousness, art, nature, ancient wisdom, and deep humanity. Michiel has been focused on unlocking human potential and vitality by creating personalized learning journeys based on users' unique biology.

An International Phenomenon

Exponential Organizations proved to be a phenomenon. It has sold more than 600,000 copies in more than 20 languages, making it one of the most successful business books ever written and one of the most successful books ever published in Silicon Valley. It set off a global movement. As companies implemented their own exponential programs, they swapped notes and best practices. Soon, they were knocking on Salim's door in droves.

Faced with this onslaught of interest, Salim created OpenExO, a community and ecosystem of 24,000 consultants, entrepreneurs, innovators, and academics that serves as a clearinghouse for exponential transformation. OpenExO is a dynamic archive of companies implementing the exponential attributes and detailing their successes and frustrations along the way. Inevitably, it has grown into an ecosystem that helps companies and governments transition to this new world.

Salim quickly became an in-demand speaker, not just to large corporations but also to industry groups and even national governments around the world. He understood if organizations didn't get on board quickly, this point of inflection would leave them behind forever, with no way to catch up.

ExO and The Fortune 100

This realization has proved correct. In the original book, the authors and the ExO community analyzed the Fortune 100 companies, ranking them against the ExO model for flexibility, scalability, and agility. In 2021, they conducted a seven-year trailing[4] analysis. How had those companies performed?

The results were stunning, confirming what we had predicted about ExO companies and proving just how much competitive advantage these firms had over their traditionally organized peers. Between 2014 and 2021, the top 10 most ExO-friendly companies in the Fortune 100 blew away the bottom 10 (least ExO-friendly) in the following metrics:

- Revenue Growth: 2.6 times higher
- Profitability: 6.8 times higher
- Return on Assets: 11.7 times higher
- Total Shareholders Return
  (CAGR):   **40 times higher**

Let's just repeat that last one: over an eight-year period, of the largest 100 American corporations, *the companies that most emulated the attributes of the ExO model delivered shareholder returns that were a staggering 40 times better than those of the companies that least followed the model.*

The ExO Top 100

As part of the book's genesis, Salim also worked with a group of 160 ExO experts across 45 countries to research and grade multiple startups and scale-ups founded after 2005, as well as several incumbent organizations. He used a diagnostics of their Exponential Quotient (ExQ), an aggregate score compiled from responses to a 21-question survey on exponential attributes. The survey identified the Top 100 exponential

---

4   "Solving for 10x," OpenExO, https://old.openexo.com/f100/.

organizations:[5] the most scalable and adaptable of the firms assessed. An eight-year trailing analysis[6] for these Top 100 Exponential Organizations, similar to that of the Fortune 100, revealed equally fascinating results. The ExO Top 100 boasted:

- 80% of the Top 100 generated positive shareholder returns,
- an impressive 26% average annualized growth in valuation—twice as much as the S&P 500 for the same time period, and
- a staggering 46.6x jump in valuation for startups and scale-ups.

This is the data that wasn't available in 2014. It suggests that not only were our co-authors' early predictions not overly optimistic—as some suggested at the time—but rather that, in many cases, they *weren't optimistic enough.* Ten-times growth is eminently achievable to those willing to board the exponential bullet train, and that kind of growth becomes sustainable for years.

As we dug deeper into these companies' operations, it became apparent that going exponential was not simply a matter of adopting the right technologies and implementing different operational schemes. Rather, they also adopted *a new cultural paradigm* that, in short order, transformed their very nature.

---

5   "The Top 100 Exponential Organizations," OpenExO, https://old. openexo.com/top100/.

6   "Eight-Year Trailing Analysis," OpenExO, https://old.openexo. com/top100-report/.

The Exponential Leadership Mindset / Abundance360

While Salim was developing the ExO community worldwide, Peter was building and exclusively running Abundance360,[7] which is Singularity's highest-level program. Abundance360 is a year-round leadership program designed for founders, executives, and investors who are ready to create meaningful impact and leave a legacy. It is for those exponential entrepreneurs who desire to develop their Massive Transformative Purpose (MTP) and take on Moonshots (both of which are discussed in greater detail throughout this and the original book).

The Abundance360 membership and faculty meet in person in Los Angeles every March during a five-day, five-star summit. They also gather quarterly online for implementation workshops and member meet-ups. The Abundance360 programming focuses on:

1. Artificial intelligence
2. Understanding exponential technologies
3. Shaping MTP and Moonshots
4. Longevity breakthroughs
5. Building a community of exponential entrepreneurs seeking to uplift humanity

Peter has committed to run A360 for 25 years through 2038. As of 2023, the program was entering year 12. Access to A360 is by application only and is highly selective. More information is available at Abundance360.

---

[7] "Abundance360 by Peter Diamandis," abundance360, https://www. abundance360.com/summit.

The Movement is Well Underway

Today, there are an estimated 20,000 ExOs worldwide. That's an impressive number, but it's still a tiny fraction of the number of enterprises on the planet. Many incubators like Rokk3r Inc. in Miami use the model to build all their companies. A product called ExO Builder even leads cohorts of startups in building out ExOs as a standardized process.

Bringing together the Top 100 ExO data,[8] the Fortune 100 results,[9] ten years of anecdotes, and the various case studies from governments, we strongly believe that over the course of this decade, every organization, every startup, every non-profit, every government department, and every impact project will be structured as an ExO. The data is incontrovertible: the model is just better and can deliver exceptional stakeholder outcomes.

In this new and revised playbook, we further document the ExO, drawing on the rich store of details, case studies, and content that has transformed our understanding of this phenomenon over the past decade.

We don't claim to have all the answers. But, based upon our own experiences, both good and bad, we believe we can offer management teams a path through this era of hyper-accelerated innovation and competition, as well as into the new opportunities (and responsibilities) presented by our rapidly changing world. As we said in the first book: If we can't guarantee you success, we can at least put you on the right playing field and show you the new rules of the

---

8   "Top 100 ExO Data," OpenExO, https://old.openexo.com/top100-report/.

9   "The Fortune 100 Results," OpenExO, https://old.openexo.com/f100/.

game. These two advantages, plus your own initiative, offer good odds for being a winner in the world of Exponential Organizations.

We hope this book will provide a taste of what the exponential future looks like—and leave you hungry to learn more. We intend to expand on this body of work with a series of books over the next few years that each take on a particular topic in the field: for example, MTP and corporate transformation, as well as a detailed operating manual for corporations on applying exponential theory to social institutions, including nonprofits and governments. This library builds on the following critical books:

- *The Singularity Is Near* by Ray Kurzweil
- *Abundance: The Future is Better Than You Think* by Peter Diamandis and Steven Kotler
- *Exponential Organizations* by Salim Ismail, Yuri van Geest, and Michael S. Malone (with Peter Diamandis)

We hope that this growing set of ExO books will not only elucidate an all-encompassing vision of exponential theory as a fundamental new cultural force but will also provide a detailed roadmap of how to get there.

Kurzweil's Law of Accelerating Returns and Moore's Law long ago broke from the confines of semiconductors to utterly transform human society. Today, Exponential Organizations are the latest embodiment of acceleration in human culture and enterprise. And they are overhauling commerce and other aspects of modern life at a scorching pace, rapidly leaving behind the old world of "linear" organizations. Those enterprises that don't jump aboard soon will be left on the ash heap of history, joining Iridium, Kodak,

Polaroid, Philco, Blockbuster, Nokia, and a host of other once-great, industry-dominant corporations that failed to adapt.

Claim your ExOPass

What you hold in your hands is a passport to a transformative future. Since publishing the original ExO book in 2014, we have been building a community of thousands of exponential thinkers and doers—and you can join them. By visiting the link below, you can access a wealth of resources and knowledge, a growing community, and exclusive content. Together, we can transform the world for a better future.

1

Our World Is Changing Exponentially

The future is faster than you think.

–Peter H. Diamandis & Steven Kotler

The global COVID-19 pandemic—which persists as this book is being written—was an unexpected and historic event. It was also shocking, not just because millions of people died and hundreds of millions more fell ill, but because of its sheer speed and the disruption it left in its wake.

As sophisticated and technologically astute citizens of the 21st century, we thought we had acclimated to the blistering rate of change that had characterized the past decades of technological revolution in the global economy. Then came COVID, infiltrating the entire world in a matter of months. Its speed left little time for strategy or thoughtful consideration. We were simply, suddenly, overwhelmed by a life-threatening force that propagated at speeds that rapidly outpaced any technological change, forcing society and business, workers and leaders, to reinvent every aspect of our daily work and home lives almost overnight.

The true nature of exponential growth and impact became painfully clear, acted out in real-time every day for more than two years.

The Curve of the Modern World

This curve of accelerated change is driving us towards a more digital, dematerialized, and democratized world, notably via computation and high-speed networks. Two things are important to note:

First, this process didn't begin only 50 years ago. On the contrary, with his Law of Accelerating Returns (LOAR), Ray Kurzweil realized that it actually began generations ago with the earliest computers, which were powered first by mechanical systems, then relays, and then vacuum tubes. It's just that the early stages of exponential growth are deceptively slow. Double a small number like 0.01 to 0.02, 0.04, 0.08, and so on, and it still looks like zero.

This is what Peter Diamandis and Steven Kotler describe as the "deceptive phase" of exponential growth in their book *Bold: How to Go Big, Create Wealth and Impact the World.* They note that the doubling of small numbers (as shown above) seems unimpressive to the casual outside observer. But later, as the doubling continues, it transforms everything. If you double something thirty times, it ends up more than a billion times bigger, what Peter refers to as the *disruptive* phase. And, as we shall soon see, the digitization of products and services ultimately results in the dematerialization, demonitization, and democratization of those products and services.

Only in retrospect did we recognize that the explosion of new inventions at the beginning of the 20th century was an augury of things to come. In other words, this exponential process has been going on for a long time, and we are now at the point on the curve where each increment is massive, with even more ahead.

Gordon Moore recognized that, between 1958 and 1965, the number of transistors on Intel's integrated chips doubled every 12 to 18 months while the costs involved halved—an observation that would come to be known as "Moore's Law." But even Moore didn't imagine that those little silicon chips, each bearing dozens to hundreds of transistors, would, in time, each carry trillions of transistors. Frankly, he *couldn't* imagine that because it was beyond human imagination and beyond our understanding of physics: it was a number too great for the human mind to comprehend. Moore assumed that at some point, his curve would have to run into some physical barrier and flatten, and the current era of exponential transformation would end.

But it didn't end. And it hasn't ended. And, given the extraordinary efforts of human ingenuity over several generations of scientists, it is likely to continue for many decades. Today's microprocessor chips bear little resemblance to those memory chips of the early 1960s: the design, materials, software, and myriad other characteristics have changed radically. And with the recent rise of quantum and photonic computing and other new architectures, further radical change is all but guaranteed.

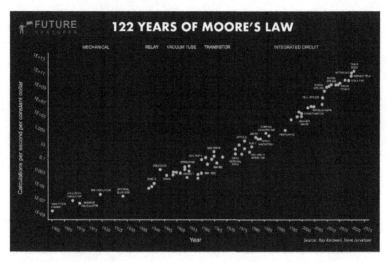

Source: Ray Kurzweil, updated since 2008 by Steve Jurvetson

Which brings us to our second point: If you are counting on all of this change to slow in your lifetime, you are probably making a very big mistake. Indeed, change is accelerating.

And that's just the beginning because exponential growth is no longer confined to the world of technology. Indeed, it hasn't been for a long time. Tech has long since invaded and transformed the world of business, non-profits, defense, finance, consumer products, and, most important of all, daily life. It began quietly: the mainframe computer down the hall handling payroll, digital readouts showing up in airplane cockpits, a processor in your car's fuel-injection system, a calculator on your desk, etc.

Look around you. More than 30 billion processors are currently in use in the world, containing as many transistors as the number of raindrops that fall on the Earth each year. They are embedded in every corner of our daily lives, growing smarter, more connected, and more capable by the year. All that has happened in less than a single lifetime. Now, imagine change on that scale occurring in a single year. Next year. Then again in the following six months, along a wide front, from medicine to education to space exploration to transportation and communications. As Peter, Ray, and others have noted, we'll experience more progress in the next decade (2023–2033) than we saw in the past century (1923–2023).

There's more. Waiting in the wings is a long list of game-changers: artificial intelligence (AI), Big Data, quantum technologies, the Internet of Things (IoT), robotics, mobile medical monitoring and diagnosis, the extended human healthspan, hypersonic travel, and the colonization of space, to name just a few. Each of these has the potential to create a massive disruption in the patterns of our daily lives (and to create new, trillion-dollar industries in the process). Salim Ismail talks about this as "20 Gutenberg Moments," referencing the dramatic transformation created by the printing press in the 15th century. Today, solar energy will have that same impact. But so will blockchain. So will AI, and CRISPR, and passenger drones, and life extension. And so on.

Metatrends

The convergence of exponentially growing technologies, especially artificial intelligence, will reinvent every business model and accelerate the global pace of change. Such convergence will disrupt old industries and create a multitude of new trillion-dollar opportunities in the coming decade.

In order for exponential entrepreneurs to surf on top of this tsunami of change rather than being crushed by it, it is critical to understand the key metatrends shaping the decade ahead.

Peter has created a list of ten such metatrends that are likely to define the period between 2023 and 2033. Paying attention to these trends is how an entrepreneur can peer around the corner and see the future.

1. **The rise of artificial intelligence (AI).** Artificial intelligence is projected by Ray Kurzweil, Elon Musk, and the team at Google's DeepMind to reach human-level performance before the end of this decade. Today, large language models such as Open AI's GPT-4, Google's BARD, and NVIDIA's Megatron-Turing NLG are increasing tenfold in capability every year. In 2022, DeepMind announced Gato-AI, a "generalist agent" AI that is able to carry out complex tasks from stacking blocks to writing poetry. Later in 2022, OpenAI rolled out ChatGPT and took the internet by storm, followed rapidly by AutoGPT. AI is expected to penetrate every industry and product. Combined with the explosion of low-cost microscopic sensors, the deployment of high-bandwidth networks, and the connection to AI cloud services, every device will soon become intelligent. A toy remembers a child's face and name. Appliances respond to voice commands and anticipate user needs.

2. **AI, robotic, and human collaboration.** The rise of "AI as a Service" (AIaaS) platforms will enable humans to partner with AI in every aspect of their work, at every level, in every industry. Reid Hoffman, founder of LinkedIn™, predicts that by 2028, every profession will have an "AI-Copilot" available. AI technologies will become entrenched in everyday

business operations, serving as cognitive collaborators to employees: supporting creative tasks, generating new ideas, and tackling previously unattainable innovations. At the same time, humanoid robots are expected to flourish in the decade ahead. Whether fully autonomous, driven by GPT-4 or GPT-5, or human-driven avatars, these robots will take on jobs that are dull, dangerous, or dirty. The most famous is Tesla Bot (also known as Optimus), which Elon Musk announced in 2022 as Tesla's most important future product. "Optimus will upend our idea of what the economy is ... It will be able to do basically anything humans don't want to do... It's going to bring an age of abundance," he said.[10]

3. **Ultra-low-cost global gigabit connectivity.** The world is rapidly being blanketed in wireless bandwidth, connecting everyone and the Internet of Things (IoT). 5G will connect 3 billion users by 2025, with 6G (100x faster) already under development. Starlink has deployed 3,000 satellites, with the projected 30,000 satellites in orbit by the end of the decade. Other constellations, such as Kuiper and E-space (with 100,000 satellites), are also under development. According to McKinsey, IoT will create $6.2 trillion of new economic value by 2025.

4. **Web3 and Metaverse transforming retail, educational, and human interactions.** Citibank estimates

---

10   Evannex, "At Cyber Rodeo, Musk Says Tesla's Future Will Bring 'an Age of Abundance,'" InsideEVs, April 8, 2022, https://insideevs.com/news/578756/tesla-musk-cyber-rodeo-age-of-abundance/.

that the Metaverse could be worth $13 trillion by 2030 and have up to 5 billion users. Powered by a combination of virtual reality and augmented reality (VR and AR), 5G networks, blockchain, AI, Web3, and Metaverse will transform everyday life, impacting every industry from retail and advertising to education and entertainment. High-resolution, lightweight virtual-reality headsets will allow people to shop for everything from clothing to new homes from the convenience of their living rooms. AI will know users' detailed body measurements and whip up a fashion show featuring that user's avatar wearing the latest 20 designs presented on a virtual runway. In education, the use of VR- and AI-driven avatars with new apps promise a powerful future of gamelike, immersive education and training.

The metaverse is a virtual virtual-reality space in which users can interact with each other and share knowledge, data, and best practices. ExOs can leverage a metaverse's assets to test multiple environments and user interactions. ExOs can also leverage metaverse users' computing power to power the environment.

Web3 is a new, decentralized World Wide Web based on blockchain technology and decentralized assets. Web3 incorporates crypto features like token-based economics and fractionalized IP. It allows users to leverage assets by distributing ownership and costs of ownership across a large group of people. Conceptually, fractionalized ownership is not new: the shares of any company are essentially fractional ownership.

5. **Autonomous vehicles and flying cars** (i.e., electric vertical take-off and landing aircrafts, or eVTOL) will redefine human travel, making it increasingly faster and cheaper. Fully autonomous vehicles, car-as-a-service fleets, and aerial ride-sharing will be operational in most major metropolitan cities in the coming decade. The cost of transportation will plummet three-to-four-fold, transforming real estate, finance, insurance, the materials economy, and urban planning. Already, a half-dozen eVTOL companies have gone public, raising billions of dollars to fuel their growth. These vehicles are real and will help define the decade ahead.

6. **Curing genetic disease with CRISPR and gene therapy.** In 2022, the cost of reading a single human genome (3.2 billion letters) decreased to $200 (from $3 billion 23 years earlier) and took approximately seven hours, down from nine months back in 2001. At the same time, CRISPR, for which the 2020 Nobel Prize was awarded, has given us the ability to precisely edit our genomes with the promise of curing a wide range of genetic diseases (e.g., sickle cell anemia, thalassemia, and certain forms of congenital blindness) as well as infectious diseases ranging from AIDS to Ebola. As of early 2023, there were 130 human trials using CRISPR to cure various genetic diseases. The tools to read, write, and edit DNA and RNA will usher in a biological revolution in the decade ahead.

7. **Extending the human healthspan by 20+ years.** A dozen game-changing biotech and pharmaceutical

solutions will reach consumers this decade, adding decades to the human healthspan. Technologies include epigenetic reprogramming, stem-cell supply restoration, Wnt pathway manipulation, senolytic medicines, a new generation of vaccines, GDF11, and supplementation of nicotinamide mononucleotide and nicotinamide adenine dinucleotide NMN/NAD+, among several others. The speed of biotech breakthroughs is accelerating, giving us the potential to reach "longevity escape velocity": the point at which science extends life for more than a year for every year that a human is alive. Advanced full-body diagnostic testing (imaging, genomics, and biomarkers) will also help to identify disease at its earliest point when it is more readily curable. The societal implications to a longer-lived, healthier population are staggering. In 2022, Harvard, Oxford, and the London School of Business estimated that an additional health year added to the global population is worth $38 trillion to the global economy.

8. **Cellular agriculture and vertical farming providing cheaper, healthier, high-quality local food supplies.** The next decade will witness the birth of ethical, nutritious, and environmentally sustainable protein production systems. Stem cell–based "cellular agriculture" will allow for the production of beef, chicken, and fish anywhere, on demand, with far higher nutritional content and a vastly lower environmental footprint than traditional livestock options. In addition, vertical farming in downtown cities will grow dozens of different crops at scale,

where they can be delivered rapidly at low cost with high nutrient content.

9. **The rise of globally abundant, cheap, and renewable energy.** Continued advancements in solar, wind, geothermal, hydroelectric, nuclear, and localized grids will drive humanity toward cheap, abundant, and ubiquitous renewable energy. The price per kilowatt-hour will drop below one cent for renewables as storage cost drops below three cents per kilowatt-hour, resulting in the majority displacement of fossil fuels globally. New companies will be able to mine sunlight and water to create cheap, abundant hydrogen as a storage medium. Fusion Power is also on the brink of crucial breakthroughs, promising commercial-scale production in the decade ahead. What are the socioeconomic implications as the petro-dollar diminishes on the global stage and the poorest countries (which are also the sunniest countries) become net-energy exporters?

10. **Sustainability and the environment.** An increase in global environmental awareness and concern over global warming will drive companies to invest in sustainability, both from a necessity standpoint and for marketing purposes. Breakthroughs in materials science, enabled by AI (and soon quantum technologies) will allow companies to drive tremendous reductions in waste and environmental contamination. In the process, one company's waste will become another's profit center. Visionary venture capitalist John Doerr said, "Climate change brings economic

opportunity that's bigger than the internet boom."[11] And Microsoft cofounder Bill Gates said, "Carbon capture tech will create the next Microsoft, Google and Amazon, and the next eight to ten Teslas."[12]

The ExO Community has, with a working group, identified as many as 15 new industries created by these metatrends and valued at potentially $90 trillion—with many more such disruptive industries likely to appear in the decades to come. The question for you, the reader, is:

How are you planning to incorporate these metatrends into your current or future organization?

Anticipating the Unexpected

One more category of events signals the further acceleration of the pace of change. Peter refers to these sudden shock moments as "Asteroid Impact events." Asteroid Impacts are massive disruptions that cause a sudden shift in the environment. Organizations that are slow and lumbering, unable to rapidly adapt (e.g., the dinosaurs), will rapidly go extinct. Companies that are nimble (e.g., furry little mammals),

---

[11] Jon Swartz, "VC Legend John Doerr Says Climate Change Brings Economic Opportunity That's Bigger than the Internet Boom," MarketWatch, November 9, 2021, https://www.marketwatch.com/story/vc-legend-john-doerr-says-climate-change-brings-economic-opportunity-thats-bigger-than-the-internet-boom-11636466626.

[12] Catherine Clifford, "Bill Gates Says Climate Tech Will Produce 8 to 10 Teslas, a Google, an Amazon and a Microsoft," CNBC, October 21, 2021, https://www.cnbc.com/2021/10/20/bill-gates-expects-8-to-10-teslas-and-a-google-amazon-and-microsoft.html.

evolve rapidly, and fill open opportunities will initiate a Cambrian explosion of innovation.

Beyond its more obvious impacts, the COVID-19 pandemic has acted as an Asteroid Impact accelerator to an already rapid rate of change. Nowhere was this more obvious than in the development of multiple COVID vaccines and their production in billions of doses in record time. Even the "experts" predicted that this accomplishment might take years. In actuality, it took less than a year, enabled by new mRNA vaccine technology and by a series of actors and organizations that resembled more than anything else a collection of Exponential Organizations.

At the same time, the pandemic acted as an accelerant to cultural changes that were already underway. Pundits had spoken for decades about the phenomenon of working "virtually" from locations other than the traditional office. But the process had gone so slowly that it had become the accepted view that it might take another decade or more to become dominant in the world of work.

Needless to say, the global lockdown forced by the pandemic accelerated the adoption of virtual work from the predicted decades to mere days. Workers on every continent went home for months (and yet were still expected to be productive). Supporting that social shift was teleconferencing—the ubiquitous Zoom call—leading millions to quickly adopt and adapt to a technological vision that Bell Labs had imagined nearly 70 years earlier.[13]

COVID, we now see, was not a monolithic event but rather one that created numerous ancillary disruptions—many of

---

[13] Andy Patrizio, "The History and Evolution of Video Conferencing," WhatIs.com, August 17, 2021, https://www.techtarget.com/whatis/feature/The-history-and-evolution-of-video-conferencing.

them quite beneficial, despite their dangerous origins. The societies, enterprises, and individuals who responded best to those disruptions succeeded the most. Those that failed to respond risked being left in the dustbin of history.

Similar Asteroid Impact events are waiting in the wings—or are already in motion. The most notable of these is climate change, which is already profoundly impacting the world economy and creating vast misery. It will take prodigious human innovation and effort to survive its corollary effects, such as drought, famine, and disease.

It is a frightening prospect. But there is a ray of light in this gathering darkness. It is that our tools to meet and solve these challenges are also increasing in number and improving at exponential rates. In this arms race, they are giving us an increasingly powerful ability to address emerging problems.

Technology has always been a major driver of human progress. Indeed, Ray Kurzweil contends that it might be the only major driver of that progress. Now that we have a dozen technologies riding on top of the exponentially growing power of computation, there is indeed cause for optimism. As Peter likes to say, "The world's biggest problems are the world's biggest business opportunities," and "If you want to become a billionaire, help a billion people."

The Oldest Dream

In the midst of all of this technological advance, there is one disruption that is so stunning, so positive, and so unprecedented in human history that we still have trouble imagining that it can possibly be true.

That disruption is abundance.

The story of humankind has been continuously defined by shortages—food, warmth, health, medicine, and shelter.

Scarcity, in fact, has been the driving force for homo sapiens since the species emerged. Scarcity has led to untold deaths during famine, war, disease, and natural disasters. By comparison, periods of abundance have been brief, in small geographic locations, and available only to a few powerful or lucky individuals.

But now, for the first time, we appear to be entering into an Age of Abundance. It is such a stunning turn of events that it's hard to wrap our minds around the impact that abundance is having and will have on humanity. Something astounding is happening. And what is driving this ultimate disruption is, once again, the exponential pace of technological innovation.

Peter has written extensively on this topic, including his *New York Times* best-selling book, *Abundance: The Future is Better Than You Think*. In his second book, *BOLD*, he argued that six exponential forces—the "Six *D*s"—are driving us towards universal abundance:

1. **Digitalization.** Once something goes from physical to digital (i.e., from atoms to ones and zeroes), it gains the ability to grow exponentially and can spread at the speed of the internet.
2. **Deception.** As discussed above, when a product or service is digitized and starts on its exponential growth, the initial numbers are small, and their growth goes largely unnoticed to outside observers.
3. **Disruption.** At some point, the new exponential technology grows so fast and spreads so far that it completely disrupts the status quo. Double something 30 times, and it's a billion-fold bigger. This is how the digital camera devastated Kodak film, Netflix ate Blockbuster for lunch, and Google upended libraries and advertising.

4. **Demonetization.** When a product or service becomes fully digitized, the cost of replicating and transmitting that product or service becomes effectively zero. This completely changes the economics. Software is less expensive to design, iterate, and perfect than hardware. And again, proliferation of software becomes virtually free. Meanwhile, downloadable smartphone apps enable access to terabytes of information—music, books, entertainment—at near-zero costs.

5. **Dematerialization.** When we digitize a wide variety of "things," they physically disappear and become apps. Everything from alarm clocks, cameras, records, books, videoconferencing equipment, and flashlights has dematerialized to apps on our smartphones.

6. **Democratization.** When a product or service becomes fully digitized, the cost of transmitting that digital product to anywhere on the planet also approaches zero. As such, rather than marketing in your neighborhood, state, or nation, a success in one location can be a success everywhere. True democratization can happen at shocking speeds. You need to look no further than early 2023 when ChatGPT went from announcement to a million global users in five days and to 100 million users in only two months.

Put all of these *D*s together. Add networking effects, with 8 billion humans participating. Imagine everyone's application of these technologies to fields as essential to human existence as energy, water, education, food production, communications, and healthcare. And then witness the emergence of a new world, defined by unprecedented abundance for everyone, even the most impoverished. Consider the following developments documented in "Our World in Data[14]":

- Between 1820 and 2015, the proportion of humanity living in extreme poverty plummeted from 90% to 10%.
- Between 1800 and 2016, the global literacy rate increased from 15% to more than 80%.
- Between 1800 and 2017, the global child mortality rate plummeted from 42% to under 5%.
- Between 1779 and 2019, average global life expectancy skyrocketed from 30 to more than 75 years.

It's no longer an unusual sight to see a person in, say, Lusaka, Zambia, selling handicrafts on eBay on a smartphone, or an AIDS orphanage raising donations via crowdsourcing, or villagers in a remote corner of India having their hearts tested by a mobile device and the data transmitted for analysis a continent away. Children in isolated villages and towns around the world are getting a real education via YouTube and other Internet sites.

After millennia characterized by periods of devastating famines, droughts, and other lethal shortages; of unequal distribution of medicines, money, and knowledge; technology has come to humanity's rescue. It is the force that is converting scarcity into abundance. And, incredibly, its impact is being felt not just at the bottom of Maslow's hierarchy of needs—in basic nutrition, shelter, and safety—but at the top as well, as every human has an increasing chance at achieving love, esteem, freedom, and self-actualization.

The prospect of endless abundance is a heady dream. But it doesn't come without challenges. For one thing, it's

---

14   "Our World in Data," https://ourworldindata.org/.

happening very quickly—and our ability to adapt to this new reality will be an enormous test for our established institutions, social orders, and collective and personal relationships to the world. As co-author Mike Malone observes, technological revolutions arrive slower than we predict but faster than we are prepared for them.

In addition to COVID, the last decade saw worldwide protests against racial discrimination and a war in Ukraine. There is little doubt that disruptive events will continue to come at us thick and fast. The social and cultural upheaval created by these disruptions and the responses to them—from bureaucratic incompetence to violence and hysteria to repression to euphoria—is not heartening. Humanity needs to evolve its organizations and enterprises to better deal with these potentially civilization-threatening challenges. Just as important, we need to change the nature of our culture. Noted biologist E.O. Wilson summarizes it best: "We have Paleolithic emotions, medieval institutions, and godlike technology."[15]

Consider that all the tensions and conflicts in the world come from the gaps between those three layers: emotions, institutions, and technology. Developing tools to solve those disparities is the work of every world leader in this century. The ExO model is one of those tools. It has the flexibility, adaptability, and velocity of execution to navigate our continuously accelerating world.

In the next chapter, we'll explain why linear organizations, even the most successful ones today, are undependable in the short term and doomed in the long term.

---

[15] "Looking Back Looking Forward: A Conversation with James D Watson and Edward O Wilson," YouTube, October 14, 2014, https://www.youtube.com/watch?v=N8_W2cBAO7s&list=PLcuB9ocQRZCm4-n_TuQKie_L2jlC9Pq2h&t=606s.

2

The Death of the Linear Organization

As technology brings us a world of abundance,
access will triumph over ownership.

—*Exponential Organizations*, First Edition

Ownership Equals Value

Human beings have always worked to own valuable items and then trade access to them. This behavior started in tribes, was adopted by clans, and then spread to empires, nation-states, and, most recently, global markets, making possible ever-larger human institutions. Value has always been generated by owning more land, more equipment, more machinery, more people. Ownership was the perfect strategy for managing scarce resources and ensuring a relatively predictable, stable environment.

The more you had—that is, the more value you "owned"—the wealthier and more powerful you were. Of course, to manage your assets, you needed people. Lots of them. If a plot of land was twice as big, you needed twice as many people to farm or protect it. Luckily, because our span of control couldn't reach very far across the landscape, this was a workable arrangement.

Of course, once we reached the critical mass of people needed to manage or protect our owned assets, we created hierarchies. In every tribe or village, there was an implicit or explicit hierarchical order to the power structure. The bigger the tribe, the bigger the hierarchy.

Then, beginning in the Middle Ages but not fully taking hold until the Industrial Revolution and the rise of the modern corporation, that local hierarchical structure was ultimately mapped onto companies and government. That model has, with limited modification, endured ever since.

Beyond Arithmetic

Today, we still manage and measure ourselves on a linear scale. That is: x amount of work takes y amount of resources; $2x$ needs $2y$, and so on. Although automation, mass production, robotics, and even computer virtualization have altered the slope of this line, it remained linear. If one concrete mixer truck replaces 100 laborers hand-mixing concrete, then two trucks replace 200 laborers. Similarly, much of society is also measured on this basis: the number of doctors per 100,000 patients, class size per teacher, GDP, and energy per capita. Labor is paid hourly, as are legal fees, and housing is priced by the square foot.

In business, the way we build most products and services continues to mirror this linear, incremental, sequential thinking. The classic way to build a product, be it a giant airliner or a plastic toy, is through a template stage-gate process called New Product Development, or NPD. It includes the following steps:

1. Idea generation
2. Idea screening
3. Concept development and testing
4. Business analysis
5. Beta and market testing
6. Technical implementation
7. Commercialization
8. New product pricing

So codified is this process into the DNA of modern business that there is even a designated industry association for it, called the Product Development and Management Association (PDMA).

This linear paradigm also remains pervasive across the world economy, merely taking on different names in its different incarnations. In software development, for example, it's been called the *waterfall approach*. And while new development methods, like Agile, have cropped up to short-circuit this approach and parallelize some of its steps, the basic paradigm is still linear and incremental. Whether you are making locomotives or iPhone apps, linear product development remains the dominant paradigm.

Revisiting COVID-19, let's note that a pandemic is an exponential problem. Yet for many months, the responses were incremental and linear, and the problem exploded on us. Human institutions largely implement linear solutions because our brains can process and comprehend them.

But as we see from Chapter 1, the world is now operating at exponential speeds. So how have organizations responded? For the most part, they have not. If you attempt disruptive innovation in a traditional organization, it will get attacked by the organization's internal immune system. One of two outcomes is typical. Either the disruptive idea is rejected outright, or it gets so diluted by consensus-building that all its disruptive aspects are lost.

As the ExO community has found, many companies let their "innovation departments" put on a show of pursuing radical innovation, mostly to impress customers and shareholders. In reality, however, they are content when those departments contribute nothing—or, at most, incremental, linear advances—to disrupt the status quo. Many teams are actually discouraged from the radically disruptive thinking that might get their company out of its box, much less thinking that might get the company out of the industry within which it's comfortable. Thus, linear thinking actually reinforces inertia and lack of risk-taking—characteristics that are fatal in an Exponential world.

The bottom line is this: when you think linearly, when your operations are linear, and when all of your measures of performance and success are linear, you cannot help but end up with a linear organization, one that sees the world through a linear lens. Linear organizations tend to be:

- Sequential in thinking and operations
- Organizationally top-down and hierarchical
- Driven primarily by financial outcomes
- Restrained by budgets that aren't linked to impact goals but rather short-term outcomes and shareholder return

- Focused on manageable, incremental growth (10% versus 10x)
- Driven by innovation primarily from within
- Focused on the past when it comes to strategic planning
- Risk intolerant
- Inflexible in process
- Resigned to needing large numbers of employees
- Committed to owning all of their own assets; and,
- Ultimately, massively invested in the status quo.

As noted business author John Hagel once quipped, "Our organizations are set up to withstand risk and resist change from the outside," rather than to embrace those changes, even when they're useful. Famed aerospace engineer Burt Rutan (creator of SpaceShipOne) further observed: "Today's organizations are designed to defend and not to question."

Not surprisingly, given all of these limiting—and even destructive—characteristics, linear organizations rarely disrupt their own products or services. They haven't the tools, the tolerance, or the mandate to do so. Moreover, their well-established corporate cultures will actively sabotage such activities.

Instead, what they will do, and what they are built to do, is keep getting bigger in order to take advantage of economies of scale. Scale—but linear scale—is the very reason for the existence of linear organizations. John Seely Brown calls this "scalable efficiency" and maintains that it is the paradigm that drives most corporate strategies and architectures.

Clayton Christensen immortalized and warned against this type of thinking in his business classic, *The Innovator's Dilemma: When New Technologies Cause Great Firms to Fall*. Still, the strategy of scale dominates business life throughout the world. Reid Hoffman and Chris Yeh document this quest in their book *Blitzscaling: The Lightning-Fast Path to Building Massively Valuable Companies.*

Lost in the Matrix

One of the biggest innovation challenges faced by most large corporations is that they organize in a matrix structure.

In this scheme, product management, branding, and sales are typically aligned vertically, and support functions, such as legal, HR, marketing, finance, and IT, are usually horizontal. Thus, for example, a person handling legal operations often has two reporting lines: one to the head of product (who has revenue accountability) and the other to the head of legal (whose job it is to ensure consistency across numerous products). The support functions rarely use cross-functional teams.

Typically, the internal data these operations handle exists in silos. At one point, Citigroup had more than 300 different customer databases, with each product team (e.g., mortgages, loans, savings) jealously guarding their data from others in the same company.

The appeal of this model is obvious: it is great for command and control, and that's what management loves even more than productivity.

On the other hand, the matrix structure is terrible for accountability, speed, and risk tolerance. Every time an innovative or ambitious employee tries to do something fresh and new, that employee has to obtain authorization from all the risk-averse managers in HR, legal, accounting, and much of the rest of the management ranks. That process takes time, and approval typically depends on a veto held by one or two people with the least amount of intelligent and useful data on the proposed project. This, of course, naturally leads to proposals with facts and figures "massaged" to beat the system at the cost of a realistic chance of success. Eventually, that innovative or ambitious employee gets so tired of such a dysfunctional process that they typically either quit or get fired.

Salim has observed another major issue with matrix structures: over time, power accrues to the horizontals. Because HR and legal value conformity over innovation, they have little incentive to say yes. Thus, over time, their default answer becomes a blanket "no" (which is why HR is often referred to as "inhuman resources"). It's not that HR people are bad people. But, over time, their incentives end up at cross purposes with those of product managers.

The Cost of Size

Over the last few decades, the all-consuming race to achieve economies of scale has resulted in an explosion of large, globalized corporations. At the same time, the comparable pressure for higher and higher profit margins has led to such phenomena as offshoring, international expansion, and mega-mergers in the name of cutting costs, increasing revenues, and improving the bottom line.

Of course, as we've learned in recent years, each of these strategic moves has come at a great (and usually) unexpected cost. That's because the flip side of increased size is decreased flexibility. However hard they try, large companies with extensive facilities and tens of thousands of employees scattered around the world are increasingly challenged to operate nimbly in a world that's continually speeding up. As Jim Harris, bestselling author and ExO community member remarks, "Disruption completely confounds most experts and executives because it renders traditional business models of large, well established, incumbent industry players completely irrelevant."

Large, matrixed organizations—not to mention small and medium-sized businesses—tend to find it extremely difficult to be agile enough to implement and maintain the disruptive changes like those we saw during the pandemic. The global lockdown forced the world's corporations to accelerate their recognition of this phenomenon and to act accordingly. ExO Africa cofounder Kelley Rowe noticed early on in the pandemic that the lockdown helped many enterprises finally see that many—perhaps most—of their employees could in fact work from anywhere in the world and that they did not need to sit at the same desk, in the same building, eight hours a day, day in and day out. Increasingly, senior executives realized that not every business needs massive, fixed overheads to achieve productivity from their employees. But then, as the lockdowns lifted, many employers again demanded that employees return to their desks.

(S)Mothered by the Immune System

If you read the original *Exponential Organizations*, you may recall we talked about corporate "immune systems." Salim first heard this framing from Jeff Kowalski, then the CTO of Autodesk. Here's how they work: the mother company, sensing Exponential change—too much money devoted to or too many of the organization's top talents working toward a new initiative, a potentially disruptive shift in focus, or the creation of a wholly new market—initiates an autoimmune response. That is, it releases antibodies to attack and kill the startup from within. Corporate immune systems act as key retrograde forces to organizational change and innovation. You will hear comments like: "That is an unproven strategy, and we can't afford to waste capital and employee time pursuing that approach." Or declarations such as, "None of our competitions is pursuing that market. It's clearly a waste of time and resources." The ultimate killing phrases include: "That is just risking too much and could destroy the company" and "That will be too hard to even try."

Riaz Shah, the Global Head of Learning at Ernst and Young, trains 100,000 new hires annually. The following image from Riaz is his take on the immune system:

Typical Immune System Responses

We've never done it before.
Nobody else has ever done it.
It has never been tried before.
We tried it before.
Another company tried it before.
We've been doing it this way for years.
It won't work in a small company.
It won't work in a large company.
It won't work in our company.
Why change — it's working OK.
The boss will never buy it.
It needs further investigation.
Our competitors are not doing it.
It's too much trouble to change.
Our company is different.
It's too radical a change.
It's beyond my responsibility

Credit: Riaz Shah

It's not my job.
Marketing says it can't be done.
Sales says it can't be done.
The service department won't like it.
So and so says it can't be done.
It can't be done.

50 reasons
not to change

We don't have the money.
We don't have the personnel.
We don't have the equipment.
The union will scream.
It's too visionary.
You can't teach an old dog new tricks.
We don't have the time.
It will obsolete other procedures.

Customers won't buy it.
It's contrary to policy.
It will increase overhead.
The employees will never buy it.
It's not our problem.
I don't like it.
You're right, but…
It won't work in this department.
It's impossible
We're not ready for it.
It needs more thought.
Management won't accept it.
We can't take the chance.
We'd lose money on it.
It takes too long to pay out.
We're doing all right as it is.
It needs committee study.
Competition won't like it.
It needs sleeping on.
It's impossible.

Too many people who have worked for a business—especially a large enterprise—are familiar with corporate immune systems. The unlucky among them know what it's like to fall victim to their antibodies. Especially vulnerable to corporate immune systems are startup acquisitions whose dynamic culture (the reason they were acquired) is almost always quashed during integration, squandering much of the value.

This immune response can take many forms, from the passive-aggressive and anonymous blocking of approvals and necessary resources to direct, career-ending attacks. It renders big organizations extremely vulnerable to today's relentless Exponential disruption.

Abandoning Linear

Traditional linear thinking simply cannot compete in our emerging Exponential World. Salim saw this firsthand at Yahoo in 2007. Despite its Web bona fides, Yahoo operated within a classic linear matrix organizational structure. Every time a new product or feature was launched, the team behind it had to jump through multiple approval hoops—branding, legal, privacy, PR, etc. Each step took days or weeks to complete, which meant that any potential competitive advantage had already been lost by the time it was finished—usually to some new startup that sprang up to take quick advantage of the opportunity. Indeed, it was Salim's experience at Yahoo that led him to search for a better way—and to elucidate his model of the Exponential Organization.

Even the most lauded, progressive companies have not entirely escaped the linear trap. It may surprise the reader to learn that the mighty Google struggles with this, too. For example, it took two years and enormous effort to get its Google+ social network system out the door. That product was brilliantly crafted, but by the time of its launch in the summer of 2011, Facebook already had an almost insurmountable lead. In the end, Google closed down Google+ in April 2019.

While we focus in this chapter on big companies, let's not forget that the struggles we've documented are even worse in governments and nonprofits. And even some of our established institutions have terrible immune systems: academia, for example, or—even worse—organized religion. To their credit, in 2017, the Vatican asked Salim to run a workshop for their senior leaders. The immune system of the Catholic Church is 1,500 years old!

Beyond Fast

In contrast to lumbering, linear institutions, Exponential Organizations are fast. And they get faster all the time.

It's hard to overstate just how quickly an ExO can move. After all, we already live in a very fast-moving economy. Thanks to streamlined supply chains, shortened approval cycles, and improved distribution channels, even modern linear corporations boast about how quickly they can bring products and services to market compared to the slower-moving companies of the past. The timeframe from a new startup to global impact has shrunk dramatically. It used to take about 20 years to get to a billion-dollar market cap or "unicorn" status. Today, the average time to unicorn status is just over seven years.[16] Clubhouse and iCarbonX took about six months to get there; NuCom group reached unicorn status in 52 days, and Avant did it in 46. We saw the explosive launch of ChatGPT, which reached a hundred million users in under two months.

In April 2023, Jeremiah Owyang, Ben Parr, and Chris Saad tweeted a prediction: "The next billion-dollar startup will only have three employees." The culture of that startup would be "AI first," and it would use autonomous AI agents

---

[16] Irfan Ahmad, "Which Unicorn Companies Reached $1 Billion the Fastest?," Digital Information World, April 12, 2022, https://www. digitalinformationworld.com/2022/04/how-long-does-it-take-for-startup-to.html.

to get work done. All marketing and sales would be automated via AI bots, and the three employees would be:

1. **The CEO,** who would handle vision and purpose and lead public-facing marketing. She would also code and be involved in engineering.
2. **The Product Lead,** who would interface with customers and team to manage the product roadmap and drive development
3. **The Operations Lead,** who would be responsible for the outcome of the AI bots and handle finance and legal and smooth operations.

We believe that thousands, or perhaps tens of thousands, of startups are being built right now using a similar formula. Most will fail, but the cost of trying is almost zero. If only a small percentage of these succeed, they will drive the entire future of the economy.

For an existing, traditional, linear company, this mindset is very nearly impossible. As we've seen, most struggle just to get a product to market in that timeframe. Companies like P&G or Unilever typically take close to one year to launch a new product. Their decision-making and approval cycles are just too slow. So are their manufacturing lines, their supply and distribution channels, and their ability to hire additional employees.

By comparison, ExOs—and all of these unicorns are ExOs—either eschew these slow-moving processes, contract them out, or crowdsource them. That's why they can move so quickly. And that's why they can remain small and still achieve historically unprecedented rates of productivity per employee.

Exponential Organizations are founded by innovative owners who value speed and early adoption of innovation.

Think Tesla/SpaceX and Elon Musk, Amazon and Jeff Bezos, Apple and Steve Jobs. In these companies, the visionary tech founder has the ability to dictate speed and direction. From inception, these company cultures are oriented toward rapid Experimentation and data-driven decision-making rather than the comfort of humans living in the status quo.

In the very traditional CPG (consumer packaged goods) industry, Unilever or P&G takes about 300 days to go from an initial product idea to a Walmart shelf. Quirky, one of the original batch of ExOs, achieved the same task in just 29 days.

Ownership vs. Access

In 2007, two months after the launch of the Apple iPhone, Finnish mobile phone giant Nokia spent a staggering $8.1 billion to buy Navteq, a navigation and road-mapping company that had embedded physical traffic sensors in a quarter-million miles of roads in 35 cities across Europe. Nokia pursued Navteq because it could dominate mapping, as well as mobile and online local information—assets that would act as a defensive barrier against the increasing market predations of Google and Apple.

During its quest for an acquisition, Nokia actually looked at and passed over, a small Israeli company called Waze, which crowdsourced location information by leveraging the GPS sensors on its users' phones as they sped down local streets and highways.

Within two years, Waze was gathering traffic data from as many sources as Navteq had road sensors. Within four years, it had 10 times as many sources. Today, Waze has more than 140 million daily users around the world—and fully 100 times the traffic signals of Navteq/Nokia. Moreover, it doesn't own those sensors and its users upgrade their own phones and GPS devices. By contrast, the Navteq sensor system was a fixed asset—and upgrading it cost a fortune.

As you may already have guessed, the Nokia/Navteq acquisition failed spectacularly. By June 2012, five years after the first iPhones appeared in stores, Nokia's market valuation had collapsed from $140 billion to $8.2 billion—that is, about what it had spent to acquire Navteq.

Looking back, it's easy to dismiss the foolishness of Nokia's business decision. At the time, however, Nokia's move not only seemed entirely justifiable but was also viewed as bold and brilliant. Some business analysts considered the acquisition a potential game-changer—one that might enable Nokia to dominate the world's cellular phone business for decades to come.

Nokia's acquisition of Navteq is a classic example of a linear organization thinking linearly. Waze, by comparison, is an example of an Exponential Organization and non-linear thinking.

The lesson we can learn from the last dozen years embodies many of Peter Diamandis's Six Ds, described in the previous chapter. Navteq's sensors were expensive physical objects that required installation and maintenance. In contrast, Waze's use of crowdsourced data from its users' phones was a digitalization, dematerialization, and ultimately a demonetization of traffic data.

Waze's triumph and Navteq's decline should be the model for every budding ExO. Ask yourself, "Which of my products or services can I digitize and dematerialize?" and "How can I use the Six Ds to leapfrog my biggest linear competitors? How can I use them to demonetize and democratize my products and/or services?"

Since we wrote *Exponential Organizations*, several fully exponential companies have climbed quickly into the top ranks of their industries. Uber, for example, has been valued at more than $80 billion—with few assets and no driver employees. Airbnb, with a similar valuation, does not own the properties rented on its site; they are owned by non-employee "hosts." Both companies are growing exponentially.

With that book, and in the years since, we have tried to make a strong case to you that the world is currently undergoing an "asteroid impact" period of rapidly accelerating change. As with the dinosaurs 65 million years ago, the slow and lumbering companies—those unable to make rapid and nimble changes—will go extinct. Those companies who are born as, or become, ExOs have the opportunity to dominate the new world ahead. Today's asteroid impact has created the right conditions for the creation and cultivation of a new breed of organization.

Key Takeaways

1. While the information-based world is now moving exponentially, most of our organizational structures are still very linear (this is especially true for the largest organizations and governments).
2. Linear organizational structures evolved to deliver predictability and to maximize efficiency. This model works well for scarcity, but the world is moving towards increasing abundance.
3. We've learned how to scale technology; now it's time to scale organizations.
4. Matrix structures don't work in an exponential, information-based world.

5. The Six *D*s of exponential growth—Digitization, Deceptive growth, Disruptive growth, Dematerialization, Demonetization, and Democratization—are a road map for companies that want to become ExOs.

David S. Rose, author of the best-selling book *Angel Investing: The Gust Guide to Making Money and Having Fun Investing in Startups*, sums it up most dramatically:

"Any company designed for success in the 20th century is doomed to failure in the 21st."

3

What is an Exponential Organization?

Indeed, the rate of change is so high everywhere these days that
you now must assume that someone will disrupt you, and often
from a direction you least expect.

—*Exponential Organizations*, First Edition

In the original *Exponential Organizations*, we told the story
of one of the most iconic events of the era: the introduction of the Apple iPhone in January 2007. The birth of
the iPhone was an augury of a revolution in the business
world. Everything in high tech turned upside down that day.
All existing strategies in consumer electronics were quickly
rendered obsolete. Almost instantly, the entire future of the
digital world was up for grabs to those willing to pursue the
implications of this new model.

Six months before the iPhone launch, however, a less heralded but ultimately much more important event took place, at least for our purposes. In August 2006, Amazon launched its EC2 cloud services, now known as AWS or Amazon Web Services.

These two events, occurring within months of each other, comprise the asteroid impact that changed the business world forever. This was the birth of the Exponential Organization. The iPhone created a new model for consumer engagement via the App Store. AWS allowed any startup to move computing off the balance sheet to a variable cost. Collectively, these two developments applied Peter's Six *D*s to computing. The cost of a Silicon Valley startup dropped from several million dollars to several thousand dollars, and a Cambrian explosion of new organizational forms emerged.

What's an ExO?

Here's how we defined an ExO back in 2014:

> *An Exponential Organization (ExO) is one whose impact (or output) is disproportionally large—at least 10x larger— compared to its peers because of the use of new organizational techniques that leverage accelerating technologies.*

We have updated this definition for two reasons. First, what happens if multiple companies all operate as ExOs? How do you distinguish 10x (10x of what?)? Second, we discovered that the fundamental economic driver of an ExO is that it finds ways of radically dropping the marginal cost of supply (e.g., Waze or Airbnb).

So, in 2023, here's our new definition of an ExO:

An ExO is a purpose-driven, agile, and scalable organization that uses accelerating technologies to digitize, dematerialize, democratize, and demonetize its products and services, resulting in a 10x performance increase over its non-ExO peers.

ExO Attributes

Let's now list the major characteristics of Exponential Organizations. These are based on our original research plus the last eight years of experience.

The first stands alone: Massive Transformative Purpose (MTP). As the name suggests, MTP is the ExO's core reason for existing. MTP is the foundation upon which all company actions take place. It establishes a long-term goal for the company so sweeping and profound that it is always within reach yet always unreachable. It sets a moral foundation for all company interactions between all stakeholders. It keeps the company disciplined and on target. It inspires employees and customers. And it galvanizes employee morale and retention.

Beyond MTP, 10 key attributes define and power ExOs. The first five characteristics are the "outward-facing" traits of an ExO and are encapsulated by the acronym SCALE.

SCALE: Outward-Facing Characteristics

1. **Staff on Demand:** Increasing speed and functionality by leveraging external workers according to need rather than hiring internal employees.

2. **Community and Crowd:** Attracting, engaging, and leveraging communities and the crowd, whose like-mindedness adds to creativity, validation, and even funding efforts.
3. **AI & Algorithms:** Leveraging automated functions (machine learning, deep learning, etc.) to obtain new insights and automate operations and services.
4. **Leveraged Assets:** Accessing, sharing, renting, or otherwise outsourcing assets to remain nimble and reduce capital expenditures.
5. **Engagement:** Leveraging outside interest through gamification, digital reputation systems, incentive programs, and crypto economics to create network effects and positive feedback loops.

The next five attributes of an ExO are inward-facing. They are encapsulated by the acronym IDEAS.

IDEAS: Inward-Facing Characteristics

1. **Interfaces:** Different ways of interacting, processing, and automating the SCALE attributes so the organization is doing the right work at the right time.
2. **Dashboards:** Making real-time information, with essential company and employee metrics based on Objectives and Key Results (OKRs), accessible to everyone internally, with short feedback loops.
3. **Experimentation:** Introducing lean startup methodology in all departments, with new ideas and processes, culturally enabling rapid, validated learning.
4. **Autonomy:** Instituting a flat structure that allows individual employees or multidisciplinary teams to operate independently and effectively.

5. **Social Technologies:** Leveraging peer-to-peer collaborative tools to facilitate transparent, real-time conversations across the organization.

As we mentioned in the beginning of the book, in the Note to the Reader, we have found the best visual metaphor for the ExO model is the brain and its two hemispheres. We call this the ExO Mind Map™. The five SCALE attributes represent creativity and growth, and the five IDEAS attributes deliver the control framework and drive culture.

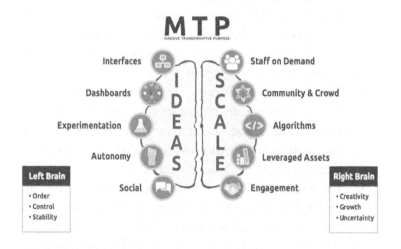

Beyond these attributes, an ExO also exhibits certain unique characteristics. Many of these are found in other companies, but they are intrinsic to and inherent for ExOs:

- **Environment:** The ExO is a worthy steward of the environment and a net contributor to the planet's health. This contribution is many times that of its more traditional competitors. In practice, this means an exponential reduction in negative impact (environmental CO_2, reduction of plastic waste, use of recyclables, etc.) combined with a massive positive impact created by the company's offerings.

- **Sustainable Development Goals:** This is a corollary to the MTP. A successful ExO establishes challenging but realizable sustainable development goals to guide its development on the path to its MTP target. Most MTPs will attempt to solve the Sustainable Development Goals (SDGs).
- **Ethics:** An ExO, from the start, develops, unanimously ratifies among all stakeholders, and adheres to a globally valid code of ethical conduct that will discipline and color all of its operations for the life of the enterprise.
- **People:** The ExO rates higher than its traditional competitors on all measures of employee and customer satisfaction, loyalty, and retention. It does so by creating a rewarding work environment and providing a sense of career purpose.
- **Productivity:** ExO employees, by leveraging the multiplier power of technology, exhibit a productivity per employee that is a 10x multiple of linear competitors. This, in turn, means total employment numbers that are a fraction of those of their competitors.
- **Near-zero marginal costs:** ExOs are uniquely able, due to new technologies, innovative organizational models, social networks, crowdsourcing, and other tools, to drive the cost to as near zero as possible for the manufacture, market, and sales of each unit.
- **Income:** Due to the radical drop in costs and the ability to scale externally with community and leveraged

assets, ExOs enjoy fast and consistent growth in both revenues and profits.

- **Intangible assets:** ExOs exhibit measurable improvement in social, environmental, and societal capital through continuous, rapid growth in intellectual (as opposed to physical) capital.

The Outstanding Performance of ExOs

In 2014, in the original *Exponential Organizations,* we listed the top 100 companies[17] that used the ExO model the most. Listed below are the top 10 from that overall list and how they've done since 2014.

ExO	2014 valuation	2022 valuation	Comments
Github (founded 2008)	~$2 billion	~$7.5 billion	Bought by Microsoft in 2018 for $7.5 billion
Airbnb (2008)	$13 billion	$105.8 billion	IPO in 2020
Uber (2009)	$17 billion	$81.3 billion	IPO in 2019
Indiegogo (2008)	$300 million	unknown	Still private
Google (1998)	$359 billion	$1917 billion	Still the 2nd largest company

---

[17] "The Top 100 Exponential Organizations," OpenExO, https://old. openexo.com/top100/.

ExO	2014 valuation	2022 valuation	Comments
Quirky (2009)	$4.6 million	0	Failed
Kaggle (2010)	unknown	unknown	Acquired by Google— unknown $$, but registered users increased 20x since 2014
Pinterest (2009)	$5 billion	$23.7 billion	IPO in 2019
Reddit (2005)	$412 million	$14.1 billion	Raised Series F in 2021
Etsy (2005)	$1.2 billion	$10.3 billion	IPO in 2015

For the top 10 ExOs, the average increase in market cap (where fully measurable) was 990% (9.9x) over eight years. The S&P companies grew an average of 2.5x over that same time. In other words, our top 10 ExOs outperformed the S&P by about four times. This is consistent with the results we saw measuring the Fortune 100.

**In general, organizations fully applying the ExO Model outperform
those that don't use the attributes by a multiple of
about 4x.**

ExOs and Governments

Since the launch of the ExO model in 2014, several dozen governments have used the book to organize their activities. Nishan Degnarain used the ExO model to organize the Ministry of Oceans in Mauritius. The City of Miami and Miami-Dade County have implemented the model in various ways. Medellín, Colombia, has actively deployed the ExO model in Ruta N, the city's innovation arm. The Prime Minister of Thailand tagged his election campaign as "Exponential Thailand." Lord Anthony St. John proclaimed on the floor of the UK House of Lords, "We should run the NHS on this [Exponential Organizations] book" while waving a copy. And the United Arab Emirates has essentially become an ExO country, with 10x targets for many of its government ministries. The third book in this series is planned as "ExOs for Government and Society." Note that governments have a natural MTP of serving the citizenry.

The Challenge for Big Corporations

As the economy skews increasingly exponential, the largest corporations will have to adapt and ultimately become ExOs, in order to survive.

This is clear from the Fortune 100 data. Shareholders, watching their company's market share decline, profits shrink, and stock prices fall, will demand that those companies change, even if it requires a shareholder revolt and the firing of senior management—which will be replaced with a more progressive one, committed to making the firm exponential. Those who don't make the move—or who move too slowly—will limp along for a few years until their assets are ultimately acquired by successful ExOs, or are driven into bankruptcy.

Many of the companies that were born in the 20th century, in an analog and linear world, will need to transform. Their traditional products and services will no longer be relevant, nor will they be competitive. Most will be unable to cope with a digital, exponential world. With disruption coming, how will society deal with the massive unemployment and dislocation that will follow their demise?

For big companies, there is, in fact, a prescriptive path to transforming into an ExO. Indeed, the ExO community has worked over the last eight years to successfully transform big corporations. To date, we have engaged with more than 100 blue-chip corporations. We will cover corporate transformation extensively in our second planned book in this series (anticipated in 2024), but in summary, here's the top-level, three-step plan for transforming an existing corporation:

- **Step 1 - Awake:** Run an "Awake" session to alert senior management to an exponential future. The CEO and board must accept the need for disruptive change and ultimately drive this transformation.
- **Step 2 - Sprint:** Run a 10-week ExO Sprint,[18] which transforms culture at scale and solves the immune system problem.
- **Step 3 - Incubate:** Create an incubator at the edge of the company that takes a portfolio of disruptive ideas and executes them, aiming at adjacent industries.

---

[18] "Exo Sprint," OpenExO, July 20, 2023, https://openexo.com/exo-sprint/.

It's not obvious, but the biggest companies in the world already operate like this. Google built an incubator called GoogleX to incubate radical ideas (the organization is now known simply as "X" within the Alphabet ecosystem). Amazon is the quintessential ExO in its ruthless application of Dashboards, Experimentation, and other ExO attributes.

But perhaps the biggest master of the ExO technique is the largest company in the world, Apple. Apple has a very simple modus operandi. Yes, it has an incredible design team, and yes, it has an amazing technology supply chain, but others have access to these. Salim maintains that Apple's secret is its organizational design. Unlike any other company, Apple forms small, hyper-disruptive teams, places those teams at the edge of the company, keeps them secret, and then directs those teams to disrupt some industry. The result is that Apple has a portfolio of teams at the edge of the organization analyzing different industries. When they think retail—or watches, or payments—is ready for disruption, they pounce: entering that market and folding that offering back into the vast Apple ecosystem. That's it. That's why they're the biggest company in the world. And there is no limit to Apple's size. They just pick an industry, challenge it, own it, and then wash/rinse/repeat. What's coming next? Healthcare, automotive, finance? When Apple broke through $1 trillion of market capitalization, Salim was one of the first to say they'd break two trillion very soon afterward. As of this writing, they have just surpassed $3 trillion.

• • •

For his book *Reinventing Organizations*,[19] author Frederic Laloux researched those rare organizations around the world that have thrown away the traditional top-down organizational structure and created organizations of distributed intelligence and distributed power. Essentially, he's describing ExOs. These companies were located all around the world, across multiple industries, and many have been in operation for decades in very tough markets. Yet they outperform the competition every time. They did it, and so can you.

Every reader of this book—whether you are a long-time follower of ExO theory or you are just learning about it for the first time—has the potential to learn its lessons, implement its tools and join the ranks of those wildly successful firms. No matter how old or hidebound or traditional your enterprise, the door is still open to transform yourself into a fast-moving, world-changing, Exponential Organization. It takes only the will to start down that path. And to motivate you a bit more, remember that you don't really have a choice: any other alternative will likely lead to oblivion.

---

[19] "Reinventing Organizations," REINVENTING ORGANIZA-TIONS, https://www.reinventingorganizations.com/.

Key Resources/Links where you can learn more

- Organizing and running an Awake Session
    - https://help.openexo.com/en/articles/34
      67603-organizing-and-running-an-
      awake-session
- Learn more about a Sprint
    - https://openexo.com/exo-sprint/
- The Fortune 100 List
    - https://openexo.com/f100-list/
- ExO Database
    - https://openexo.com/exo-global/
- Peter Diamandis puts out two weekly blogs on
  Exponential Technologies and Longevity
    - http://www.Diamandis.com/blogs
- Peter's Abundance360 Summit for exponential
  leaders
    - http://www.A360.com
- Singularity University's programs
    - http://www.SU.org

4

Massive Transformative Purpose

In an ExO world, purpose trumps strategy and execution overrides planning.

—*Exponential Organizations*, First Edition

The three things you'll learn in this chapter

- Every ExO should have a Massive Transformative Purpose (MTP)—it's the one mandatory attribute of an Exponential Organization.
- How your MTP guides you and your organization.
- How to create both an individual and an organizational MTP.

I n 2015, Paul Polman, CEO of the UK-based consumer products giant Unilever, read *Exponential Organizations*. He was so intrigued by its ideas and predictions that he had Salim speak to the top 200 Unilever executives. The company subsequently ordered every one of its brands to take on a purpose-driven, MTP-driven future. As of 2020, the five most profitable Unilever brands were the ones most driven by an explicit Massive Transformative Purpose.

A Company's Most Important Asset

Eight years spent gathering hard data have convinced us more than ever that the Massive Transformative Purpose (MTP) is the single most important attribute of a true Exponential Organization.

Most people spend the majority of their waking hours working. Sadly, much of that work is not connected to something meaningful—and thus, it is often unfulfilling in the long run. MTPs are transformative because they connect work to a broader sense of meaning and purpose.

We live in an increasingly secular age in which emerging generations want more meaning in their work lives. Today, this desire remains largely unfulfilled. We believe being part of an organization or enterprise driven by an MTP can help fill that void by providing all-important context and meaning. We further believe this trend will only accelerate.

Living up to your MTP is hard work and will inevitably entail countless risks, setbacks, and restarts. But when you are trying to make a dent in the universe or solve the world's biggest problems, it will be worth it.

As Suman Sasmal maintains, "Very few things don't happen in the world because people didn't have the knowledge to do it. Most things don't happen because they did not have an intent to do it".

MTP Defined

A Massive Transformative Purpose reflects an organization's highest aspiration: the core, defining purpose of its existence. An MTP describes the change in the world that you want to achieve, the fundamental problem you are trying to solve, while recognizing that that change will not be accomplished, the problem solved, in the short term. The MTP is designed to inspire focused action, express your passions, and create an emotional connection that drives you and others toward meaningful, positive, and common change.

By definition, an MTP is likely never fully realizable. For example, Google's MTP is to "Organize the world's information." Google will never fully organize *all* the world's information—but that MTP still will remain its goal.

MTPs are distinct from simple "purpose." All MTPs are purpose-driven, but purposeful organizations aren't necessarily Massive or Transformative. Rather, MTPs are *passion*-driven and provide clarity on an organization's emotional drivers: What gets you super excited? What drives your passion? And because they are passion-driven, MTPs instill an emotional energy and create a gravitational force around which communities gather. This is the most important outcome of a proper MTP: it generates the kind of cultural movement—that is, it generates a community—that authors John Hagel and John Seely Brown have called the *Power of Pull*.[20] The MTP is so inspirational that an aggregation

---

[20]   John Hagel, John Seely Brown, and Lang Davison, *The Power of Pull: How Small Moves, Smartly Made, Can Set Big Things in Motion* (New York, NY: Basic Books, 2010).

of followers forms around the ExO and then spontaneously begins operating on its own.

Ultimately, this aggregation creates its own community, tribe, and culture that, in time, generate their own style, mores, and attitudes. Think of those lines outside the Apple Store, the waiting list for TED's annual conference, or the vast crowds at Comic-Cons: these are people who likely have never met, yet they share a common attitude and purpose. When they do meet, they feel as though they've known each other forever. The MTP is the most human aspect of any organization, thus, the most relatable.

Peter describes an MTP to the companies and CEOs he mentors as follows: "Your MTP will be the filter through which you see opportunities in the world and will serve as your North Star in a world of ever-increasing abundance, distractions, and demands on your time."

The MTP is *not* an advertising slogan or even a traditional "mission statement," which focuses on what the company does. Rather, an MTP is declarative. It doesn't say, "We are going to try," but rather, "We will." It is a call to action for a community to gather and help solve a problem.

Apple and TED, in particular, have created enterprise-specific ecosystems based on their MTPs. That is, they have created communities so excited about being part of their products or services that they pull those products and services out from the core organization and assume ownership of them, complete with marketing, support services, and even design and manufacturing.

Francesco Derchi, an adjunct professor at EHL in Lausanne, Switzerland, offered this definition as part of his PhD thesis: "The MTP is an intangible asset, part of the core of the ExO that simultaneously impacts the internal dimension of the enterprise and its culture, the brand and its external activities as well as its competitive strategy."

The MTP Advantage

A strong MTP is especially advantageous to first movers. If the MTP is sufficiently sweeping, there's no place for competitors to go but beneath it, in its shadow. After all, it would be very hard for another organization to pop up and announce, "Hey, we're *also* going to organize the world's information, but better."

By keeping its eye on its MTP North Star, a company can move quickly and strategically to deal with changing circumstances—while never losing its way. As a result, competitors are forced to deal with the previous shift while the company has already moved on to the next one. An MTP further serves as a stabilizing force during periods of rapid growth and enables organizations to scale with less turbulence.

A strong MTP also serves as an excellent recruiter for new talent, as well as a vehicle for retaining top talent—both increasingly difficult tasks in today's hyper-competitive talent marketplace. Further, it is an effective attractor and retainer for customers and for the company's larger eco-system (developers, startups, hackers, NGOs, governments, suppliers, partners, etc.). As a result, it lowers the acquisition, transaction, and retention costs of these stakeholders.

Suman Sasmal, an ExO evangelist in Bangalore, India, puts it nicely "Money can't buy certain things that MTP can—which are emotions. MTPs release an extraordinary amount of emotional capital, which is often left on the table. Finance is not the only capital. Emotional capital can do magical stuff!"

• • •

Of course, MTPs don't operate in isolation. Rather, they create and illuminate a community around them that influences every part of the organization. An impressive example of this is Red Bull, whose MTP is "Giving You Wings." This MTP has empowered the company to look beyond its product line—energy drinks—to the entire world of energy-driven alternative sports, including skateboarding, climbing, and motocross, as well as more established sports like car racing, boxing, baseball, and cricket, both at live events and on television. Indeed, it's hard to find a sport anywhere in the world where Red Bull isn't present as a sponsor.

The result is that a company that otherwise might have been just another player in the energy-drink market has become *the* dominant presence in the worldwide market, with unmatched visibility and a deeply loyal customer base. Meanwhile, employees are hugely proud to be part of such a celebrated company.

The success of companies like Red Bull has not been lost on other firms. As a result, the number of companies devising and adopting their own MTPs has grown exponentially. As a consequence, more and more companies like Unilever are becoming deeply aspirational in their operations. After all, you can't pursue an MTP if you are not prepared to aspire to the uniquely high bar it sets. MTPs create a solid bridge between a brand promise and the real world—a challenge many brands have struggled to overcome.

That aspirational attitude creates its own positive effects: customers feel good about the products and are increasingly proud to be part of a larger, virtuous movement. Employees are proud to give unmatched service and support. Suppliers promote their relationship with the company. Aspirational branding helps lower costs, improve effectiveness, and accelerate learning by leveraging intrinsic, rather than external, motivation.

Finally, embracing an MTP comes with economic advantages. In a world facing many grand challenges, as Peter has noted, "the world's biggest problems are the world's biggest business opportunities." As a result, it's likely that smart investors will incorporate MTPs into their stock portfolio strategies over the next decade. And, of course, customers will want to be associated with a company they see as making the world a better place.

Working with a Purpose

In a paper published in the *Harvard Business Review*, authors Thomas W. Malnight, Ivy Buche, and Charles Dhanaraj described an eight-year study of three forces believed to be the biggest drivers of company growth: creating new markets, changing the rules of the game, and serving larger stakeholder needs.[21] In the process, they found a fourth driver that proved to be the most important of all: *purpose.* They wrote:

> Companies have long been encouraged to build purpose into what they do. But usually, it's talked about as an add-on—a way to create shared value, improve employee morale and commitment, give back to the community, and help the environment. But as we worked with the high-growth companies in our study and beyond, we began to

---

[21] W Malnight, Ivy Buche, and Charles Dhanaraj, "Put Purpose at the Core of Your Strategy," Harvard Business Review, August 27, 2019, https://hbr.org/2019/09/put-purpose-at-the-core-of-your-strategy.

recognize that many of them had moved purpose from the periphery of their strategy to its core—where, with committed leadership and financial investment, they had used it to generate sustained profitable growth, stay relevant in a rapidly changing world and deepen ties with their stakeholders.

This, to us, is an excellent definition of Massive Transformational Purpose.

Malnight, Buche, and Dhanaraj weren't alone in their findings. Indeed, over the last few years, the notion of purpose as a company's defining force has been elucidated in the most unexpected places. For example, Larry Fink, CEO of investment giant BlackRock, has stated that his company will focus on purpose-driven organizations. And the Unilever example from above shows the concrete positive monetary outcome.

During the same time period, several new financial terms and organizational structures have emerged, reflecting a new emphasis on purpose. These include Benefit or B Corporations, the Triple Bottom Line, L3Cs, the Conscious Capital movement, and the Slow Money movement. These entities leverage their MTPs to integrate social and environmental issues—as well as profits—into their business processes. Many of them fall under the rubric of social enterprises.

The Social Life

Social Enterprises (SEs) are emerging in the 21st century as a distinct—and growing—movement. This trend has been led by a number of different foundations (e.g., Ashoka, Skoll), regional movements (e.g., Grameen Bank in Pakistan under Muhammed Yunis), and university business schools (e.g., Oxford, Harvard, Stanford). A 2022 study estimated that there were 11 million social enterprises globally.[22] All of these enterprises, almost by definition, are pursuing their own MTPs and have proclaimed them publicly.

Though their definition remains somewhat amorphous, social enterprises are structured and behave like traditional companies but include strong social benefits in their operations. In theory, SEs generate enough income that they can operate independently without relying on regular capital injections from charitable institutions. To date, only a fraction of SEs have reached that level of self-sufficiency.

Needless to say, not every enterprise can be a social enterprise. On the contrary, the world's economy runs on profit-generating, wealth-creating commercial operations.

That said, the rise of social enterprises has undoubtedly had an impact on the explosion of corporate social responsibility (CSR) programs over the last decade. In 2012, 57% of Fortune 500 companies published a CSR report—double the number from the previous year.[23] By 2019, 90% of the companies on the S&P 500 Index, that bellwether of US stock market performance, published sustainability, corporate responsibility, or citizenship reports in their annual reports.

CSR initiatives are add-ons to most companies' core business. For social enterprises, however, CSR initiatives are

[22] Julie Pybus, First Global Social Enterprise Census reveals 'one of the largest ..., June 7, 2022, https://immersives.pioneerspost.com/how-many-social-enterprises-worldwide/index.html.

[23] "We Can Eat Our Way out of the Climate Crisis," Sustainable Brands, http://www.sustainablebrands.com/news_and_views/articles/sustainability-reporting-among-sp-500-companies-increases-dramatically.

the core business. The Massive Transformational Purpose takes the middle ground: it captures the importance of CSR to social enterprises but embeds it at the center of the ExO—then supercharges it with the highest possible goals. This shift now has been embodied by some larger companies—for example, Patagonia—where positive social impact becomes a core driver of strategy.

Recruiting Off the MTP

Becoming an Exponential Organization, armed with a powerful MTP, is an unmatched recruitment tool for the best and brightest talent.

Martin Seligman, an expert on positive psychology, notes that there are three states of happiness: the pleasurable life, the good life, and the meaningful life. MTPs play a key role in that last state: that of finding purpose, transcending ego, and working toward a higher goal.

Millennials—those born between 1984 and 2002—show an unprecedented orientation towards seeking meaning and purpose in their lives. Worldwide, they are becoming increasingly aspirational and, as such, will be drawn as customers, employees, and investors to equally aspirational organizations—that is, to companies that manifest their beliefs. Ultimately, it is highly likely that this generational cohort will come up with their own MTPs, which will juxtapose, overlap, and symbiotically exist with organizational MTPs.

OpenExo Chief Learning Officer Jaroslav Dokoupil offers the following summary of MTP:

Shoot the Moon

If the most important force in the Exponential Organization is its Massive Transformative Purpose, then the actual execution of that MTP can be viewed as the Corporate Moonshot.

What is the relationship between an MTP and a Moonshot? Think of the MTP as a canvas upon which a company "paints" its Moonshot initiatives. Moonshots need to be pursued within the context of an MTP, both fueled and restrained by it.

How many Moonshots can a company take? As many as it desires and resources allow. Put simply: a company has one MTP, but that MTP can be manifested in multiple Moonshots. Alphabet, for example, has created a division called "X" (their Moonshot factory) led by Astro Teller, their captain of Moonshots. Today X has thousands of employees and dozens of Moonshots at any one time at various stages of development: in medical technology, AI, robotics, communications, and more. Each of these Moonshots is a strategy, a plan to get closer to the MTP. Every Moonshot is fueled by, and in service of, the MTP. The grander the Moonshot, the more its achievement will depend upon exponential technologies.

The name may be new, but great companies have long pursued the philosophy of Moonshots, usually through their research laboratories—think Bell Labs, IBM, Xerox PARC, and 3M. Thanks to today's technology, these activities can now encompass every department within a company in real time.

Importantly, unlike the MTP, Moonshots actually can be achieved. So, if "Making humanity multiplanetary" is an MTP, then "establishing a permanent and self-sustaining presence on Mars" is a Moonshot. The first may never be really accomplished (there are always more planets), but we can complete the second.

Just imagine the possible network effects in a global economy populated by thousands of Exponential Organizations pursuing moonshots to realize world-changing MTPs.

Prerequisites and Interdependencies

The MTP is unique in that it is the prerequisite for all other ExO attributes. As such, it comes before all other attributes and necessarily guides them all. Perhaps the most important prerequisite for an MTP is that the leaders must walk the talk and always position the MTP as central to their activities. It's essential when formulating the MTP that all three letters of the acronym are fully acknowledged and covered.

The Benefits of an MTP

The Massive Transformative Purpose offers a myriad of benefits, including fostering a sense of community by answering the fundamental question of an organization's existence, attracting and retaining top talent through purpose alignment, providing a focused compass for growth, and shifting the organizational focus outward towards delivering value. It also aligns seamlessly with impact-driven models, catalyzes innovation, instills deeper meaning and purpose, facilitates transformation for traditional companies, ensures coherent growth, enhances cultural cohesion, promotes agility and learning, and acts as the organizational glue that binds other attributes of an Exponential Organization.

- **Community Building**: The MTP fosters a sense of community by answering the fundamental question of the organization's existence—Why do you exist? This creates a movement among stakeholders that strengthens the organizational fabric.
- **Talent Attraction and Retention**: An MTP not only attracts top talent but also plays a crucial role in retaining them by offering a purpose that resonates with their career aspirations and personal values.
- **Focused Growth**: During periods of hypergrowth, the MTP serves as a compass that helps the company stay focused and avoid distractions or unnecessary diversions.
- **Outward Focus**: An MTP helps shift the organizational attention from internal politics to delivering value externally, thereby keeping the focus on customers, impact, and stakeholders.

- **Alignment with Impact-Driven Models**: The MTP is highly compatible with impact-driven entrepreneurial models, such as B-Corps, Conscious Capitalism, and Triple Bottom Line, serving as an overarching philosophy for these subsets.
- **Innovation Catalyst**: By setting a transformative agenda, the MTP inspires the development of new products, services, and activities that align with its overarching purpose.
- **Meaning and Purpose**: The MTP provides a deeper sense of meaning and purpose for not just the core team but also the wider community engaged with the organization.
- **Transformational for Traditional Companies**: The MTP is not limited to startups; it also helps traditional companies pivot and transform themselves in alignment with changing market needs and values.
- **Coherent Growth**: MTPs serve as a unifying force that enables coherent exponential growth by aligning collective aspirations and efforts within an organization.
- **Cultural Cohesion**: The adoption of an MTP helps align organizational objectives and fosters a cooperative, non-political culture among team members.
- **Agility and Learning**: An MTP encourages agility and a culture of continuous learning within an organization, making it more adaptable to change.
- **Organizational Glue**: The MTP acts as the glue that binds other attributes of an Exponential Organization, creating a cohesive and effective organizational unit.

Challenges to Implementing an MTP

Implementing and maintaining a Massive Transformative Purpose is a complex task that demands commitment, discipline, and a strategic approach. This section outlines the challenges faced by organizations in retrofitting an MTP, holding onto the vision, integrating the MTP at all levels, keeping it alive, dealing with market pressures, managing multiple product lines, and the role of governments in having a natural MTP.

- **Retrofitting Challenges**: Incorporating an MTP into existing companies is challenging and carries the risk of it being reduced to a mere brand promise rather than serving as a profound existential motivation.
- **Long-Term Vision Holding**: Sustaining the vision of the MTP over time, amidst economic and cultural changes, is difficult and requires resisting short-term temptations, as demonstrated by Kodak's struggle with digital cameras.
- **Discipline and Top Management Support**: Embedding the MTP into every level of an organization and living it daily demands great discipline and consistent support from top management.
- **Keeping MTP Alive**: Once initiated, it is crucial to keep the MTP alive to retain the community that has been painstakingly built and nurtured.
- **Public Companies' Dilemma**: For public companies, aligning with the MTP is often challenging due to the pressure of meeting market demands for quarterly and annual returns.
- **Multiple Product Lines**: Companies with multiple unrelated product lines often develop a separate

MTP for each division, as seen in conglomerates like Samsung, which has divisions for electronics, life insurance, securities, and biologics.

- **Government's Role**: Governments inherently have a natural MTP to serve their citizens, and it is expected that these MTPs will become explicitly stated and integrated into their operations.

Famous MTP Examples

Here are some notable examples of successful companies with great MTPs:

- **Google:** With its goal to **"Organize the world's information,"** Google is the poster child for MTPs. Note that this MTP is not about what the company *does* but rather a call to action for its larger community to use Google's tools and platforms to achieve the company's stated MTP.
- **Uber:** **"Go anywhere, Get anything."** Uber's MTP targets not only the transportation of individuals but also allows the company to explore multiple business models. Ultimately, we can see Uber becoming a platform for all kinds of mobility-based services (e.g., Uber Health, etc.).
- **Danone:** **"Bring health through food."** Danone has established itself as a world leader in four businesses: dairy and plant-based products, early life nutrition, medical nutrition, and water. Crucial to the company's success is that it evaluates all its projects based on its MTP.
- **XPRIZE:** **"A bridge to abundance for all."** As you might guess, XPRIZE's MTP was devised by Peter.

This MTP is sufficiently wide to encompass a vast range of different initiatives—from prizes for space-flight to cleaning up oil spills to ocean health to a medical tricorder—while keeping with the guard-rails of competition and awards.

- **Infarm: "Feeding the cities of tomorrow."** Germany-based Infarm is the world's fastest-growing urban farming company, operating out of thousands of stores in 30 cities in 10 countries. The company provides modular units that grow food in supermarket aisles and inside restaurants. These "farms" are owned and controlled remotely by InFarm through a combination of big data, IoT, and cloud analytics. Note how the company's MTP puts it on a path to create a worldwide farming network to help cities become self-sufficient in their food production while significantly improving the safety, quality, and environmental footprint of their food. The actual nature of this delivery system and the products themselves remain unspecified.

- **Colossal Biosciences: "Bring back extinct animals."** Colossal is a "de-extinction" company whose goal is to develop a process to create and use everything from artificial wombs to advanced software engineering—as well as established tools like CRISPR—to return to existence species that have been gone for thousands, even millions, of years. It is currently implanting modified genes from frozen woolly mammoth cells into female Asian elephants to produce a new species. Note that Colossal's MTP doesn't restrict it to either a single process or species. Rather, it has built absolute flexibility into the MTP to allow for a variety of species and the invention of new techniques and tools.

- **Wise.com: "Money without borders."** Wise is a fast-growing fintech company that started with low-fee cross-border transfers and has since grown into a multi-currency, fully digital global bank that provides nearly instant global transfers within its network and saves billions for both people and businesses. Wise was co-founded (and backed by Richard Branson and others) by two Estonians frustrated with traditional ways to send money across borders.
- **Spanx: "Elevating Women."** Sara Blakely devised this MTP to build a multi-billion-dollar enterprise from $5,000 of personal savings.

Now, consider once-famous companies whose demise can largely be blamed on the lack of an MTP:

- **Blackberry:** This legendary personal-communication device company never had an MTP. As a result, once it experienced its great global success (remember when everyone important had a Blackberry?), the company had nothing to drive it forward, no larger goal around which to focus its energy and creativity. As a result, between arguing over the company's direction and pursuing merely incremental improvements in its product line, the company eventually turned inwards and collapsed.
- **Kodak:** This venerable organization was one of the most successful consumer companies of all time. And yet, Kodak never developed a larger purpose, such as "Capture the images of human life and the natural world." It stuck with film and analog cameras, rather than shifting to software applications and digital cameras—and was destroyed in the process.

The Future of MTP

We believe the concept of an MTP will pervade all forms of organizations in the future. Some key futures include the following:

- **Entrepreneurs and MTPs**: In the coming years, most entrepreneurs will commence their entrepreneurial journey with an MTP as the foundation for building their companies.
- **Established Companies' Search**: Established companies will increasingly search for an MTP that aligns with their existing business model, starting as brand promises but gradually becoming the company's modus operandi. The MTP will evolve from being an add-on purpose to the very reason for the company's existence and a determinant of its future operations.
- **Hiring and MTP Alignment**: Hiring decisions will be influenced by the alignment between prospective candidates' MTPs and the organizations' MTPs, emphasizing the importance of shared purpose and values.
- **Hierarchy of MTPs**: For large companies, it is anticipated that there will be a hierarchy of MTPs for each product line or division, all serving the broader organizational goal.

Seven Reasons Why an MTP is Critical

Still have doubts about the necessity for a corporate MTP? An MTP matters because:

1. It gives you a target to shoot for and helps you evaluate if you are on track to hit that target.
2. It perpetually inspires you and your team, even during difficult times.
3. In an era of "opportunity abundance," it helps you choose what to focus on (and what to walk away from).
4. It helps your stakeholders and the general public know what you stand for.
5. It provides the "launch pads" and trajectories for your Moonshots.
6. It provides critical cultural support for several other ExO attributes, such as autonomy (it creates common culture and allows autonomy), Experimentation (where to point experiments), Dashboards (what are you measuring?), and common culture (shared context).
7. It provides the focus and emotional energy you'll need for the trip.

Case Study: The SpaceX Story

To understand the power of—and sometimes the sacrifice required by—truly adopting an MTP for your company, consider the story of one of the most celebrated companies of our time: SpaceX.

In founding SpaceX, Elon Musk's MTP was to take humanity to Mars—and in the process, to make humanity a multi-planetary species.

According to co-author Peter, who was friends with Elon during the early days of SpaceX, when Elon and his team finally got Falcon-1 operating (after three sequential failures), rather than continuing to sell that smaller launch vehicle,

Elon decided to "burn the ship," so to speak. He no longer pursued the sale of Falcon-1 rockets to potential customers, instead focusing 100% on the new, unproven Falcon-9 production line. Why? Because the move was more aligned with SpaceX's MTP of making humanity multiplanetary.

Fast forward a couple of years. As Peter remembers:

"I was in Musk's office one day. It was a casual meeting, and Elon looked agitated, even depressed.

"'What's up?' I asked.

"He replied, 'Well, I just figured out that I've got to completely reorganize SpaceX because there's no way that the Falcon-9 is going to get us to Mars.'"

Recalls Peter: "What he meant was that the Falcon-9, even with its extraordinary success record and the reusable first stage, wasn't sufficient to meet SpaceX's MTP of making humanity a multiplanetary species. Soon after he realized that, Elon announced that he would shift the company's future from the Falcon-9 to Starship. In other words, once again he was going to "burn the ship" and kill the Falcon-9 production line, the most successful rocket in human history, and instead focus all the company's resources on Starship.

"And that is what he is doing. Burning the boats once again, he made the precipitous decision to kill the Falcon-9, sacrificing it at the altar of the Starship rocket. The lesson is: If you're not going to constantly reinvent yourself, then someone is going to disrupt you."

When you see something that's not serving the MTP, kill it because you're spending a lot of time and energy supporting something that's not directly aligned with your broader purpose. Otherwise, you'll waste energy, and you will never achieve your MTP.

• • •

Getting Started on Your Enterprise's MTP

According to the United Nations, extreme poverty has decreased worldwide by 72% (from 36% to just 10%) over the last 30 years. The people emerging from deep poverty will add a sizable new cohort to the five billion people who were already online in 2020.

Many of these people will become part of ExOs as they climb Maslow's Hierarchy of Needs. With their physiological and safety needs, and (hopefully) love and belonging needs met, they will be looking further to self-esteem and, at the highest levels, self-actualization. This last will be a quest they will share with people in developed nations.

Exponential Organizations, with their defining MTPs, present the greatest opportunity yet developed for people at all levels of the organization chart, from all backgrounds, and from anywhere in the world, to find an enterprise that will enable them to strive for this highest degree of human existence.

So, how do you create an MTP worthy of your enterprise?

It's important to reiterate that an MTP is not the same as a mission statement. As an example of the latter, consider Cisco's mission: "Our mission is to shape the future of the Internet by creating unprecedented value and opportunity for our customers, employees, investors, and ecosystem partners."

While there's some Purpose there, and it's somewhat Massive, it's certainly not Transformative. Furthermore, at least a dozen other Internet companies could use it. It's nothing special.

By comparison, if we were to write Cisco's MTP, it would be something along the lines of "Connecting everyone, everything, everywhere—all the time." Now that would be exciting. Wouldn't you rather work for *that* company?

As Salim has written, "MTPs provide focus to enable exponential growth. A strong MTP forces your mind to break all the old models about how to achieve a task. It inspires innovation. And it gives you permission to think outside your own constraints and create a new model to support exponential growth."

We have learned that the biggest imperative of a worthy MTP is its Purpose. Building on visionary ethnographer Simon Sinek's seminal work, this Purpose must answer the following critical "why" questions:

- Why should we do this work?
- Why does this organization even exist?
- Who are we serving?
- What do we strive to do better than anyone?

Until you can answer those questions, you will never be able to formulate a true MTP for your enterprise.

Creating an MTP and Moonshot is so important for every CEO and entrepreneur that Peter has made having an MTP and Moonshot a core prerequisite of his Abundance360 Summit Leadership Program. Before any member can participate in the five-day Summit, they are required to develop a working MTP and Moonshot (at least in draft form). As Peter coaches his membership, "We are living in a world of increasing abundance. In the days ahead, you are going to hear about so many amazing opportunities across a dozen exponential technologies that unless you have a clear MTP to help you filter and focus, you'll go crazy."

As American lawyer, author, entrepreneur, and transgender rights advocate Dr. Martine Rothblatt has said, "The difference between successful and very successful people is that the former says NO to most things, and the latter says

NO to almost everything." Your MTP can help you decide when to say *yes* and when to say *no.*

Because authoring an MTP and Moonshot can sometimes be a challenge, Peter and his Chief AI Officer, Steve Brown, created a Generative AI tool to help his members in crafting them, available for free at www.Diamandis.com/MTP and www.Diamandis.com/Moonshot.

With the MTP, you have taken the crucial first step. You are now poised to become an Exponential Organization. In the remaining chapters, we will show you how.

Key Resources/Links where you can learn more

- Purpose Power Index 2022 Executive Summary
  - https://static1.squarespace.com/static/5dcb58b2bce3d618517c3882/t/62fe60eedea0fa66b1d9856d/1660838130774/Purpose+Power+Index+2022+Executive+Summary.pdf
- Put Purpose at the Core of Your Strategy
  - https://hbr.org/2019/09/put-purpose-at-the-core-of-your-strategy
- Purpose-Driven Companies Evolve Faster Than Others
  - https://www.forbes.com/sites/caterinabulgarella/2018/09/21/purpose-driven-companies-evolve-faster-than-others/?sh=bbb341f55bcf
- Meet the 20 Most Purpose-Driven Brands of 2022 | Inc.com
  - https://www.inc.com/rebecca-deczynski/power-of-purpose-list-impact-driven-companies.html

---

- All The Books Written By Simon Sinek
  - https://simonsinek.com/books/
- MTP - ExO Insight
  - https://insight.openexo.com/tag/mtp/

PART 2
SCALE

5

Staff on Demand

If you build communities and you do things in public," he says,
"you don't have to find the right people, they find you.

—*Exponential Organizations*, First Edition

The three things you'll learn in this chapter

- Companies that use Staff on Demand (SoD)
  have the fastest scaling capability and the most
  agility to survive industry disruption.
- SoD creates an enormous challenge to the social
  contract.
- Most SoD provisioning will be via platforms
  and communities.

With the all-important MTP properly documented, we now look at the externalities that an ExO can leverage. These map onto the acronym SCALE. The first of these, Staff on Demand, will examine how an ExO can scale by utilizing a workforce outside the organizational boundaries.

What is Staff on Demand

SoD means utilizing a pool of prequalified workers, hired on an as-needed basis, to conduct operational elements of a company's business. Responsibilities range from simple tasks to complex work and may even include mission-critical processes.

The Great Resignation

The Great Resignation was big. Millions of people around the world quit their jobs rather than returning to the status quo of their working lives before the COVID-19 pandemic and the resulting global lockdown.

The pandemic only accelerated trends that had been building for most of the century. Over the last four decades, the half-life of learned skills has dropped from 30 years to fewer than four, in large part because of the accelerating pace of change driven by the tech revolution. According to noted business visionary John Seely, this trend will continue to accelerate in the years ahead. While employees were forced to work at home, the reason they *could* work at home was thanks to technological breakthroughs like Zoom, smartphones, ultra-high-speed broadband, and more. Further, many of them liked working from home better than going to a traditional office. And, thanks to the rise of the economy over the previous decade, they also found they could earn a living without being at the mercy of a single employer.

The result was the biggest shift in the workforce since the Industrial Revolution.

Many companies saw the Great Resignation as a serious threat to their future. In fact, it may be a benefit. For one thing, it may help them escape the boom/bust cycle—and the attendant chaos and strife—of hiring and laying off workers according to the vagaries of the business cycle. The Great Resignation suggested enterprises that retain employees as their productivity degrades will hurt their competitiveness. On the other hand, organizations that can easily adjust employment levels in response to economic shifts and who can employ workers with the most up-to-date skill sets will have a distinct competitive advantage.

That means taking advantage of the new phenomenon of Staff on Demand.

Description of What is Staff on Demand?

The term "Staff on Demand" (SoD) is only about a decade old, but the idea is hardly new. Rather, it dates back to the beginning of the last century. In a nutshell, it refers to the practice of retaining an external pool of human resources with the ability to add and subtract more staff as needed. A classic example is the temp agency, which contracted out independent workers—typically clerks and other non-professionals—to corporate clients for temporary (hence the name) duties.

A second notable precursor of SoD is Hollywood movie productions. Studios would draw upon the large professional community of camera operators, sound technicians, electricians, etc. to staff individual films, sometimes on location. As such, these productions can be considered the first example of what are now called "virtual corporations."

But there have always been "temp" workers in the corporate world. The difference with Staff on Demand is that:

- **It is a profession.** Today's gig workers don't see themselves as taking on temporary work as a way to earn a living between full-time jobs. Rather, a surprising percentage say this type of work is their career.
- **It is valuable.** Traditional temp work typically consisted of per-hour jobs that required little (filing) or specialized (typing) training or expertise. SoD jobs can include traditionally professional positions that can rise to the top of the organization chart.
- **It has its own infrastructure.** Micro-payments, individual health insurance, remote work tools—an entire safety net has emerged to support gig workers and overcome the historic obstacles to temporary and contract work. The result is a work environment that can be as good, if not better, than a full-time job, even before we factor in the unequaled level of freedom for workers. These benefits will increasingly draw the best and brightest to move to SoD roles for their own careers—and for companies to increasingly draw upon these resources.

Some of today's SoD platforms include:

- **TaskRabbit:** Local repair and odd jobs as a service. As a measure of its success, TaskRabbit has been acquired by Ikea (e.g., "Build my Ikea furniture," "Help me move").

- **Amazon Mechanical Turk (MTurk):** A micro-task platform for information-gathering and data-processing tasks
- **Upwork** (the merger of Desk + elance): A global marketplace for freelancers
- **Gigwalk:** A marketplace to contract micro-tasks to distributed, local workforces (e.g., "Check the placement of an item on a shelf in all the Walmarts in your area, and take a picture of each.")
- **Fiverr:** An Israeli online marketplace for listing and applying for small, one-off jobs.
- **Molly Maid:** The oldest service on this list, a 500+ franchise home-cleaning service
- **Kaggle:** A community of data scientists solving "challenges" and "competitions" provided by enterprises
- **99Designs:** A competitive freelancer platform for graphic design
- **MBO Partners**: For larger companies, MBO manages all your contractors in areas like payroll, background checks, on-boarding, off-boarding and training and can dramatically drop the cost of managing contractors.

Staff on Demand is the present and future of work: Between 2005 and 2015, 94% of new jobs created were in the gig economy,[24] enabled by—among other things—technological breakthroughs, new legislation that protects gig workers, and the rise of an online global marketplace that enables companies to hire from anywhere on the planet. For

---

[24] Kate Sitarz, "The of the Gig Economy: A 2018 Perspective," Babson Thought & Action, October 4, 2019, https://entrepreneurship.babson.edu/the-state-of-the-gig-economy/.

example, in 2020, there were more than 3 million app-based gig workers in Mexico and an estimated 12 million across Latin America. Fifty-eight million freelancers work in the United States, contributing more than $1.4 trillion to the national economy. Not surprisingly, freelancing is predicted to become the US majority workforce by 2027. SoD exemplifies the new Zeitgeist of the sharing economy, crowdsourcing, and the shift of power to ordinary people (the "Army of Davids") over big business, Big Media, and Big Government.[25] An obvious example is OpenAI beating the mighty Google to the punch with Chat GPT, but there are many others.

All these forces converge to make possible what co-author Mike Malone calls the "Protean Corporation": an enterprise with a small, solid core of long-serving full-time employees who preserve the company's culture and purpose, surrounded by a cloud of on-demand contract staffers with different skills.

The result, which structurally resembles the modern image of an atom, would show the company as a shapeshifter: highly capable, able to quickly wax and wane in size with the vagaries of the market, and able to nimbly reorganize and take off in pursuit of new business opportunities.

But, Malone warns, a Protean Corporation will succeed only if the organization has powerful training tools to quickly build gig-worker loyalty and understanding of the company culture—as well as precise and efficient recruitment, hiring, and payment systems.

---

[25]   Glenn H. Reynolds, *An Army of Davids: How Markets and Technology Empower Ordinary People to Beat Big Media, Big Government, and Other Goliaths* (Nashville, TN: Nelson Current, 2007).

Probably no company in the last decade has leveraged SoD as well as the ride-sharing success story Uber. Indeed, Uber is synonymous with Staff on Demand. Uber likely wouldn't work if it was a full-employment company. If it were, Uber would have an estimated 5 million employees and be the largest employer on the planet.

Needless to say, Uber initially had a brilliant MTP. "Everyone's Private Driver" is simple and short—and nebulous enough to eventually allow for everything from airplanes to personal helicopters. It's easy to focus on the second and third words of Uber's MTP: that the company provides users with private chauffeurs. In fact, the most important word may be the first. "Everyone" commits the company to make its service available to anyone who wants to use it everywhere. That may seem an impossible goal, but that's the point of MTP, isn't it? And the use of Staff on Demand enables Uber to reach every small neighborhood on the planet.

As most readers know, there are downsides both to Uber's business model and its practices: price surge pricing, lack of transparency, insurance issues, and tensions surrounding the employment status of its drivers. But there's no denying the pervasive breadth and depth of the company's success.[26]

There also is no denying that the success of Uber has stirred economic, legal, and legislative tension around the world. Indeed, the rapid dominance of Uber in hired transportation across the planet, supplanting full-time employees

---

[26] Thomas Reiner, "$uber with a Strong Report, Finally Seeing Meaningful Profitability (and Importantly FCF). GBV +33%, EBITDA $364M (4.5% Rev Margin, 1.3% GBV Margin) $382m of FCF, and Reaffirm Long Term Ability to Hit $5B of EBITDA (with $4b+ of FCF) in 2024 Pic.Twitter.Com/Tdhbhc0osd," Twitter, August 2, 2022, https://twitter.com/treiner5/status/155 4449907422859264?t=qSpdW7mjcShv5nLvnR4bXA&s=19.

(taxi drivers in particular) with "gig" workers, has forced a re-think of the social contract between workers and employers. That debate is just beginning.

Case Studies: Staff on Demand

- **Netflix Prize.**[27] In September 2009, Netflix was still an online DVD-rental company making forays into video streaming. It announced a contest—with a prize of $1 million—for the best online filtering algorithm to predict user ratings based on previous ratings. Teams of the best and brightest code writers from around the world formed and in time merged. Over three years, the winning team—BellKor's Pragmatic Chaos—beat Netflix's own algorithm for predicting ratings by 10.06%. Meanwhile, the competition made Netflix famous.
- **Dabbawala.**[28] The teeming Indian metropolis of Mumbai, it is said, is built upon Dabbawala, a network of an estimated 5,000 bicycle-based food delivery workers. The box lunches they deliver are prepared by women, often working out of private homes and taken to a nearby train station. The train carries the boxes downtown, where they are distributed workers in various offices. Dabbawala delivers as many as 200,000 lunchboxes a day, on time and with an accuracy of 99.9%.

---

[27] "Netflix Prize," Wikipedia, August 11, 2023, https://en.wikipedia.org/wiki/Netflix_Prize.

[28] Stefan Thomke, "Mumbai's Models of Service Excellence," Harvard Business Review, August 1, 2014, https://hbr.org/2012/11/mumbais-models-of-service-excellence.

- **Catalonia.** The government of Spain's Catalonia region manages a globally distributed intelligence network of expat experts that serves as mentors on specific topics. Catalonia Trade & Investment (CT&I), a government agency under the Ministry for Business and Knowledge of the Government of Catalonia, is responsible for strategies that enhance Catalonia's position as a global center for business, innovation, and talent. The 40 offices of the CT&I global network provide services to 24,000 companies a year and work with committed companies to build capabilities, innovate, and internationalize. In January 2019, CT&I launched Catalonia Exponential, based in Silicon Valley, to accelerate the innovation economy in Catalonia and the transformation of Catalan startups, SMEs, and large companies. Catalonia Exponential found a novel, low-cost way to do just that: a Staff On Demand program that manages a distributed intelligence network of loyal expatriate Catalonian experts to mentor local companies on becoming ExOs. Notably, they developed an MTP: to increase Catalonia's impact on the world economy.
- **Medellín, Colombia.**[29] The Colombian Supreme Court set out to transform the country's justice system. It did so by inviting teams of entrepreneurs to participate in an incentive-prize program with alternating periods of cooperation and competition. The goal: use exponential technologies to develop breakthrough solutions to create massive positive change.

---

[29] Steve Cohen, "Economic Growth and Environmental Sustainability," State of the Planet, January 27, 2020, https://blogs.ei.columbia.edu/2020/01/27/economic-growth-environmental-sustainability/.

The program's radical openness is a critical part of its success. The cooperation of local government, business, and educational communities, in combination with dedicated and passionate local community members, creates unprecedented connection and common purpose and strengthens the likelihood that changes will "take." As a result, interested parties no longer instinctively react negatively to new ideas but instead have a commitment to their success.

- **Amazon's Mechanical Turk (MTurk).**[30] MTurk connects and commodifies human labor to accomplish micro-tasks—officially called "Human Intelligence Tasks"—such as information gathering (completing surveys, online research) or data processing (e.g., image identification). Once a micro-task—for example, transcribing line items of a scanned receipt or labeling image data for machine learning—has been codified into a process, it can be created and bundled on the Amazon MTurk platform. This way, human labor can be accessed to accomplish tasks that may not yet be possible (or that may be cost-prohibitive) to accomplish with full automation. Typically, each task takes only seconds to accomplish and carries cent- or sub-cent-level rewards. Labor around the world can flexibly sign up and carry out work packages of tasks at their own pace and availability. For individuals, the comparative hourly rate is often competitive or superior to local job opportunities and also more flexible.

---

[30]   Amazon Mechanical Turk, https://www.mturk.com/.

- **Sweep South.**[31] This South African domestic cleaning service, founded in 2014, is disrupting the industry by using technology to provide customers with verified, highly-rated cleaners, gardeners, and other domestic workers from what has, until now, been an otherwise informal labor segment. Sweep South uses a proprietary online platform that handles bookings, worker ratings, and other salient data and services. As a measure of its success, Sweep South has been one of the country's most successful enterprises in terms of obtaining international investments.

The Future of Staff on Demand

Staff on Demand may be an ExO attribute, but it is one with an expiration date. Automation is waiting in the wings: in the not-too-distant future, we are likely to look back at SoD as little more than an interim step before the Age of AI & Robotics.

Contrary to popular fears, this transition isn't likely to result in drastic unemployment. More likely, it will see workers migrate towards jobs that feature direct human-to-human contact while lower-end work will be done by AIs, deep learning, or robots. We will also see the workforce team up with AIs, where most professions will have an AI co-pilot.

As part of this migration, the most successful human workers will begin to behave, as celebrated venture capitalist Reid Hoffman has described, as a "Startup of One." That is, everyone becomes a lifestyle business. A pioneer of this new personal entrepreneurship is Etsy.

---

[31] SweepSouth, https://sweepsouth.com/?gclid=EAIaIQobChMI2Pu Zkra76gIVirTtCh39JACGEAAYASAAEgIBzfD_BwE.

Until then, we are likely to see some fundamental changes in SoD as it becomes more pervasive, more accepted, and more powerful culturally and politically. We're likely to see:

- **Connecting Supply and Demand through MTP Platforms**: Platforms dedicated to Massive Transformative Purpose (MTP) communities, such as Kaggle, serve as crucial connectors between supply and demand. These platforms facilitate the exchange of resources, knowledge, and opportunities, enabling community members to collaborate and contribute towards a shared purpose.

- **Evolution of Employment and Labor Laws**: The changing landscape of work, driven by the rise of gig economy and remote work, necessitates the development of new employment and labor laws. These laws must be designed to protect the rights of workers while also accommodating the flexibility and dynamism of modern work arrangements.

- **Emergence of New Forms of Organized Labor**: As the nature of work evolves, so too must the forms of organized labor. New structures and organizations will be required to represent and advocate for the rights and interests of workers in an increasingly decentralized and fragmented labor market.

- **Formation of SoD Voting Blocs, Candidates, and Lobbyists**: The rise of Staff on Demand (SoD) will lead to the emergence of distinct voting blocs, candidates, and lobbyists that represent the unique interests and concerns of on-demand workers. These groups will play a critical role in shaping public policy and advocating for necessary changes.

- **Reimagining the Social Contract, Citizenship, and Sovereignty**: The transformation of work and the rise of decentralized networks will necessitate a reexamination and redefinition of fundamental concepts such as the social contract, citizenship, and sovereignty. New frameworks will be required to address the challenges and opportunities presented by a more interconnected and decentralized world.
- **Adaptation of Health Insurance, Welfare, and Work-Life Balance Rules**: As work becomes more flexible and decentralized, there will be a need to adapt rules and regulations related to health insurance, welfare, and work-life balance. This will involve creating new models that provide adequate support and protection for workers while also accommodating the diverse and dynamic nature of modern work.

How will Staff on Demand take advantage of the emerging virtual world of the Metaverse? The people and staffing companies that figure out this opportunity first—and best—will have a decisive competitive advantage.

Benefits of Staff on Demand

Staff on Demand is one of the key attributes of a successful Exponential Organization. The more the modern ExO can outsource, the better. Thanks to the rapidly growing gig economy, implementing company-wide SoD today offers some powerful competitive advantages, including:

- **Flexibility in Scaling**: The capability to promptly expand or contract according to the situation.

- **Swift Market Adaptation**: The ability to rapidly reorganize and enter new markets by quickly assembling teams for new operations.
- **Technical Competitiveness**: Staying technologically competitive by sustaining a workforce that is consistently at the forefront of knowledge and training.
- **Access to Top Talent**: The opportunity to tap into the best talent and expertise, even if they wouldn't join your company full-time.
- **Enhanced Cognitive Diversity**: Access to diverse perspectives from workers who are not confined by the same biases or conventional thinking as permanent staff.
- **Specialized Expertise**: The ability to break down work projects into smaller segments and hire freelancers with specialized knowledge in each area.
- **Reduced Administrative Burden**: Minimized time and money spent on managing employee benefits, health programs, and retirement plans, facilitated by companies specializing in remote worker services.
- **Empowerment of Gig Workers**: Providing gig workers with greater control over their time and resources, the ability to work remotely, a selection of employers, diverse work, and the opportunity to pursue their own personal MTP.

Challenges of Staff on Demand

As we've already hinted, implementing Staff on Demand effectively isn't easy—internally or externally. That's partially because SoD fundamentally threatens the social contract. The gig economy contravenes the world of pension plans, employer healthcare, taxation, and unemployment insurance. Regulatory obstacles, many created by political forces in the name of worker rights and conditions, often interfere with the ability to implement SoD. Enabling widespread SoD requires fundamental reform. Governments that embrace this reform—engaging with thorny questions like tax revenues—will create a thriving future. But SoD also presents specific personnel challenges:

- **Lack of Engagement with MTP:** The gig worker may not have Engagement with your MTP—and thus become a distracting force.
- **Mixed Loyalties:** Without specific standards to the contrary, freelancers may find themselves working on multiple platforms for multiple companies. As a result, they may exhibit mixed loyalties.
- **Task Description Overhead:** Management will spend a great deal of time carefully describing tasks for freelancers; these tasks would be second nature for full-timers.
- **Limited Cultural Onboarding:** There will be little time to train freelancers in the company's culture or operating style.
- **Differential Investment in Success:** On-demand staff may have a stake in doing the best possible job, but they won't have the same stake in the company's long-term success.
- **Risk of Exploitation:** Gig employees risk being exploited by employers if they aren't prepared to walk away.
- **Self-Marketing Requirement:** Gig employees must learn to market themselves to get work.

Staff on Demand: Requirements and Prerequisites

Importantly, a company should never outsource its MTP or culture. These features are carefully wrought from experience and are enduring; they should not be touched by temporary workers. In order to establish purpose-oriented relationships (rather than simple freelance contracts), on-demand staff should be engaged around the MTP.

When a company plans to implement Staff on Demand, it must first make sure that its existing core team understands that SoD is not meant to replace them but rather to act as a complement to and enhancement of their own and the organization's capabilities.

Often, some SoD contractors will become part of the company's core team, while others will leave. It's crucial that appropriate steps are taken to ensure the core always is left stronger and more capable and that all new knowledge is retained. This is one of the fastest and most affordable methods to inject new capabilities into an organization. An effective SoD platform offers the following:

For the Organization	For the Worker
An online marketplace	Maximum flexibility
Standardized, modular work assignments	The ability to do one's own marketing and sales
Significant availability of external talent	Competitive per-unit compensation
For the Organization	For the Worker
A reputation system (rating, quality, skills)	Automated and transparent billing and payments

For the Organization	For the Worker
Easy and standardized onboarding processes	Safety and security while on the job
Dashboards and tracking mechanisms	Exposure to new ideas
Pay for performance	Accountability overall sits with the organization

Case study: Marriott versus Airbnb

During the initial stages of the COVID-19 global pandemic, Marriott Hotels, with its 1.4 million rooms in 7,399 properties globally, furloughed tens of thousands of jobs and slashed executive salaries by 50%. Needless to say, the stress on the remaining employees and on the quality of guest services was extreme. Marriott's well-tended image took a major hit. Marriott Hotels' EBITDA between 2019 and 2020 was slashed by 75%, dropping from $2.2 billion to $562 million.

Meanwhile, competitor Airbnb, which had 4 million hosts in 220 countries, faced similar challenges. They lost 80% of their business in just eight weeks.

The difference? Airbnb is a fully Exponential Organization, using all 11 attributes of the ExO model.

Airbnb refunded $1 billion in deposits to people who couldn't travel. They paid $250 million from their balance sheet to the hosts. They cut 25% of their core staff—just 2,000 people—but also added customized services (enhanced cleaning) for the pandemic. They noticed a significant rise in domestic travel (people needing a holiday who couldn't travel abroad, people who needed a home office, and people visiting their families but not wanting to stay with them). Even on significantly lower revenue, their 2020 adjusted EBITDA was $251 million—almost identical to their EBITDA of $253 million in 2019.[32]

As CEO Brian Chesky summarized, "This crisis revealed just how adaptable our model is. Whatever is in store for me won't be as bad as losing 80% of our business in eight weeks. After what we've been through in the last eight months, we're absolutely prepared for what is to come."

SoD: How to Get Started

- Make a list of tasks that could, if needed, be outsourced to Staff on Demand platforms. Then identify the positions responsible for those tasks. Convert more of these employees into contractors.
- The pandemic plus Zoom have shown us that employees can operate anywhere on the planet. Use that "geographic arbitrage" to contract gig workers where the low cost of living, high education rates, and quality of infrastructure give on-demand staffing a decisive advantage.
- Overcome your own prejudices about "temp" workers and recognize that modern freelancers may have superior skills and experience than your own employees.

• • •

---

[32] Airbnb, "Airbnb Fourth Quarter and Full Year 2020 Financial Results," Airbnb Newsroom, April 19, 2021, https://news.airbnb.com/airbnb-fourth-quarter-and-full-year-2020-financial-results/.

Take a large army of on-demand staffers surrounding an ExO. Add to that army the vast numbers of customers and other stakeholders that result from immense scaling possible by technology. The result? Crowds and Communities will inevitably become more important to an ExO than to any form of enterprise before it. Those attributes are the subject of the next chapter.

Key Resources/Links where you can learn more

- List of gig economy companies - Wikipedia
  - https://en.wikipedia.org/wiki/List_of_gig_economy_companies
- The Great Resignation: How employers drove workers to quit - BBC Worklife
  - https://www.bbc.com/worklife/article/20210629-the-great-resignation-how-employers-drove-workers-to-quit
- What is the gig economy and what's the deal for gig workers? | World Economic Forum
  - https://www.weforum.org/agenda/2021/05/what-gig-economy-workers/
- Gig economy | Financial Times
  - https://www.ft.com/gig-economy
- Gig Economy: Definition, Statistics & Trends [2023 Update]
  - https://zety.com/blog/gig-economy-statistics
- The Startup of You
  - https://www.startupofyou.com/
- Staff on Demand - ExO Insight
  - https://insight.openexo.com/tag/staff-on-demand/

6

Community and Crowd

Are you primarily a community or are you primarily a company?
The reason you have to ask yourself this is because sooner
or later the two will come in conflict.

—*Exponential Organizations*, First Edition

The three things you'll learn in this chapter

- What we mean by Community versus Crowd, and why each is a critical asset for building and scaling an ExO.
- The value of a community and how to create one.
- The value of crowds and how to tap into them.

I n the previous chapter, we discussed the importance of non-employee, on-demand, contract staffers as a critical new resource to help enterprises better innovate, operate, and adjust to sudden changes in the vastly accelerated Exponential economy. We went so far as to suggest that without Staff on Demand, no company could succeed in this economy, much less become an Exponential Organization.

But there's another non-traditional asset, an even larger cache of surplus cognitive talent, that may prove even more important to an ExO than Staff on Demand. What's more, the expertise and talent of this asset is provided voluntarily, without any contract—and, often, without a paycheck. This is the all-important "Community" and "Crowd," the subject of this chapter.

What are Community and Crowd?

A Community, in the ExO context, is a large, global group of individuals who are passionate about your MTP and are directly involved in the main functions of your organization. They are loyal to a shared goal and devoted to solving the grand challenges surrounding your organization's purpose.

In a nutshell, Communities facilitate peer-to-peer value creation. This is also true for Crowd, with some variations, which we will get to later in this chapter. In particular, Community is defined by many interactions between individuals, while Crowd operates via one-to-one interactions between individuals and an entity (the ExO).

Once again, the heart of this ecosystem is the organization's Massive Transformational Purpose (MTP), which creates and drives a deep and emotional connection between the Community and the enterprise. An organization's Community and the Crowd it attracts can help validate new ideas and learnings. Crowd and Community amplify ideation and marketing, which can accelerate the implementation of new products and services.

Let's take a closer look at these two forms of company volunteers:

- **Communities** are cohorts of individuals who have a relationship with the company. Put another way, a Community is the public personification of the MTP. This includes customers, fans, vendors, partners, suppliers, and alumni of the organization. Often, these individuals have a special bond with the company—and that may make them willing to donate time, expertise, and even money to make and keep the company successful. In our opinion, true Community is achieved when an organization has converted a sizable percentage of these interested parties into dedicated volunteers who add value to the organization. Kevin Kelly, the founding editor of *Wired* magazine, believes that you need only 1,000 "True Fans" as a threshold for success.

- **Crowds,** simply, are everyone else. That is, they are the remainder of the 8 billion people on Earth who do not have a relationship with your organization but can be potentially incentivized by reward or interest to engage with it in some fashion that adds value. Whereas members of a Community are in regular contact with the company and each other, Crowds form around a company only briefly—and only for some kind of singular, transactional reward, whether that's monetary, to quench a curiosity, or to build status among a peer group. Therefore, one of the best ways to draw in a Crowd is through Engagement,

such as competitions and incentive prizes, publicized and amplified via social media platforms.
Evocative public-relations efforts, such as clickbait
on Buzzfeed, can also draw Crowds. For an ExO, the
goal of these transactions is to convert Crowd members into Community members.

Graphically, the relationship between the organization,
its Community, and its Crowd looks like this:

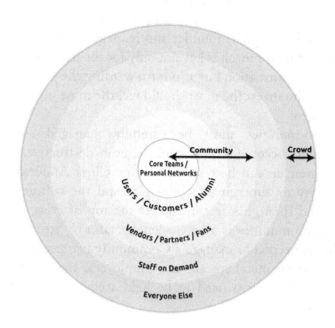

Interactions between an Exponential Organization
and its Community are not simply transactions. The
Community should hold an elevated position in an ExO's
universe: granted special favors, given insider insights and
forward looks on future offerings, rewarded with gifts, and

honored with special levels of trust. Community members are the Elect. While they are not necessarily actual employees, they are pseudo-employees, citizens of the ExO's larger sovereignty.

Of course, the more open Community membership is, the more careful an organization must be about how much insider knowledge it can safely share. One solution to that dilemma is to create levels of Community membership based on tenure and contribution so that the most vetted and trusted members have the highest degree of company access, while the rest must still earn their way. Futurist Jaroslav Dokoupil, cofounder and manager of RQ Genesis, believes this approach is key not only for the management of sensitive information but also for rewarding the community. Those who invest the most should feel the most "inside" and privileged.

Communities must be carefully managed so that they don't become an antagonistic, even destructive, force. Entrepreneur and best-selling author Chris Anderson, an authority on emerging technologies and the cultures that surround them, has remarked, "At the top of every one of these communities is a benevolent dictator."[33] Strong leadership is needed to manage a Community because although Community members are not employees, they still have responsibilities and need to be held accountable for their performance.

---

[33] "Chris Anderson on Why Community-Driven Companies Will Always Win," BCG Global, January 8, 2021, https://www. bcg.com/publications/2014/technology-strategy-innovation-chris-anderson-why-community-driven-companies-will-always-win.

Case Study: Ethereum

Ethereum is one of the most established and largest open-source blockchain cryptocurrencies, second in market capitalization only to Bitcoin. Officially named Ether ("Ethereum" describes the universe of millions of users it has created), Ethereum is one of the defining examples of the power of Crowd in modern business history.

Founded in 2013 and launched in July 2015, Ether itself was crowdfunded. It was designed from the start to be radically decentralized and open, allowing any user to place their own applications on its site. As a result, it has accumulated a vast library of decentralized finance (DeFi) applications that, because they obviate the need for intermediaries like banks and brokerages, have proved wildly popular among businesses and individual users. Remarkably, other cryptocurrencies have used Ethereum blockchain for their own offerings. Ethereum also enables users to create and exchange non-fungible tokens (NFTs).

The intelligent use of Crowds has been a constant feature of Ethereum's operations. In 2014, the non-profit Ethereum Foundation was founded and developed by way of an online public Crowd sale. This funding itself was unusual in that investors bought Ethereum value tokens with, of all things, Bitcoin. Two years later, the DAO (decentralized autonomous organization)—essentially, a library of smart contracts developed on the Ethereum platform—raised $150 million in funding via a Crowd sale—a record at the time. Today, all of Ethereum's fungible and non-fungible tokens are launched via crowdfunding.

- **Apple.** The world's most valuable company is legendary for its huge, intensely loyal, and enduring community of customers, product reviewers, YouTubers, and websites.
- **Axie Infinity.** A powerful example of a play-to-earn model, this Vietnamese firm has developed a token-based online video game that uses Ethereum-based cryptocurrencies. Players collect and mint NFTs that represent the company's digital pets.
- **Roblox**. Roblox enables creators in its Community to launch and co-develop new video games and deploy them to Roblox's marketplace. The platform thus democratizes not only the distribution of but also the tools to create video games.
- **GitHub.** "Where the world builds software." GitHub, Inc. provides Internet hosting for software development and version control. As the name suggests, it uses Git: a free, open-source distributed version control system
- **Kaggle.** This Google subsidiary is an online Community of data scientists and machine-learning experts. It enables users to publish data sets, collaborate, build models, and enter competitions to solve data-science challenges.
- **LinkedIn.** A business and employment-oriented online service, LinkedIn manages its enormous Community (880 million members) through websites and mobile apps.
- **Peloton.** As a result of the boom in home exercise equipment ignited by COVID lockdowns, Peloton

became the largest fitness platform in the world, with a loyal community of more than 1.4 million members.

- **Fitbit.** This maker of wearable, wireless exercise devices, as well as the web-based analytical software that supports their use, has more than 120 million devices used by 29 million Community members in more than 100 countries.
- **Reddit.** A great example of a powerful Community. Reddit has just 700 employees, most of whom manage the platform. It sees an estimated 20 billion visits per year from 430 million users. Incredibly, Reddit hosts 130,000 different communities.
- **The Open-Source Software.** Community dates back to the late 1980s. Users of FOSS (free and open-source software) devote long hours to testing and validating new versions and fixes, and provide detailed descriptions and reproduction cases of failures.
- **Amazon.** The world's biggest Community uses Crowd to understand what products it should focus on.
- **Stack Overflow.** A question-and-answer website for programmers, Stack Overflow features high-quality, long-form answers to questions on a variety of highly specialized areas of digital technology. It has become the go-to tool for technologists and developers looking to solve challenging problems or find canonical answers for approaches. Community members are rewarded with a Karma-based point system. A key value to Community members is the ability to strengthen their profile and amplify employability.
- **XPRIZE** is a worldwide community of innovators who self-organize into teams to attack and solve very

clear, specific incentive-prize challenges. In 2021, the XPRIZE launched a $100 million competition, funded by Elon Musk, to remove gigatons of carbon from the atmosphere and oceans. More than 1,200 teams registered to compete. In April of 2023, the foundation launched an $11 million "Wildfire" XPRIZE, asking teams to build and demonstrate the technology to identify a fire at ignition, and then autonomously put it out within 10 minutes.

The Growing Power of Crowd

The Crowd is the feedstock for building Community. And today, for the first time, Exponential Organizations have the power to reach and tap into the potential of the global Crowd. Thanks to the global deployment of 5G, and low-Earth orbiting constellations like Starlink, the 8 billion citizens of this planet are increasingly connected. Over the past few years, we've seen 5G connections grow from 13 million in 2019 to an expected 2.8 billion by 2025. Soon, high-bandwidth connectivity will be available to every person on every square meter on the planet. And researchers are developing 6G, which will be 100 times faster—fast enough to download 142 hours of Netflix in a second!

Take this information-gathering capacity. Expand its reach to literally billions of potential participants. And then stoke the enthusiasm and energy unique to newly formed gatherings of human beings. The result? You've created the conditions for possibly the greatest business engine ever devised.

Case Studies: Crowds

ExOs are uniquely adept at aggregating and tapping into Crowds. The epitome of leveraging the crowd, of course, is the **XPRIZE Foundation**. Here are some others:

- **GoFundMe.** This Silicon Valley–based, for-profit[34] crowdfunding platform helps people raise money to cover the costs of life events that can range from injuries and accidents (often subjects of major media attention) to weddings and personal debt.[35] Between 2010 and 2020, GoFundMe raised nearly $10 billion from more than 120 million donors. Strictly speaking, GoFundMe is a Crowd play, with only a minority of regular donors and just 500 employees.
- **TaskRabbit.** Founded in 2006, TaskRabbit is a mainstay of the gig economy. This mobile online marketplace connects consumers with 60,000 freelancers ("taskers") to tackle basic, everyday tasks, such as handyman work, moving, and product assembly. In 2017, TaskRabbit was purchased by furniture giant IKEA, although it still operates independently.
- **TikTok.** Founded in 2018 in China (where it is known as Douyin), TikTok allows users to create and post short videos. By 2020, the company had achieved 2 billion downloads and was rated the world's third-fastest-growing brand. By 2021, it was rated the most popular website in the world. Given the autonomous nature of its postings, TikTok is

---

[34]   "For-Profit," Wikipedia, November 14, 2010, https://en.wikipedia. org/wiki/For-profit.
[35]   "Crowdfunding," Wikipedia, August 23, 2023, https://en.wikipedia. org/wiki/Crowdfunding.

essentially a giant, Crowd-based company with almost no organized Community. It's been so successful that lawmakers are alarmed at the addiction it creates in users and are considering banning the application altogether.

- **Kiva** is the world's first online lending platform, connecting online lenders to entrepreneurs across the globe. Kiva's MTP is "to expand financial access to help underserved communities thrive."
- **Wikipedia.** The Crowd populates, but the Community validates. The world's encyclopedia, Wikipedia, averages more than 18 billion page views per month, making it one of the most visited websites in the world. The site adds more than 20,000 new articles each month and has 27 million registered users. It contains many times the content of the traditional encyclopedia, can be accessed at light speed, links from one topic to another, and it is updated every second of every day. Best of all, it is free.

The Future of Community and Crowds

In the future, almost every organization in the world will engage with Community and Crowds. In fact, most organizations will be *just* Community and Crowd. Several major predictions can also be made:

- **Tokenomics**: Cryptocurrencies as an asset class will be worth more than $1 trillion. The combination of crypto-economics and gamification will act as a staggering accelerant for assembling and incentivizing communities. (We'll discuss this further in the chapter on Engagement.)

- **MTP Communities**: MTP-based communities will increasingly grab attention and mindshare from traditional corporations.
- **UN SDGs**: As grand challenges are natural MTPs, Communities focused on the UN Sustainable Development Goals (SDGs) will attack global problems.
- **Web3 Elements**: Techniques developed in the Web3 arena (i.e., blockchain, cryptocurrencies, NFTs, and the metaverse) will move into corporate and even government circles.
- Increasingly, large corporations will realize the value of Community and seek to build theirs (usually around the brand promise).
- **AI Tools**: As AI tools like ChatGPT propagate, the importance of Community will be enhanced while the importance of the Crowd will diminish.
- **AI replaces Crowds**: To explain the prior point, the Crowd is a proxy for AI. Tapping into the Crowd requires prescriptively describing tasks. Once a task can be described in efficient detail, AI can handle it as well as a human being. Thus, over time, the Crowd will be replaced by AI bots.
- **Crowd into Community = Winner**: Certain industries—for example, blockchain—have become very good at leveraging Community. The corporate world will soon catch up. Organizations will increasingly compete for limited attention and mindshare. The organizations (ExOs) that successfully attract a Crowd and convert their members to Community will be the winners.

Benefits of Community and Crowd

Why are Community and Crowd so important to an ExO? Because they add value to an organization. How? Because they tap the world's surplus cognitive capacity.

No company, no matter how large, employs more than a minute fraction of the world's most brilliant minds. Bill Joy, cofounder of Sun Microsystems, famously said, "No matter who you are, most of the smartest people work for someone else." Moreover, those talented experts are scattered around the planet, and most don't have the time or interest in working for you.

That's why ExOs cultivate their own Communities. A company can have some of the best developers and data scientists on its payroll—but nothing beats a large, engaged Community.

Similarly, machine-learning models rely on large datasets, which are not easy to find. The Kaggle Community finds them. Kaggle offers many open datasets to build, train, and test machine-learning models. Community members can share solutions and be ranked according to their results. They can also participate in data competitions with cash prizes for winning solutions.

An Exo's Community of loyal users and fans is similarly valuable for product development, alpha testing, word-of-mouth marketing, and other business. The Apple iPhone community—given its size and complexity, it might more accurately be called a "universe"—serves the company as a sounding board, conscience, expert consultant, field tester, app designer, and a huge and steady purchasing audience that not only helps the company determine future Apple product models and upgrades but then all-but guarantees the commercial success of those offerings.

Some other benefits of Community and Crowd include:

- **Creating new intellectual property.** From game characters on Roblox and Axi Infinity to news postings on Reddit and Facebook, Community creates content that is used to engage other members.
- **Generating data.** Community and crowd-generated data that can be used by an organization's Algorithms and AI to create further value—for example, identifying and developing new markets. Fitbit and Nest are two examples.
- **Supporting interactions** that can help build an organization's products or services. The act of engaging with an organization—through platforms like Wikipedia, Reddit, or GitHub—often ends up building products and/or services.
- **Marketing support** by promoting the company at no cost to friends and prospective customers.
- **Creating comradery and connection** that keep members coming back to engage with their friends. Peloton is a good example.
- **Value for acquisition.** A robust Community can act as a value multiplier, making a young company particularly appealing for acquisition. Indeed, the Community itself has its own value. In January 2021, for example, Fitbit was acquired by Google at a valuation of $2.1 billion, most of which accounted for the company's user roles and data.
- **Gathering knowledge.** For ExOs, Communities become a powerful means to gather, curate, and store knowledge for later use.

Challenges of Community and Crowd

Navigating the intricacies of Community and Crowd management presents a spectrum of formidable challenges. Here are the primary ones:

- **Community Building Takes Time**: Building the Community or Crowd to a size that can create a meaningful impact requires time, work, and patience.
- **Control and Trust**: Loss of control and lack of trust are significant challenges in managing a Community or Crowd. Asking a direct report for something yields a more certain outcome than requesting the Community or Crowd and hoping for results.
- **Trust Extension by Big Companies**: For large companies, extending trust into the community presents an enormous challenge.
- **Group Management**: Managing any group is always challenging, but it becomes particularly difficult when the Community is very large. Crowds, being usually large and independent, cannot be managed but only influenced.
- **Cultural and Linguistic Misunderstandings**: Misunderstandings arising from cultural and linguistic differences can cause significant and unnecessary stress.
- **Time Zone Challenges**: A large community usually spans multiple time zones, making communication a challenge.
- **MTP Alignment**: Ensuring everyone aligns with the MTP is critical but challenging. Moreover, gauging engagement with the MTP is difficult as individuals vary in their level of commitment and involvement,

making it tough for the core team to navigate the variations.

- **Crowd Unpredictability**: The most significant challenge of dealing with a Crowd is the unpredictability of the outcomes. There is no way to know for sure what you will get.

Crowd and Community: Requirements and Prerequisites

Here is what you need to successfully implement a Community—and attract a Crowd:

- **MTP.** As we've said throughout this book, a powerful MTP precedes everything in an Exponential Organization. This is especially true regarding Communities and Crowds because traditional employee salaries and benefits are not available to them. The MTP allows organizations to create an emotional connection within a Community.
- **AI and Algorithms** necessary to track and analyze interactions between and within Crowd and Community.
- **Engagement.** An effective ExO "gamifies" everything from incentive prizes to crypto-economics to make Community Engagement sticky. Engagement is extremely tricky because, inevitably, some Community members think they know more than the company—and grow resentful when their ideas aren't adopted.
- **Interfaces** so that the Community can self-provision the tools they need to build.
- **Dashboards** to track Engagement and metrics.

- **Experimentation** so that a Community can design and run experiments in line with the organization's MTP.
- **Autonomy** so that the Community can act on its own and have a sense of freedom and independence.
- **Social networking** so that both Community and Crowd can have rich interactions over distance and time.

Crowdfunding

Crowdfunding harnesses the power of the web to raise capital—and market interest—by assembling very large numbers of comparatively small investors. It is the best-known example of using the Crowd to serve a higher purpose—such as investing in a new technology, developing a new product prototype, or even creating a new company. It also enables people to participate in acts of charity or social justice and to make political statements.

Nearly $20 billion is raised each year through more than six million different crowdfunding campaigns—an amount that grows by a third every year. Successful campaigns average nearly $30,000 per campaign. Some of the best-known examples of crowdfunding companies include Kickstarter, Indiegogo, FundRazr, Patreon, Wefunder, GoFundMe, and, for social causes, Chuffed.

With crowdfunding platforms like Kickstarter, we can, for the first time in business history, get market validation for a product before building it. In fact, Sony Corporation is listing anonymous Kickstarter projects and funding the successful ones.

How to Get Started: Creating, Nurturing, and Managing Communities

How do you create Communities? You probably don't have to. As Salim has said, "If you do good things in public, you don't have to find the right people—they find you." You just need to give them an easy onramp to get involved.

Once a Community begins to form around an ExO, the company can take five steps to aid its growth and strengthen its membership:

1. Use a powerful MTP to attract and engage early members/early adopters.
2. Offer them an easy mechanism to join and show their affiliation.
3. Engage with and nurture the community: confer with the community, solicit its advice, and recognize its contributions. A variety of key tools—websites, blogs, bulletin boards, and social media—are integral here. True Community sparks when peer-to-peer Engagement and value creation occurs.
4. Enable a mechanism that provides recognition for Community members' efforts and contributions via points or badges (see Engagement).
5. Create a platform to automate peer-to-peer Engagement and to allow Community members to create value for themselves and support each other in terms of reputation (GitHub), followers (Twitter), or revenue (YouTube).

Given their sheer size, Communities and Crowds cannot be managed individually. Rather—and this is true as well for employees and customers in ExOs—it requires the assistance of powerful software programs that can respond quickly and effectively. In other words, it requires Artificial Intelligence and Algorithms, the subject of our next chapter.

Key Resources/Links where you can learn more

- XPRIZE Foundation
  - www.xprize.org
- Top 20 Best Online Communities Sites - Aelieve Digital Marketing & Web Design Ranked - 2021
  - https://aelieve.com/rankings/websites/category/online-communities/best-online-communities/
- Kevin Kelly's essay, The Technium: 1,000 True Fans
  - https://kk.org/thetechnium/1000-true-fans/
- People Powered: How Communities Can Supercharge Your Business - Jono Bacon
  - https://www.jonobacon.com/books/peoplepowered/
- Community: The Structure of Belonging by Peter Block
  - https://www.amazon.com/Community-Structure-Belonging-Peter-Block/p/1605092770/
- How to Build a Meaningful (and Massive) Community, From Someone Who's Done it Twice
  - https://buffer.com/resources/build-a-meaningful-and-massive-community/

- The Ultimate Guide for Building a Community From Scratch
  - https://www.bevy.com/blog/ultimate-guide-for-building-community
- CMX Hub
  - https://cmxhub.com/
- Community & Crowd - ExO Insight
  - https://insight.openexo.com/tag/community-crowd/

7

Artificial Intelligence and Algorithms

Artificial intelligence could have more profound implications
for humanity than electricity or fire.

−Sundar Pichai, CEO Alphabet

Companies have to race to build AI, or they will be made
uncompetitive. Essentially, if your competitor is racing
to build AI, they will crush you.

−Elon Musk, CEO SpaceX, Tesla, Twitter

There will be two kinds of companies at the end of this decade:
those who are fully utilizing AI, and those who are
out of business.

−Peter Diamandis

The three things you'll learn in this chapter

- The broad definition of Artificial Intelligence, its various approaches and strategies, and the implications of each for your business.
- The power AI will have across every industry in the decade ahead and why it will be critical for every company to incorporate AI into every aspect of their business.
- The initial steps the company must take to start its AI journey.

S taff on Demand, and the cultivation of Crowds and Community, are appealing in theory. In reality, their practical application demands massive amounts of digital technology to account for their sheer scale and complexity. Further, that technology must be connected to real-life applications. That connection comes in the form of Algorithms, which are managed not by human beings but by Artificial Intelligence (AI), the topics of this chapter. With the rise of large language models (LLMs) like ChatGPT and Stability AI, the World Economic Forum predicts that nearly 25% of jobs will be disrupted in the next five years. PwC Global estimates that AI will contribute $15.7 trillion to the global economy by 2030. The world's biggest companies have already noticed—and they are leading the way in implementing AI.

What are AI and Algorithms?

An Algorithm is a step-by-step set of instructions used to automate a task or solve a specific problem. Artificial

Intelligence (AI) explores how algorithms can be made "intelligent," allowing digital systems to both learn to solve problems without predetermined instructions and discover solutions to new problems without human intervention. AI enables computer systems to behave or "think" like humans by learning to improve performance over time.

Case Study: AlphaFold—The Power of AI and Algorithms in Predicting Protein Structures

AlphaFold is an AI program developed by DeepMind that predicts protein structures. To understand its significance, we first need to know what proteins are and why their structure is important.

Proteins are made up of chains of amino acids that fold into 3D structures. These structures determine the protein's biological function. The "protein-folding problem" is a major challenge in biology because it's difficult to figure out how the amino acid sequence of a protein determines its 3D structure.

Scientists have used expensive and time-consuming methods like X-ray crystallography, cryo-electron microscopy, and nuclear magnetic resonance to determine protein structures. However, these methods have identified only the structures of around 170,000 proteins, while there are more than 200 million known proteins across all life forms. If we could predict protein structures only from their amino acid sequences, it would greatly advance scientific research. That's where AlphaFold comes in.

AlphaFold uses AI and deep learning to predict protein structures. It has competed in the Critical Assessment of Structure Prediction (CASP) competition, which challenges scientists to produce their best protein structure predictions. In 2018, AlphaFold 1 ranked first in the competition, particularly excelling at predicting structures for difficult targets where no existing template structures were available.

In 2020, AlphaFold 2 repeated this success, achieving a level of accuracy much higher than any other group. It scored above 90 out of 100 for about two-thirds of the proteins in the CASP global distance test (GDT), which measures how similar a predicted structure is to a structure determined by lab experiments, with 100 being a perfect match.

AlphaFold 2's results were considered "astounding" and "transformational" by researchers. While it still has room for improvement, the achievement is impressive.

DeepMind trained AlphaFold on more than 170,000 proteins from a public repository of protein sequences and structures. The program uses a form of attention network, which is a deep-learning technique that helps the AI identify parts of a larger problem, then piece it together to obtain the overall solution. This training and the subsequent predictions showcase the importance of AI and Algorithms in tackling complex problems like protein folding.

AlphaFold is a prime example of how AI and Algorithms can be used to make significant advancements in scientific research. By predicting protein structures from amino acid sequences, AlphaFold opens up new possibilities for understanding biological processes and developing treatments for various diseases.

Description of AI and Algorithms: Key Concepts

To better understand this rapidly evolving field, let's explore some key terms and concepts:

- **Narrow AI.** Current AI technology is "narrow" because it can solve only the tasks for which it is trained. It can't extrapolate from its experience to entirely different areas of intelligence or understand broader concepts without specific training. Narrow AI systems may also suffer from "catastrophic forgetting," losing the ability to solve previous tasks when they are trained for new ones.

- **Artificial General Intelligence (AGI).** AGI refers to an intelligent agent that can understand or learn any intellectual task a human can do. It is a long-standing goal in AI development, exemplified by the Turing Test, designed by Alan Turing in 1950.

- **Machine learning.** Instead of programming machines with explicit instructions, machine learning enables machines to deduce concepts or outcomes directly from data. This process includes building models for machines to learn.

- **Neural nets.** A type of machine-learning model loosely based on human brain neurons. Neural nets are digital operating units that produce outputs based on inputs. They are arranged in layered networks, with more neurons enabling a greater capacity to learn complex concepts and relationships.

- **Deep learning.** A type of machine learning based on artificial neural networks that uses multiple layers of processing to extract progressively higher-level features from data. Deep learning can lead to superior results in applications such as computer vision, speech recognition, natural language processing, drug design, and medical image analysis.

- **Generative adversarial networks (GANs).** GANs are neural network models where a generator and a discriminator serve as adversaries. The generator creates synthesized outputs to fool the discriminator while the discriminator tries to detect if the output is fake.

- **Natural language processing (NLP).** NLP focuses on creating computers and digital agents that can interact with humans using regular human language. It aims to develop devices that can analyze vast amounts of natural-language data in near-real-time.
- **Federated learning.** Federated learning is a decentralized, distributed machine-learning technique that trains AI models across multiple devices holding local data samples, such as smartphones or IoT devices, without sharing the actual data. This approach allows the AI model to learn from a wide range of data sources while preserving privacy and reducing the need for centralized data storage. In federated learning, devices collaboratively update a shared global model by sending only the model updates, such as gradients or parameters, to a central server, which then aggregates these updates to improve the global model. Federated learning unlocks information for AI applications without requiring devices to surrender and share data, making it a standard for meeting privacy regulations.
- **Large language models (LLMs).** LLMs are advanced machine-learning models designed for natural-language processing tasks. They excel in understanding and generating human-like text based on context, thanks to innovations in deep-learning techniques, particularly the Transformer architecture. Trained on massive text datasets, LLMs like OpenAI's GPT-4, Google's Bard, and Stability AI have demonstrated remarkable capabilities in various applications, such as summarization, translation, and

question-answering. Their ability to generate coherent and contextually accurate text has made them a powerful tool in the world of Artificial Intelligence.

By understanding these key terms and concepts, we can appreciate the ongoing advancements in AI and its potential to revolutionize various aspects of our lives.

Why AI? Overcoming Human Cognitive Biases

We have traditionally relied on human intellect and intuition for decision-making. However, these processes are often flawed due to a variety of cognitive biases, such as:

- **Availability bias**: Basing decisions on easily recalled information rather than considering all relevant data
- **Bandwagon effect**: Adopting opinions or beliefs because they are popular or endorsed by others
- **Hindsight bias**: Believing, after an event has occurred, that one would have predicted or expected the outcome
- **Illusory superiority**: Overestimating one's abilities and underestimating the abilities of others
- **Negativity bias**: Giving more weight to negative information than positive information
- **Sunk cost fallacy**: Continuing to invest in a decision based on the amount already invested rather than evaluating the current and future value of that decision
- **Overconfidence bias**: Overestimating the accuracy of one's beliefs or predictions
- **Anchoring bias**: Focusing too much on one piece of information while ignoring others

- **Apophenia**: Finding connections between unrelated events or data points
- **Cognitive dissonance**: Disregarding or modifying conflicting information to maintain existing beliefs
- **Confirmation bias**: Interpreting information in a way that confirms pre-existing beliefs.
- **Logical fallacy**: Allowing irrational factors to influence decision-making or conclusions.
- **Truthiness**: Believing in the logic of a process based on the plausibility of the outcome.

AI has the potential to overcome many of these human biases in decision-making. However, it is crucial to note that AI can also exhibit these biases if they are present in its programming. Additionally, AI has its own set of potential flaws that need to be considered and addressed.

Case Studies: AI and Algorithms

> The next 10,000 business plans will be for an entrepreneur to take a domain and add AI to it.
>
> —Kevin Kelly, Founding Editor, *Wired* magazine

Artificial Intelligence and Algorithms have become part of daily life in most of the world. Today, they are so ubiquitous that we barely notice them: Google's page rank, Amazon's recommendation engine, airline pricing, newspaper financial stories, air-traffic control, etc. Let's look at some brief case studies on these attributes.

- **FutureScope.** This marketing firm uses AI to generate engaging, customized daily newsletters designed to connect clients with their audiences, help generate targeted email lists, and convert audience members into paying customers.

- **ProFinda** is a workforce optimization platform powered by AI. The self-described leader of "the Future of Work," ProFinda maps an organization's skills, knowledge, expertise, connections, and availability to build a single view of its talent pool, allowing employees to find expertise internally and enabling more efficient team-building and production.

- **Cainthus.** In 2014, brothers David and Ross Hunt set out to provide affordable digital measurements to farmers to make data-driven decisions. Cainthus, now a part of Ever.Ag,[36] combines computer vision and Artificial Intelligence analytics to "enable individual animal management at scale." "The whole point," David told us, "was 'How do you give farmers information that they can use, information where they can make more money by using it?' Farmers could take the data that we gave them, implement it into their day-to-day activities, and then feel confident that those changes either saved them money or made them more.

"When cows are stressed, they don't eat, they don't drink, they don't produce milk," explains David. "If you don't treat your cows well, you earn less money because they don't produce enough milk. If

---

[36] "Ever.Ag: Empowering Supply Chains to Feed a Growing World," EverAg, 2022, https://c212.net/c/link/?t=0&l=en&o=3573292-1&h=2879909087&u=https%3A%2F%2Fnews.ever.ag%2F&a=Ever.Ag.

you have a higher cow comfort index, the more milk you'll get."

The Hunt brothers and their engineers created a "cow comfort index" using Algorithms and applied computer vision to score large-scale bovine comfort. Insights from the data helped optimize feed management and pen-level monitoring of cow behavior to ensure maximum welfare and, therefore, milk production. The outcome was an average increase of $254,760 farm profit with an $82,500 cost—a more than threefold ROI, plus improved cow comfort.

- **Khanmigo** is a new AI-powered guide from Khan Academy that aims to mimic one-on-one tutoring experiences by providing tailored support, prompting critical thinking, and suggesting relevant resources. Khanmigo is still under development, but the entire Khan Academy ecosystem is excited about the potential of a customized AI tutor for every child.

The Future of Artificial Intelligence and Algorithms

Artificial intelligence will regularly be used in the daily operations of companies to model future products and services and design organizations. The future is incredibly difficult to foresee, reflecting its enormous potential–the future of AI is literally the future of the world. We make the following predictions:

- AIs will run astronomical numbers of digital experiments for companies, including generating hypotheses.
- As AI becomes increasingly humanlike, it will ultimately make recommendations on when and how it will be used. AGI, as it exhibits ever-greater

emotional sensing, will likely penetrate further into our private lives.

- We are likely to see more AI-human collaboration in more places. For example, we will see AI at the top of corporations, including on boards of directors and at the senior management level. We may even see a "digital twin" C-suite, in which every C-suite role will feature a validation and logic-checking AI partner.

- We also will see an explosion of AI-driven decentralized autonomous organizations (DAOs)—that is, company operations that are entirely AI, complete with decision-making powers. Not surprisingly, AIs that are part of a company will develop their own Algorithms that will gather and develop their own data to maximize desired outcomes.

- In short: Companies that do not use AI as core to all of their products, services, and operations will not survive.

A final word on the future of AI and how it will be implemented. Every company will need to navigate the tsunami of change and opportunity that is coming from all aspects of AI, from Machine Learning to Generative AI. How do you stay on top of the disruptive dangers and extraordinary opportunities for leverage? Peter has recently coined the phrase "Chief AI Officer" and has been encouraging every company he chairs, invests in and advises to get one.

So what is a Chief AI Officer? As Peter explains, "It's not someone in your company coding or training a Large Language Model. Instead, your Chief AI Officer is a strategist reporting directly to the CEO and CTO of the company. This person is in charge of monitoring the latest emerging companies, apps, and AI strategies and determining which are of the greatest value to different parts of your company. Your Chief AI Officer is building partnerships, acquiring licenses, and also training your employees. He/She is also making recommendations on how and where to flow in AI at every level of your ExO."

Benefits of AI and Algorithms

In a world exploding with data, human intellect can no longer handle the vast amount of information generated each millisecond by countless numbers of sensors and devices. Artificial Intelligence and Algorithms are necessary to pull the signal from the noise. Further, they can process the information at enormous speed. AI and Algorithms are often orders of magnitude more effective than humans at certain tasks—for example, assessing medical scans or driving. And they can be trained in virtual environments, racking up years of learning in hours or minutes of computer time. For example, many self-driving Algorithms are being trained in virtual worlds to complement their real-world training, covering millions of miles in time spans impossible in the real world.

Other benefits include:

- **Scale:** By far, the biggest benefit of AI and Algorithms is their ability to scale products and services. Netflix is the most famous example: their AI-based recommendation engine drove enormous engagement.
- **New data:** AI and Algorithms leverage new data streams from connected devices and sensors.
- **Reliability:** A much lower error rate stabilizes growth and bolsters predictability.

- **RPA:** Robotic Process Automation frees up other team members' time for more creative and value-added work.
- **Cost and speed:** Product managers can push many more features (e.g., personalization or complexity simplification and analysis) due to lower costs. They can also create new products and services much faster and generate customized user experiences automatically.
- **Persistence:** AIs operate on a 24/7 basis and never need time off (though they do get sick sometimes).
- **Reduced cognitive bias:** AI and Algorithms help overcome the cognitive biases that characterize human decision-making processes—although AI can exhibit such biases if its source programming reflects them.

Challenges of AI and Algorithms

While Artificial Intelligence and Algorithms have many benefits, they also come with considerable challenges. The governance and ethics of AI and Algorithms will dominate public discourse for several years to come. Some challenges related to these attributes include:

- **Garbage in/garbage out.** One of the oldest truths in computing is that the quality of the result depends upon the quality of the data supplied. Bad input data does not somehow magically turn into accurate, reliable, and actionable results.
- **Not sure what it's doing and how it's working.** AIs and Algorithms are often a "black box" about which the user knows next to nothing. As tools like

ChatGPT become prevalent, decisions will be made and/or implemented with few clues about the underlying process. Thus, organizations risk using good data but getting bad results or, worse, seemingly good results that don't actually meet their needs.

- **Hallucinations.** As ChatGPT and GPT4 have come online in 2023, the term "use but verify" and Hallucinations have come into vogue. Often, AI spits out inaccurate information. For example, Peter queried GPT4 about "the top 5 awards and recognitions he had received," GPT4 delivered three that were correct and two that were false (although conceptually on point since they were in the space field).
- **Lack of quantifiable effects.** Artificial Intelligence can be very appealing to implement. It's trendy, can be very efficient, and it looks good to customers and shareholders. But it can also be a black hole for investment. Hold off on AI and Algorithms until you can find definitive, empirically tracked positive effects on productivity and ROI.
- **Ethics.** Artificial intelligence is a computer-based technology. Its behavior is entirely defined by its programmers and/or the large data sets it was trained on, and its current algorithms make no allowance for human emotion, needs, or freedom. This limitation, combined with its ability to function at superhuman speeds, makes it a powerful, world-changing tool. And the same qualities can also make it intrusive, controlling, and even dangerous if left unmonitored.
- **Liability.** Beyond the moral implications of AI, note that you and your enterprise—not your AI—will be held responsible for any damage that it incurs.

- **Governance.** AGIs communicating and working with each other to solve the world's problems is a hugely appealing notion. But that scenario could also prove to be the stuff of science-fiction nightmares if these new systems are inadequately controlled, or their operating functions are misdirected. As we progress further into the Age of Artificial General Intelligence, these challenges will inevitably multiply.
- **Deepfakes.** These AI hoaxes use deep-learning technology, including neural networks, to swap faces on videos and other digital content for propaganda, entertainment, and criminal purposes. The widespread use of deepfakes has already begun to undermine the public's trust in video imagery.
- **Negative public perception.** There's a persistent public fear that robots or AI will replace workers, putting people out of jobs and driving poverty. Dystopian depictions of robots/AI in movies (think *2001: A Space Odyssey, Terminator, The Matrix*) don't help.
- **Data availability and management.** With exponentially increased amounts of data come exponential increases in data management. How will your organization access data (partnerships, open sources, etc.)? How will data be accounted for: as an asset similar to cash, plants, facilities, and customers? How will that data asset be managed? Will your organization focus first on finding good data over building more complex models?
- **Legal.** Is your organization prepared to deal with privacy and liability issues? What risks are you willing to take while waiting for legislation to catch up with faster-moving technology?

- **Modeling.** Can you use your customer data to train a model? If a customer opts out (as per the European Union's general data protection regulations (GDPR)), do you need to re-train those models?

AI and Algorithms: Requirements and Prerequisites

- **MTP.** As with everything in an ExO, the use of Artificial Intelligence and Algorithms must be preceded by the creation and adoption of a company's MTP. The MTP is crucial because it will guide, and keep within strategic guardrails, the implementation of these attributes and—more importantly—the results they generate. In particular, the MTP will determine which of those results are to be implemented and which are to be put aside.
- **Data.** Data is cleaned and labeled, allowing AIs to make greater sense of it.
- **Leveraged assets.** AI and Algorithms require extensive computation capabilities. Cloud computing is almost mandatory.
- **Dashboards** are critical to track any AI-based experiments. Because AIs can run millions of experiments using both real and simulated data, the tracking of those experiments needs to operate at the same scale.

Closing Story: OpenAI and LLMs

Fittingly, GPT-4 wrote our closing story on AI and Algorithms. We prompted GPT-4 to answer the following questions from Peter and Salim's perspectives. (We could have also asked Google's Bard and would expect a very similar answer.)

1. What is GPT-4?

GPT-4 (short for "Generative Pre-trained Transformer 4") is an advanced language model developed by OpenAI. It is a successor to GPT-3 and has been designed to understand and generate human-like text based on the input it receives. GPT-4, like its predecessors, is built using a transformer architecture, which allows it to excel at tasks like machine translation, question-answering, summarization, and text generation. Estimates indicate that its capacity is about a trillion ML parameters.

2. How did GPT-4 originate?

GPT-4 is the fourth generation of the GPT (Generative Pretrained Transformer) language processing model developed by OpenAI. The first generation of GPT, known as GPT-1, was released in 2018 and was followed by GPT-2 in 2019. Both of these models were based on the Transformer architecture, which was originally introduced in the paper "Attention is All You Need" by Vaswani et al. in 2017. GPT-3 was released in 2020.

The GPT models were designed to be trained using large amounts of unannotated text data, using a technique known as unsupervised learning. This allows the model to learn the structure of natural language on its own without the need for human-provided labels or annotations. By training on massive amounts of text data, GPT-4 has been able to learn to generate human-like text, as well as understand and respond to natural language inputs.

3. What can GPT-4 do?

GPT-4 is a powerful language processing model that can perform a wide range of language-related tasks. Some of the things that GPT-4 can do include:

- **Text generation**: GPT-4 can generate human-like text given a prompt, which could be used for content creation, story writing, or any other task that requires creative text output.
- **Text summarization**: GPT-4 can condense large amounts of text into shorter summaries while preserving the most important information.
- **Machine translation**: GPT-4 might be able to translate text between languages more accurately and fluently than its predecessors.
- **Question-answering**: GPT-4 can be capable of understanding and answering questions based on context, making it an even more powerful conversational AI.
- **Sentiment analysis**: GPT-4 might be able to understand the sentiment behind text, such as whether a statement is positive, negative, or neutral.
- **Text classification and categorization**: GPT-4 can be used to categorize and classify text based on its content, such as spam detection or topic identification.
- **Code generation and completion**: GPT-4 can assist in software development by generating or completing code snippets based on the programmer's input.

Overall, GPT-4 is a versatile and powerful language-processing tool that can be used for a wide range of applications in natural language processing and generation.

How to Get Started with Artificial Intelligence and Algorithms

To implement Artificial Intelligence and Algorithms, ExOs need to follow four distinct steps:

1. **Gather data.** The Algorithmic process starts with harnessing data, which is gathered via sensors or human beings or imported from public or private datasets.
2. **Organize data.** The next step is to organize the data. This process is known as ETL (extract, transform, and load).
3. **Apply.** Once the data is accessible, machine-learning tools—such as Hadoop and Pivotal, or open-source deep-learning Algorithms from DeepMind and SkyMind—can extract insights, identify trends, and tune new Algorithms.
4. **Expose.** The final step is exposing the data. Opening data using APIs (Application Programmable Interfaces) can be used to enable an ExO's Community—in particular stakeholders including providers, customers, consumers, and end-users—to develop valuable services. That is, the stakeholder data layers new functionalities and innovations on top of the platform by remixing the ExO's data with the stakeholders.

Successful examples of companies making use of intelligent exposure include the Ford Motor Company, Uber, Rabobank, the Port of Rotterdam, IBM Watson, Wolfram Alpha, Twitter, and Facebook/Meta.

A word of warning: companies often get discouraged trying to implement these solutions, typically because they are working with legacy systems—or they have underestimated the amount of data needed to train their predictive data analytic systems. But if they follow these four steps, the process can be fairly straightforward. And don't forget: it is possible now to purchase models that have already been trained.

• • •

The current and future explosion of data harvested from the world's billions and trillions of sensors can be analyzed only through the deployment of Artificial Intelligence and Algorithms. Given that they are so much more objective, scalable, and flexible than human beings, Artificial Intelligence and Algorithms are the keys to the future of business in general. Exponential Organizations will lead this new economy.

Key Resources/Links where you can learn more

Please note that the links below are likely to be outdated by the time you read this. The field is evolving faster than our ability to track it. For updated links, please join the community at www.openexo.com

- Join ExO Insight and the Open ExO Community Community of On Demand Experts | OpenExO.com to stay on top of some of the latest trends and conversations.
  o https://insight.openexo.com/
  o https://openexo.com/community/#/

- MIT NEWS: How quickly do AI and Algorithms improve?
  - https://news.mit.edu/2021/how-quickly-do-algorithms-improve-0920
- 4 Stakeholders of API. About Providers, Customers, Consumers... | by Amancio Bouza | API Product Management | Medium
  - https://medium.com/api-product-management/4-stakeholders-of-the-api-5ca1ef79d4f5
- Top 50 Most Popular APIs (Updated for 2023) | Rapid Blog
  - https://rapidapi.com/blog/most-popular-api/
- Awards—API World
  - https://apiworld.co/awards/#winners
- Revolutionizing agriculture through emerging technologies—Atlantic Council
  - https://www.atlanticcouncil.org/event/revolutionizing-agriculture-through-emerging-technologies/
- Text to art platforms—Midjourney, DALL·E 2
  - https://www.midjourney.com/
  - https://openai.com/dall-e-2/
- Introducing ChatGPT
  - https://openai.com/blog/chatgpt/
- Google Bard
  - https://bard.google.com
- 100+ AI Use Cases & Applications: In-Depth Guide for 2023
  - https://research.aimultiple.com/ai-usecases/

- 7 Artificial Intelligence Examples Transforming Enterprises
  - https://www.teradata.com/Trends/ AI-and-Machine-Learning/ Artificial-Intelligence-Examples
- Algorithms - ExO Insight
  - https://insight.openexo.com/tag/algorithms/

8

Leveraged and Shared Assets

The sharing economy blows up the industrial model of
companies owning and people consuming.

—Forbes

The three things you'll learn in this chapter

- Leveraged and shared assets (LSA), which include the sharing economy and rented equipment, will become a major part of the economy in the next decade.
- A sharing economy can be built around any asset, rapidly, and with minimum upfront capital.
- If you're building a business around LSA, make sure you get the unit metrics right before you scale.

In the previous chapters, we saw the benefits of using human assets only when necessary and relying on Artificial Intelligence and Algorithms to reduce overhead and increase versatility and operating speed. Those strategies were derived from the historical techniques of renting physical equipment and tools. Today, the model of Community and Crowds has evolved and amplified the strategy of using leases and rentals into that of leveraging and sharing assets—the theme of this chapter. By effectively using leveraged and shared assets (LSA) to virtualize everything possible within its operations, Exponential Organizations will have an important competitive advantage in the economy of the future.

What Are Leveraged and Shared Assets?

"Leveraged and shared assets" is the practice of renting or sharing assets—even those that are mission-critical—to allow an organization to stay nimble and unencumbered, to begin rapidly, and to scale with minimum friction. Ideally, LSA also lowers the marginal cost of supply—to virtually zero in the case of a highly scaled model. By not owning physical or digital property, an ExO can remove the costs associated with managing that property, along with all related infrastructure costs.

Case Study: BlaBlaCar

CEO Frederic Mazzella, founded BlaBlaCar in France in 2016, after a long car ride when he noticed all the empty seats in the cars on the road around him. BlaBlacar was a pioneer of the ride-sharing economy. While most carpool and ride-share apps are designed to help you catch a ride with others to a nearby location, BlaBlaCar was created to enable users to connect with automobiles—and increasingly buses—headed for long-distance destinations.

Today, BlaBlaCar is one of Europe's fastest-growing transportation companies, with more than 90 million members in 22 European and Latin American countries. For drivers, the platform is a way to cut the cost of gas; you simply post your destination and the cost per passenger. For riders, it is a quick, inexpensive, and social way to travel without the expense of a car. Riders can choose to travel with minimum interaction ("Bla") or turn the trip into a social event ("BlaBlaBla"). There's also a "Ladies Only" feature.

Says Mazzella: "Carpooling creates a unique context: it makes possible exchanges of value between people who otherwise would not have had a chance to meet."

BlaBlaCar has recently branched into another underused mode of transportation—buses—with the purchase of Ouibus, an established budget European bus line known for its very inexpensive tickets. BlaBlaBus operates very much like BlaBlaCar, enabling the traveler to manage every aspect of their journey—and even track their ride on the BlaBlaCar app.

Critical to BlaBlaCar's success is that early on, it determined the right fee structure. Drivers charge passengers per trip, and BlaBlaCar takes a 10–12% transaction fee (typically about 10 euros) per trip. The low costs appeals to customers, while earning BlaBlaCar a healthy profit for acting as the platform. As Salim points out, "If you're using leveraged assets, you have to get the unit metrics right. If you rent and share assets, you can drop your marginal cost pretty drastically and still see healthy returns."

BlaBlaCar's MTP? "We bring freedom, fairness, and fraternity to the world of travel."

• • •

Let's take a quick look at how BlaBlaCar has implemented some key ExO attributes:

- **Interfaces:** It uses an easy app to connect travelers with drivers.
- **Engagement:** BlaBlaCar has invested in tools to engage everyone in its community. For example, it offers services such BlaBlaHelper, which helps members organize their shared car experience.
- **Leveraged assets:** It's a carpooling platform that connects assets (car drivers with empty seats) to customers (passengers looking for a ride) over an average distance of 300 km.
- **Community and Crowd:** BlaBlaCar has tapped into its vast Community and developed tools—like ratings, opinions, and strong profile verification—to generate user confidence. Says Mazzella, "We take time to get to know our users. All profiles and feedbacks are checked, so you know who you travel with."
- **Autonomy:** Because it is largely virtual, BlaBlaCar has been able to create an agile company structure, which allows for rapid interactions and decision-making; constant technological transformation; local teams working independently; and hiring processes for talent acquisition.
- **Carbon neutrality:** BlaBlaCar's environmentally and human-friendly mobility network saves 1.6 million tons of carbon dioxide and enables 120 million human connections every year.

Description of Leveraged and Shared Assets

Historically, many businesses have made an asset available by embedding it into products and services. One example is car rental, where companies such as Hertz, Avis, and National purchase fleets of automobiles and then rent them by miles of use—in the interim, storing, servicing, and maintaining those vehicles as needed. Today, companies like Uber and Lyft leverage the assets of car-owning drivers to provide essentially the same service.

In recent years, the leveraging of assets has become much more sophisticated—and virtual. The latter is especially important because when you've turned an object into information, it not only typically becomes more valuable but also becomes easier to share, not to mention infinitely more scalable. Thus, Airbnb is using its platform to enable access to millions of bedrooms around the world—something that would have been impossible if it owned and serviced all of those bedrooms.

Some key asset categories that can be leveraged include intellectual property/digital assets (e.g., Google Maps doesn't own the land), Opensource, Metaverse, and Web3.

A key subset of leveraged assets is the sharing economy, which has its own set of categories. Here are some of the most important of these (and examples of well-known companies or services) that exemplify them:

- Peer-2-Peer (Blizzard Entertainment)
- Fashion (Rent the Runway)
- Cars (Turo, Getaround)
- Co-working (WeWork)
- Offices (the next WeWork: see below)
- Computation/Cloud (Amazon Cloud)

- Manufacturing plants (TSMC)
- Prototyping (Qualcomm)
- Sharing Economy (Uber & Airbnb)
- Open data sets
- Leveraging and sharing, leading to fractional ownership (IP, real estate)

Case Studies: Leveraged and Shared Assets

- **The LAND initiative,** led by Capital Certainty, is acquiring land estates the size of small countries in key locations, beginning with the Amazon Forest. LAND tokenizes land ownership through social, productive, and environmental outputs. Its goal is to create the world's largest agrotech ecological digital hub. To fund this initiative, LAND leverages digital assets and activates sustainable business models, including carbon credits covering millions of hectares. The benefits are then reinvested in biodiversity, climate control, and local well-being while increasing the value of the land by between 30 and 200%. LAND's MTP is "Make LAND's prosperity resilient, ownership accessible, destiny diverse, and innovation global."
- South Africa's **Sun Exchange** leverages roof space in the sunniest places on earth, crowdfunding solar cells on the roofs of different organizations.
- We've talked about **Waze** already. It's so popular in urban areas like Los Angeles or Mexico City that its use actually has a macro effect on traffic efficiency in the region.
- **Microgrids** may prove to be the most important—and disruptive—shared assets in our future.

Microgrids are decentralized groups of electricity sources and loads that are part of the area power grid but that can detach themselves—typically during challenging technical (brownouts) and economic (fee increases) moments—to operate independently in "island mode."

- **LabCentral Inc./BioLabs** is a non-profit organization that operates a shared laboratory facility headquartered in Cambridge, Massachusetts. There, LabCentral offers lab and office space for approximately 60 new biotech startup companies, largely found at nearby MIT and Harvard. LabCentral's main sources of funding are revenues from user fees, as well as grants and sponsorship contributions. Biolabs, a related for-profit equivalent company, serves as home for more than 300 startups in eight cities. BioLabs companies routinely account for more than 20 percent of all Seed and Series A Venture Capital invested in life sciences in the US. The company is currently opening labs around the US, wherever biolab space is in short supply.

The Future of Leveraged and Shared Assets

In the future, we'll see two distinct types of companies emerging - those that own, operate, and outsource assets, and those that leverage outsourced assets from others. The companies caught in between, with underutilized assets, may face challenges. The future of Leveraged and Shared Assets will take the following forms:

- **Assets as Platforms**: The future will witness a widespread transformation of company assets into platforms, allowing them to be accessed and utilized by third parties.

- **Platform Business Models**: As assets become more platform-oriented, businesses will increasingly adopt models centered around these platforms, enabling them to leverage shared resources and tap into new opportunities.
- **The Rise of Asset Management Companies**: With the rise of shared assets and platform-based business models, a new service industry will emerge, specializing in the management of assets for other companies. These asset management companies will help optimize asset utilization and facilitate seamless integration into platform ecosystems.
- **Outsourced Assets**: As businesses recognize the value of outsourcing assets rather than owning them outright, the demand for asset-sharing arrangements will grow, leading to increased collaboration and resource optimization.
- **Advantages for Asset Companies**: Companies that leverage outsourced assets can benefit from reduced costs, improved flexibility, and access to specialized resources without the burden of asset ownership and maintenance.
- **Challenges for Asset Companies**: Organizations that fail to effectively leverage their assets or adapt to the platform-based economy may face difficulties, such as increased competition, limited growth prospects, and potential obsolescence.
- **Industry Implications**: The transformation of assets into platforms and the rise of asset management companies will impact numerous sectors, including manufacturing, transportation, technology, and

more, fostering innovation and reshaping traditional business models.

Going forward, we predict that there will be two types of business in the world: those that own, operate, and outsource assets (e.g., 3D printing, car rentals) and those that utilize outsourced assets from others. Those in between—that is, those companies stuck with a bunch of assets they are not leveraging—will be in trouble. We predict our exponential future will be characterized by the widespread transformation of assets into platforms. Most company assets will be available to third parties, and most business models will be based around platforms. To facilitate this, an important new service industry will emerge: companies that manage the assets of other companies.

Benefits of Leveraged and Shared Assets

LSA can bring numerous advantages to your enterprise, revolutionizing traditional business models. Here are some key benefits that LSA offers:

- **Lowers Start-up Costs**: By leveraging and sharing assets, businesses can significantly reduce their start-up costs. Instead of investing heavily in acquiring all the necessary assets individually, companies can access shared resources, infrastructure, and equipment, thereby minimizing their initial financial burden. This cost-effective approach allows startups and small businesses to allocate their resources more efficiently and focus on core activities, accelerating their growth trajectory.

- **Enables Scaling**: LSA facilitates scaling operations by providing access to larger volumes of resources, leading to lower, more competitive pricing. Sharing assets with other businesses or leveraging existing infrastructure allows enterprises to benefit from economies of scale. This scalability enables organizations to expand their operations without incurring substantial costs, making it easier to penetrate new markets, meet growing customer demands, and stay competitive in the industry.
- **Lowers Marginal Cost of Supply**: By utilizing shared assets, enterprises can effectively lower their marginal cost of supply. The cost of producing and delivering additional units or services decreases as the volume increases. With LSA, businesses can tap into shared resources, manufacturing facilities, or distribution networks, benefiting from cost savings achieved through higher production levels.
- **Reduces the Need for Managing Assets**: LSA eliminates the need for businesses to manage their own warehouses, parking garages, or other physical assets. By leveraging shared infrastructure, companies can avoid the costs and complexities associated with asset management, maintenance, and storage. This allows organizations to focus their resources on core competencies and strategic initiatives, streamlining operations and improving overall efficiency.
- **Boosts the Balance Sheet**: One of the significant benefits of LSA is that it eliminates the need for businesses to maintain inventory. By sharing assets or leveraging existing resources, enterprises can avoid stockpiling excess goods or materials, resulting in a leaner balance sheet. This reduction in inventory not

only frees up capital but also minimizes the risk of obsolete or slow-moving inventory, improving financial stability and agility.

- **Increases Agility and Makes Upgrading Easier**: LSA enables businesses to adapt more quickly to changing market dynamics and technological advancements. By eliminating the need to maintain unused or outdated assets, companies can easily upgrade their infrastructure, tools, or equipment as needed. This flexibility and agility allow organizations to stay at the forefront of innovation, remain competitive, and respond swiftly to evolving customer needs and industry trends.

- **Dematerializes Office Spaces**: LSA can dematerialize office spaces, reducing the need for large physical premises and cutting overhead costs. By leveraging remote work capabilities, shared workspaces, or flexible office arrangements, enterprises can optimize their space utilization, eliminating the need for extensive office infrastructure. This cost-saving measure enables businesses to allocate resources more efficiently, invest in growth initiatives, and achieve higher profitability.

If you have an asset that is of value to others, you can turn that asset into a platform and reduce your own incremental operating expenses by sharing it with others. This is exactly what Amazon did when it opened AWS, sharing its core computing capabilities with thousands of others.

Challenges of Leveraged and Shared Assets

Understanding and mitigating the challenges of LSA are crucial for maximizing the potential of an ExO. Here are some key challenges associated with LSA:

- **Ensuring Unit Metrics Work Before Scaling**: Before scaling a business using LSA, it is essential to ensure that the unit metrics are robust and sustainable. Scaling operations without solid unit economics can lead to the amplification of losses instead of generating profits. A notable cautionary example is WeWork, that scaled without addressing fundamental unit metrics, ultimately leading to financial difficulties.

- **Increased Risk due to Leveraging Assets**: Leveraging assets introduces an element of risk, particularly during challenging times such as economic downturns or unforeseen events like the COVID-19 pandemic. Reliability and availability of leveraged assets may become uncertain, potentially impacting business operations and continuity. Enterprises relying on shared assets must carefully assess the risks associated with their reliance on external resources and implement contingency plans to mitigate potential disruptions.

- **Loss of Control**: One of the trade-offs of utilizing shared assets is the loss of control over those assets. When an organization does not own its assets, it relinquishes direct control over their management, maintenance, and strategic decision-making. This lack of control can pose challenges in terms of customization, prioritization, and responsiveness to specific business needs.

- **Inappropriate for Certain Situations**: There are instances when Leveraged and Shared Assets may not be suitable for certain organizations or specific circumstances. For example, young technology companies with breakthrough products, like Tesla, may choose to own their assets to protect trade secrets and capitalize on future demand. In such cases, asset ownership becomes critical for maintaining a competitive edge and safeguarding intellectual property.

Requirements and Prerequisites of LSA

The success of Leveraged and Shared Assets relies on several prerequisites and requirements that play a crucial role in maximizing the potential and effectiveness of LSA. Here are some key requirements and prerequisites:

- **Abundance of Easily Available Assets**: LSA heavily depends on the availability of assets that can be leveraged and shared. To fully capitalize on the benefits of LSA, an organization needs to have a substantial pool of assets that can be accessed and utilized efficiently. This could include physical assets, intellectual property, data, expertise, or any other resource that holds value and can be shared among participants.
- **Interfaces**: In order for customers to access and utilize shared assets, the interfaces through which they interact with the organization need to be intuitive and user-friendly. Easy-to-use customer interfaces enhance the accessibility and adoption of shared assets, ensuring a positive user experience.
- **AI and Algorithms**: Algorithms play a critical role in the efficient allocation and scaling of leveraged

assets. These algorithms help identify the most suitable and optimal allocation of resources, ensuring that assets are utilized effectively and in a manner that maximizes their impact.

- **Dashboards**: These are essential tools for managing and visualizing key metrics and information within an organization. Leveraged assets have a strong relationship with traditional and innovative dashboards, which provide at-a-glance insights into the performance and utilization of shared assets.

Case Study: Rent the Runway

Rent the Runway, founded in 2009, has emerged as a highly successful e-commerce platform revolutionizing the fashion industry through its unique rental model. With a vast collection of clothing and accessories from over 700 designers, Rent the Runway offers customers the opportunity to rent and wear high-end fashion items for special occasions or everyday wear. The company's business model encompasses both one-off rentals and a popular subscription service, which accounts for 75% of its revenues.

Rent the Runway's subscription service allows customers to select up to eight items per month for a fee of under $100. This affordable and flexible pricing structure has resonated with consumers, attracting a user base of almost 200,000 subscribers. On average, Rent the Runway subscribers wear approximately $30,000 worth of clothing from the platform each year, highlighting the significant value and utility the service provides to its customers.

To facilitate the rental operations at scale, Rent the Runway operates a network of giant warehouses strategically located throughout the United States. These warehouses not only store the vast inventory of designer clothing but also house one of the world's largest dry-cleaning operations. With the capacity to process over 2,000 items per hour, the company ensures that each piece of clothing is meticulously cleaned and maintained to meet the highest quality standards before being rented out again.

Rent the Runway's revenues from subscriptions and one-off rentals exceeding $100 million per year. This impressive revenue stream has contributed to the company's valuation surpassing $1 billion, underscoring the significant market demand for the rental of designer clothing and accessories.

LSA: How to Get Started

Getting started with Leveraged and Shared Assets requires a systematic approach that involves identifying assets, assessing their criticality, and transitioning from ownership to renting. By following these steps, organizations can streamline their operations, optimize resource allocation, and improve financial stability. Here's a guide on how to get started with LSA:

1. **List the Assets for Renting**: Begin by identifying the assets that your organization currently owns but could be rented instead. This includes tangible assets such as equipment, vehicles, or office space, as well as intangible assets like intellectual property or data. Consider the feasibility of renting these assets to other organizations, potentially transforming your organization into an "Edge ExO" platform that offers these assets for shared use.

2. **Assess Criticality to MTP**: Next, sort the identified assets based on their criticality to your MTP.

Evaluate how essential each asset is in directly supporting your core operations and strategic objectives. Classify them according to their level of importance, with the least critical assets being prioritized for disposal and renting alternatives.

3. **Dispose of Least Critical Assets**: Starting with the least critical assets, take steps to dispose of them and transition to a rental model. This could involve selling or divesting the assets and establishing partnerships or contracts with rental providers or shared asset platforms. By offloading these assets, your organization can reduce maintenance and management costs, unlock capital, and optimize resource utilization.

4. **Benefit from a Cleaner Balance Sheet**: As you transition from asset ownership to renting, you can enjoy the benefits of a cleaner balance sheet. By eliminating non-critical assets from your ownership, your organization becomes leaner and more agile. This streamlined approach helps improve financial stability, reduces the risk of asset depreciation, and allows for greater flexibility in resource allocation. A cleaner balance sheet provides peace of mind and positions your organization for increased efficiency and future growth.

• • •

What is the ultimate purpose of leveraging and sharing assets? To gather as many tools as possible to maximize the Engagement of your Community, Crowd, and other stakeholders. That is the subject of the next chapter.

Key Resources/Links where you can learn more

- Why Decentralized Innovation Is Critical
  - https://www.forbes.com/sites/forbestechcouncil/2022/02/14/why-decentralized-innovation-is-critical/?sh=5a77486c7a52
- Summary of the Israeli sharing community Shareitt
  - https://www.jpost.com/environment-and-climate-change/article-690181
- How Amazon Web Services Got Started
  - https://techcrunch.com/2016/07/02/andy-jassys-brief-history-of-the-genesis-of-aws/
- Amazon.com: The Upstarts: How Uber, Airbnb, and the Killer Companies of the New Silicon Valley Are Changing the World eBook : Stone, Brad
  - https://www.amazon.com/Upstarts-Airbnb-Companies-Silicon-Changing-ebook/dp/B01HZFB3X0/ref=sr_1_1
- Leveraged Assets - ExO Insight
  - https://insight.openexo.com/tag/leveraged-assets/

9

Engagement

Gamification should empower people, not exploit them.
It should feel good at the end of the day because you made
progress towards something that mattered to you.

—*Exponential Organizations*, First Edition

The three things you'll learn in this chapter

- Incentive prizes convert Crowd into Community,
  and gamification binds the Community to your
  MTP.
- With Web3 (crypto and NFTs), Engagement
  becomes exponentially more powerful.
- By the time you read this chapter, it'll be out of
  date: Engagement is the second fastest-evolving
  ExO attribute (after AI and Algorithms).

In the preceding chapters, we spoke of Community and Crowd, Artificial Intelligence and Algorithms, Leverage and Shared Assets, and other attributes vital to the successful operation of an Exponential Organization. Engagement is the "glue"—the secret sauce—that holds these attributes together. This attribute, largely unique to ExOs, enables them to grow with unprecedented speed.

What is Engagement?

Engagement is the use of techniques like gamification, incentive prizes, and—more recently—crypto economics to keep stakeholders interested, involved, and increasingly committed to an organization's MTP or shared purpose. Through Engagement, ExOs gain the loyalty of their customers and Community and convert Crowd into Community. Engagement helps to create virtuous, positive feedback loops—which in turn allows for faster growth through innovation and customer and community loyalty. Companies like Google, Airbnb, Uber, eBay, Yelp, GitHub, and Twitter all leverage different Engagement mechanisms.

Case Study: XPRIZE and the Power of Incentives

The XPRIZE Foundation is a global platform for implementing large-scale incentive competitions to drive massive Engagement and solve grand challenges. That concept isn't new. Public competitions have been around for a long time. The development of ship chronometers was spurred by an 18th-century competition to create clocks that worked accurately on a rocking ship in order to determine longitude. Charles Lindbergh flew across the Atlantic in 1927 in pursuit of the $25,000 Orteig prize for the first nonstop flight between New York and Paris. In fact, co-author Peter Diamandis was inspired to create the XPRIZE Foundation after reading about the Orteig Prize and Lindberg's flight.

Thanks to the popularity of the XPRIZE, incentive competitions are back in the news. This Engagement technique is typically used to identify promising innovators in the undifferentiated Crowd and move them into a targeted Community. Competitions are then used to challenge, leverage, and motivate that Community in order to solicit radical, potentially breakthrough ideas.

For Peter, the XPRIZE started with his love of space and his desire to create commercially viable human spaceflight capability. He was certain that some engineer or entrepreneur in the global aviation and space Crowd was capable of building a private spaceship. In 1996, under the iconic Gateway Arch in St. Louis, Missouri, Peter announced a $10 million purse for the first non-government organization able to build a reusable spaceship that could successfully carry three adults at least 100 km into space and repeat the flight again within two weeks. The purse was later funded by the Ansari family and was rebranded the $10 million Ansari XPRIZE.

On September 29 and October 4 of 2004, a vehicle called SpaceshipOne, built by famed aerospace engineer Burt Rutan and backed by Microsoft cofounder and philanthropist Paul Allen, made two consecutive flights to win the prize. The winning technology was then licensed by Sir Richard Branson, who created the spaceflight company Virgin Galactic.

• • •

An incentive prize creates a clear, measurable, and objective goal, offering a cash purse to the first team to achieve that goal. The approach offers huge leverage and efficiency: incentive prizes pay the winner only *after* the feat has been clearly achieved. They are tools that can be used by individuals, startups, medium-sized and large corporations, and even governments. But they are most powerful—and unique—in that they allow small teams or lone innovators to launch or transform industries. By tapping into the deep-rooted human desire to compete, incentive competitions push teams to deliver their very best work.

Perhaps the most important benefit of an incentive competition is that it creates an ecosystem of competing teams. Incentive competitions can engage and inspire dozens, and sometimes thousands, of teams to find innovative solutions to achieve a goal. Such innovations can galvanize not only a single company but an entire industry, spurring it forward at an unprecedented pace. In April 2021, the XPRIZE launched its largest prize to date: a $100 million purse for "gigaton carbon removal," funded by Elon Musk. More than 1,100 teams registered to compete.

To date, over its 28-year history, the XPRIZE Foundation has launched more than $300 million in prize purses, ranging in size from $2 million to $100 million. A spinoff platform called HeroX [37] allows companies to create their own smaller challenges to solve local and global challenges. HeroX enables the rapid design and launch of incentive competitions, ranging from $0 "Karma" prizes to competitions with purses of $1,000 to $1 million.

Two key aspects of incentive prizes are worth keeping in mind: First, when XPRIZE puts up an incentive prize, its Community of competitors typically spends between 10 and 20 times that amount on research and development. Thus, as

---

[37]   HeroX, http://www.herox.com/.

Peter notes, "a $10 million spaceflight XPRIZE drove initially $100 million spent cumulatively by all the teams, and eventually birthed a huge industry that will soon cross the $500 billion mark."

Second, incentive prizes deliver innovation from the most unlikely sources. For example, the second-place team in the $3 million Wendy Schmidt Oil Cleanup XPRIZE was made up of a dentist and a tattoo artist (the former got a tattoo from the latter) who tested their solution in a swimming pool. If you were an investor, would you fund that team? Very likely not, but maybe you should have, as they placed second in the competition and met all the criteria.

Today, thousands of incentive prizes are in progress worldwide. The recent emergence of computer code bug bounties is a great example: software developers reward competitors who find problems in their code.

With XPRIZE, we see the incredible Engagement potential of incentive prizes. If you're an ExO, ask yourself: *How can I use an incentive prize to tap into the most brilliant innovators in the connected world and convert my Crowd into my Community?*

Description of Engagement

The XPRIZE story is just one example of engagement. Customer Engagement is why marketers market: to build relationships with customers that will ensure they choose a product or service over its competition; enjoy and benefit from that product or service; keep coming back for more; and tell their friends, families, or colleagues to try it too.

User Engagement techniques, such as sweepstakes, quizzes, coupons, airline miles, and loyalty cards, have been around for a long time, some for centuries. All capitalize on the fact that user Engagement is the path to user commitment, which in turn elicits user contribution.

With the development and addition of digital components, Engagement has morphed considerably in recent years. Brands and businesses can no longer rely on catchy slogans or celebrity endorsements. Thanks to social media and mobile phones, they must be always "on," ready to capitalize on opportunities to engage with customers anywhere, any time. Today's Engagement initiatives are fully information-enabled, multimedia enriched, and socialized. They include digital reputation systems, online games, and incentive prizes.

In an ExO, Engagement serves up a quadruple dividend:

1. First, it helps keep current members, users, and clients happy and connected, reminding them of why they joined your organization and of the value of your product or service.

2. Second, Engagement is a means by which you can convert your Crowd into your Community. Engagement can be a mechanism that lets the Crowd find out about your product or service or as a means by which your current Community members engage their friends and families, encouraging them to join in—also known as "viral marketing." Importantly, Engagement activates Community and Crowd around your MTP.

3. Engaged members of your Community add value to your product or service, as we discussed in Chapter 6.

4. Finally, the use of Web3 and cryptocurrencies enables companies not only to monetize their Engagement, but also to create a large body of loyal "investors" that

act as a buffer to economic shocks, stock drops, and other events created by non-loyal speculators.

Today's Engagement universe finds itself with an unprecedented array of tools that can be used to build Communities and Crowds—and to bind them closer than ever:

- **Traditional** tools include user groups, corporate external communications, conferences, collateral, and discounts.
- **Virtual** tools include gamification, incentive prizes, crowdsourcing, and micropayments.
- **Web3** tools include cryptocurrencies, digital asset and crypto wallets, NFTs, proprietary user design competitions, and employee/user collaborations.

Gamification

The previous decade has seen an extraordinary rise in online gaming. E-marketer, in its US Gaming Ecosystem 2021 report, reports that more than 2.8 billion people play online games worldwide.[38] In the United States alone, 178 million people—or 53% of the total population—are gamers, and most play for more than an hour each day.

Gamification is emerging as the leading Engagement method for the next decade of Exponential Organizations, which will gamify a myriad of real-world situations and frameworks. Today, the average young person racks up more than 10,000 hours of gaming by the age of 21. That's almost

---

[38] Blake Droesch, "The US Gaming Ecosystem 2021," Insider Intelligence, March 17, 2021, https://www.insiderintelligence.com/content/us-gaming-ecosystem-2021.

exactly as much time as kids will spend in the classroom throughout middle school and high school. Gaming isn't just something that young people *do*; it is a large part of *what and who they are.*

In other words, gamers are your current and future user base. Will you use increasingly obsolete market platforms—like television, radio, or print—to reach them? Or are you prepared to meet them on their terms and engage them to find your business? Once you have attracted them, how will you keep them? In other words, how will you reward them for their Engagement and how will you manage ongoing communication once you connect? And how will you advance to even great levels of Engagement through the latest platforms, such as Web3?

The Power of Web3

Crypto Economics

The world of business—and of ExOs in particular—has changed profoundly with the arrival of new forms of exchange, notably blockchains and cryptocurrency. This new medium is driving the creation of a wholly new internet—Web3—built on the unique features and advantages of crypto and blockchain. With the rise of Web3 and crypto wallets, Engagement now intersects with cryptoeconomics, making it irresistibly sticky.

Cryptoeconomics combines cryptography,[39] computer networks, and game theory to provide secure, decentralized

---

[39] "Cryptography," Wikiversity, December 29, 2022, https://en.wikiversity.org/wiki/Cryptography.

systems that use economic incentives to provide at least in part for their maintenance. As of this writing, more than 70 blockchains are in operation, with a total market cap of over $1 billion. The most successful have grown impressively by creating Communities around a particular purpose, incentivizing Community via cryptoeconomics (e.g., early adopters get rewarded more), and gamifying the ecosystem.

The rise of cryptocurrencies has led to an Engagement revolution. Cryptocurrency creates not only a way to monetize Engagement but, just as important, a way to tie Community members closer to a company's success and thus retain them at unprecedented rates. This revolution has only just begun. As it evolves into new forms of speculation, gaming, and investing (notably, in non-fungible tokens), it promises to change Engagement in as-yet unimaginable ways. Stay tuned.

Non-Fungible Tokens (NFTs)

Non-fungible tokens, or NFTs, are a product of the rise of blockchain technology in the late 2000s and early 2010s. NFTs were conceptually introduced in 2012 with the development of the Colored Coins project on the Bitcoin blockchain. These tokens, representing real-world assets like stocks or property, were linked to small fractions of Bitcoin. However, it was Ethereum, a blockchain platform with smart contract functionality, that truly provided a fertile ground for NFTs to thrive.

In 2015, entrepreneur Eric Pulier introduced Vatoms, further evolving the concept of NFTs as unique, verifiable digital objects on blockchains. Pulier's goal was to revolutionize human engagement through gamification and the psychology of ownership, impacting sectors like ticketing, marketing, and loyalty programs. He predicted the next evolution of the internet would involve Web3 digital wallets and self-sovereign identity, leading to individuals controlling their digital identities and selectively sharing information.

The first significant mainstream breakthrough of NFTs came in 2017 with the launch of CryptoKitties, a virtual game developed by Axiom Zen that allowed users to collect, breed, and trade unique digital cats on the Ethereum blockchain. Each cat was an NFT with a distinct combination of attributes. The game quickly gained popularity, drawing attention to the potential of NFTs. This led to the emergence of platforms such as OpenSea, Rarible, and SuperRare, making it easier for users to create, buy, and sell NFTs.

Since then, NFTs have expanded across numerous domains, including digital art, virtual real estate, gaming, sports memorabilia, and music. In 2020, the NFT market gained significant momentum, with high-profile sales and celebrity endorsements propelling it into mainstream consciousness. This trend continued in 2021 when digital artist Beeple sold an NFT artwork at Christie's auction house for a staggering $69.3 million.

Meanwhile, Pulier's idea of utilizing NFTs to strengthen human Engagement started to take root. Organizations began to see the value in accessing selective information from individuals for personalized communication, reshaping the roles of intermediaries like social networks and media companies. Major brands started adopting Web3 techniques, collecting first-party data, and building personalized relationships. This shift was driven by changes in regulations, privacy concerns, and the increasing costs of customer acquisition. Pulier's company, Vatom, began to revolutionize audience engagement using gamified, personalized digital objects.

Today, with increasing interest and adoption, NFTs have become an essential part of the digital landscape, revolutionizing the way people create, own, and interact with digital assets. The dynamic nature of these digital objects not only engages users but also collects valuable data, enabling more personalized relationships and better business outcomes.

We consider most NFT projects to be ExOs. Take the FlyFish Club. Created by Gary Vaynerchuk in 2021, it consists of 3,000 membership NFTs, traded in NFT marketplaces like OpenSea, that give owners access to various restaurant events and other perks. As of this writing, FlyFish's market cap is more than $60 million. NFTs are among the few phenomena in the current economy that exhibit 10x Engagement, making them an ideal tool for Exponential Organizations. The most popular NFT project as of this writing is the Bored Ape Yacht Club (BAYC), built on the Ethereum blockchain. The collection offers profile pictures of Algorithm-generated cartoon apes. BAYC engages audiences with unique intellectual property that can be leveraged (and owned) by the community, as well as a wide variety of related experiences that galvanize a cohesive Community of enthusiasts. BAYC became a $10 billion project less than a year after it launched.

The most popular and widely used platform for brand engagement and community building is Vatom. Vatom has built the world's first and most proven enterprise-ready Web3 SaaS engagement platform. Their solution has become the Web3 infrastructure and engagement platform of choice for some of the largest companies in the world, including Google, PepsiCo, P&G, Deloitte, E&Y, Verizon, iHeart Media, Dentsu, Animoca, State Farm, and WPP, among others.

Here are five examples of how brands are using NFTs:

1. **Gucci—The NFT Collection:** Gucci collaborated with blockchain-based platform Arianee to create a limited-edition NFT collection featuring 10 exclusive digital designs.
2. **Pepsico & FIFA** joined forces with Vatom to print more than 200 million QR codes on bags of snacks, inviting consumers to take selfies and become part of the world's largest digital art project—a massive NFT soccer ball. The metrics of engagement were staggering, with 38% of all visitors registering to play, 70% engaging daily, and 40% of registered users sharing the campaign with a friend. Best of all, every player opted in for an ongoing direct relationship.
3. **Porsche** announced the creation of its first NFT project, which will offer unique, limited-edition digital collectibles to its fans and enthusiasts.
4. **Louis Vuitton** collaborated with **Axiom Zen** to create a virtual art exhibit, featuring NFTs that showcase the brand's history and heritage.
5. **Nike** and **Rarible** partnered to launch a collection of limited-edition NFTs, featuring iconic pop-culture moments, as well as original works of digital art inspired by Nike's history and brand values.

In each of these examples, digital objects and wallets are used in different ways to engage more effectively. In a discussion with the authors of this book, Pulier described the evolution of these methods, specifically the market's shift from speculation to engagement. While NFTs are designed for long-term engagement, it was clear that the early frenzy of get-rich-quick schemes and gamblers in the NFT space would dominate the news until the bottom fell out and the true value of these technologies became apparent. That time has now come, Pulier says, as organizations worldwide seek better ways to collect "zero-party consumer data" transparently and directly. Zero-party data is defined as information that a customer intentionally shares with a brand or company. Examples include preferences, purchase intentions, and even hopes and dreams—anything that the individual wishes to share to enable the highest value from the brand. This is by far the best data a group can aspire to acquire, creating win-win dynamics that any successful relationship needs to sustain over time.

Today's consumers are bombarded with marketing noise, want to engage selectively, and are increasingly careful about how they spend their time. What's the best way to find out what a particular person wants to spend time on? The answer is deceptively simple: ask them. Better yet, give them the opportunity to tell you in their own way. By engaging them upfront with digital objects of value ("take one" vs. "take my time"), combined with gamification methodologies like Octalysis (discussed below), Exponential Organizations provide the framework to establish this path. Importantly, the application of artificial intelligence to this data results in mass personalization at scale. A confluence of exponential technologies, all maturing at the same time, creates an unprecedented change in the way we engage. The result, says Pulier, is decreased customer acquisition costs, increased loyalty and retention, and personalized, one-to-one experiences at scale.

Virtual spaces—what some call the "metaverse"—are perhaps the most misunderstood form of Web3 experience for driving data. The real power here is Engagement. In the metaverse, the Engagement one seeks is more powerful *amongst* the audience than *between* brand and audience. Unlike Zoom, Instagram, Twitter, and other common forms of online social activity, virtual spaces offer a dramatic shift in how people can achieve "real world," spontaneous social interactions. In virtual spaces, you can run into someone in an unplanned manner, have a laugh, play a game, and go on an adventure.

The best way to think about this kind of Engagement, says Pulier, is as a simple improvement to the web itself. The web started as static markups of data, moved to more dynamic pages and user-generated content, and now adds "people, places, and things." with the goal of more seamlessly integrating our physical and digital lives. "People" is our identity, represented by the wallet; "things" are digital objects we truly own; and "places" are the dimensional experiences we can now "enter" to engage with each other, as we do in the physical world. Every website, says Pulier, will have a "Come in" button and will feel naked without it. The objective is not to create artificial scarcity and sell it for a profit but instead to create environments and activities where people want to come back, engage with each other, and feel comfortable sharing data to create mutually valuable relationships.

Michael Jonsson is a pioneer in the crypto space who has worked with some of the earliest coin protocols and left an indelible imprint on the evolution of this digital frontier. NFTs, he says, "are comparable to the invention of the hyperlink, paving the way for a myriad of applications that will transform the way we interact, create, and transact. Just as the hyperlink revolutionized the way we use the internet, so too will NFTs blaze the trail for unprecedented innovation and transformation across countless domains."

A final point about the power of NFTs: From a marketing perspective, the most interesting aspect of NFTs is not that they're digital but that they are *programmable*. Thus, once a set of customers has NFTs, an ExO can use frameworks like Octalysis to nudge behavior with different Engagement and gamification mechanics. That said, let's examine the Octalysis Framework.

Gamification: The Octalysis Framework

The Octalysis Framework, created by Yu-kai Chou,[40] is a human-focused engagement and gamification design framework that is designed to analyze and improve user engagement in various products, services, and experiences by applying the principles of game design. The term "Octalysis" is derived from the eight core drives that motivate human behavior, which are represented as an octagon. These eight core drives are:

1. **Epic Meaning and Calling:** People are motivated when they feel they are part of something greater than themselves or when they believe they are contributing to a larger cause.
2. **Development and Accomplishment:** Users are driven by the sense of progress, growth, and achievement they experience while engaging with a product or service.
3. **Empowerment of Creativity and Feedback:** People are motivated when they have the freedom to create, experiment, and see the results of their actions.

---

[40] "Yu-Kai Chou's Most Important Project: Octalysis Prime (OP) Finally Launches!," Yu-kai Chou, February 1, 2018, https://yukai-chou.com/gamificationnews/octalysis-prime-real-life-rpg/.

4. **Ownership and Possession:** Users become more engaged when they feel a sense of ownership and control over something, whether it's tangible or intangible.

5. **Social Influence and Relatedness:** Human beings are social creatures, and they are motivated by interactions, relationships, and competition with others.

6. **Scarcity and Impatience:** People often desire things more when they are limited, exclusive, or hard to obtain.

7. **Unpredictability and Curiosity:** The element of surprise and the desire to uncover the unknown can drive engagement and keep users coming back.

8. **Loss and Avoidance:** People are motivated to avoid negative outcomes, such as losing progress, status, or possessions.

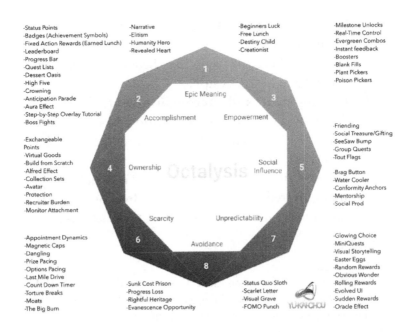

Octalysis has identified more than 150 different gamification techniques— like leaderboards, progress bars, and easter eggs —and mapped them to these eight core drives. It helps designers and developers to identify which core drives are relevant to their specific context and then to create engaging experiences that tap into these drives. By understanding and leveraging these core drives, products and services can better engage, motivate, and retain users.

A key premise of the Octalysis Framework is that systems are designed, like factory processes, to do a job quickly and well—but that human beings are not machines. Rather, they are governed by irrational factors such as emotions, fears, and rationalizations. A system designer must account for human irrationality by incorporating experiences from the Octalysis Framework that drive Engagement.

Octalysis emphasizes the balance of White Hat (purpose) with Black Hat (addiction) and Right brain (creativity) with Left brain (facts). Engagement is most successful when a system touches and balances each of these aspects.

Octalysis is the best and most comprehensive gamification and engagement framework we've seen. It is increasingly found across industries, from product design to education to healthcare. More than a billion users globally touch products designed with Octalysis. Properly used, it has been shown to increase ROI, employee motivation, product design, and—importantly— Engagement.

Case Studies: Engagement

- **Reddit.** This giant social, news aggregation, and discussion site uses its members to vote up or down on submitted content. It's the classic example of reciprocity Engagement: if you share content, you can access content, which drives Engagement and grows community and crowd. Reciprocity scales Engagement—and, therefore, your business model. Reddit boasts more than 1.5 billion monthly users.

- **TikTok.** With 700 million active users, this business phenomenon is the zenith of Community and Crowd. TikTok is also one of the best Engagement models ever devised. Its unequaled Algorithms hook users almost instantly—and turn them into fanatics almost as fast.

- **Duolingo** offers 98 language courses that teach 39 different languages. With a deeply embedded Community Engagement structure, Duolingo has more than 500 million total users and about 40 million monthly active users, representing every country in the world.

- **iHeart Media.** As the world's largest audio company (radio and podcasts), iHeart reaches hundreds of millions of consumers monthly. At their physical concerts, fans scan QR codes to get "virtual swag bags" filled with unique, dynamic digital objects. Advertisers build creative campaigns, dropping branded, gamified objects directly into fans' Vatom wallets, resulting in unprecedented rates of participation and data collection.

- **Shareitt** is an Israeli platform for sharing new and used goods. The company awards users digital tokens for items they no longer need; users can then use those tokens, or points, to acquire other shared items on the platform. Shareitt gets the ball rolling by granting points to new users and by "giving, exchanging, granting wishes, and inviting friends." Shareitt's goods travel on more than 400 routes throughout Israel.

- **Axie Infinity** is an NFT-based online video game developed in Vietnam. Players collect and create NFTs of digital pets, known as Axies, which can be bred and battle with each other within the game. But the real action is in the trading, where game developer Sky Mavis charges a 4.25% fee to players when they trade Axies.

- **Crypto DAOs.** Decentralized autonomous organizations (DAOs) are self-governing groups of crypto enthusiasts who operate under a shared goal, vote in all decisions with no government influence, and whose financial transaction records are maintained on a blockchain. Crypto DAOs often represent enormous financial power. A classic example was the Constitution Dao,[41] which in 2021 set out to buy an original copy of the US Constitution for a predicted $40 million at a Sotheby's auction. While they didn't succeed, their effort was a reminder of how powerful tokenomics can be—especially when it underscores the basic human drive towards Engagement with other like-minded people towards a common purpose.

- **Futurescope** uses Artificial Intelligence to automatically generate and distribute engaging, hyper-personalized newsletter content to connect clients with their audiences, grow their email lists, and increase revenue.

- **OpenExO**. The ExO community ran a cryptoeconomics experiment to increase Engagement via a doubling pattern using the Octalysis framework. One hundred candidates played a 30-doubling challenge,

---

[41] 1. ConstitutionDAO, https://www.constitutiondao.com/.

and 52 winners earned between 0.00002 and 10,737 tokens over 30 activities.[42] Some took 30 days, and some were delivered in a weekend! The initiative resulted in 10x community Engagement. According to Niki Faldemolaei of ExO Angels, "The combination of community engagement, dashboards, and Experimentation created a real flywheel effect in the community".

Other companies and initiatives worth investigating for their Engagement programs include: IKEA, Fender guitars, Uber, Gymshark, Apple, Greggs, Coca-Cola (check out its "Share a Coke" campaign), Tesco's virtual stores, McDonald's store overhauls, Hershey's Happygrams, chat bots that can recommend music, Domino's Pizza Hero, Pep Boys' Axonify platform, and gamification platforms like Microsoft Dynamics 365, Mambo.io, Agile CRM, Hoopla, Evoq, Engage, Gamify, and Spinify.

The Future of Engagement

TikTok users watched 167 million videos, YouTube users streamed 700,000 hours, and Facebook Live got 44 million views—all *per minute* in 2021. That magnitude of Engagement is mind-boggling.

Now, imagine that level of Engagement over weeks, months, years—even decades, for the likes of Google and

---

[42] "Exos Third Birthday Submissions," Google Drive, https://docs.google.com/spreadsheets/d/e/2PACX-1vQVryMm6ipYb-J9o84nB_9ZcUvE84XSGmJ1GQkzmE7_NcLGBj6QmdNG-Ot8sEfN3XOLx-SdMBpoah40M/pubhtml?gid=1423192804&single=true.

Facebook. And now, imagine the opportunities: co-creating products and services, launching new cryptocurrency offerings, exploring new revenue streams, and, as we have seen, manipulating elections. All of this is possible with a loyal and engaged Community and Crowd that numbers in the billions. Several significant futures are waiting in the wings for Engagement:

- To create direct, persistent, meaningful, and programmable connections with customers, brands will transform from current "push" models to the following formula: MTP + Octalysis + NFTs. The brand will own the end-to-end user experience and create direct, persistent, meaningful, and programmable connections with customers. This will dethrone Web2 platforms like Google, Facebook, and Instagram.
- Political campaigns will copy the same strategy as above.
- AI tools like AutoGPT will implement frameworks like Octalysis automagically, co-creating products and services with billions of engaged users.
- The adoption and integration of cryptocurrency into national economies will accelerate. Let's reiterate that cryptocurrencies are so powerful *not* because they are digital but because they are *programmable*.
- Play to Earn (P2E) systems will transform education into "Pay to Learn" via Engagement.
- Led by organizations like the XPRIZE Foundation, we'll address the United Nations' Sustainable Development Goals (SDGs) through crypto-leveraged, incentivized competitions with highly engaged, gamified communities, managed

and optimized by LLM tools like ChatGPT and StabilityAI.

Benefits of Successful Engagement

Engagement plays a crucial role in connecting with users and fostering a sense of community and belonging. Implementing effective engagement strategies can yield a wide array of benefits, including:

- **Inherent gamification:** The use of game mechanics in Engagement strategies enables quick iterations to optimize results, leading to better outcomes and increased user satisfaction.
- **Investment in the future:** By converting the Crowd into a Community and possibly into employees, Engagement strengthens the connection between participants and the organization's Massive Transformative Purpose (MTP), reinforcing retention at multiple levels.
- **Cryptoeconomics and NFTs:** The integration of cryptoeconomic principles and NFTs can dramatically enhance Engagement, leading to a more motivated and incentivized user base.
- **Increased loyalty, ideation, and marketing leverage:** Engagement fosters loyalty among users, stimulates the generation of new ideas and magnifies the impact of marketing efforts.
- **Play and learning:** Through engaging activities, users can explore new concepts, build skills, and have fun, resulting in a more fulfilling experience.
- **Digital feedback loop:** Engagement strategies can provide valuable data and insights from users and

Community members, driving product strategy and enabling the organization to scale more effectively.

Challenges of Successful Engagement

While Engagement is a powerful toolset, implementing effective Engagement strategies is not without its challenges. These obstacles can range from resource allocation and management to navigating the complexities of Web3 implementation and evolving engagement strategies. Some Engagement challenges include:

- **Specialized resources:** Proper implementation of Engagement strategies requires specific expertise and resources, which may be costly or difficult to obtain.
- **Risk of misalignment:** Incorrect implementation can lead to attracting the wrong Community or driving undesirable behavior, hindering the organization's goals. This can consume significant resources without yielding the desired results.
- **Web3 implementation difficulties:** While the potential of Web3 is vast, its implementation can be complex and challenging, creating obstacles to utilizing its full potential for Engagement.
- **Diverse community interactions:** Managing interactions with a varied group of Community members can be inherently difficult, as different users have unique needs and expectations.
- **Incentivization clarity:** Organizations must be cautious about what they are incentivizing, as unintended consequences, such as addiction or undesirable behaviors, can arise.

- **Balancing incentives:** Striking the right balance between positive and negative incentives can be a complex and delicate process.
- **Evolving strategies:** Many incentive structures can decay over time, requiring ongoing adaptation and evolution to maintain their effectiveness.
- **Side effects of strong techniques:** When using powerful gamification or Engagement techniques, organizations must be aware of potential side effects and ensure their strategies align with their intended outcomes.

Requirements and Prerequisites for Engagement

It's crucial to understand the fundamental elements necessary to foster effective interaction and stimulate user involvement. The requirements and prerequisites of Engagement are as follows:

- **MTP:** This should come as no surprise. As we've said consistently throughout this book, the MTP precedes and guides every activity in the Exponential Organization.
- **Community and Crowd:** This is the target and the platform for your gamification initiatives. In theory, you can reach beyond these audiences with Engagement programs, such as recruiting. But Community and Crowd come with memberships of people who are pre-qualified by interest, knowledge, and commitment, all of which increase the odds of participation.
- **Dashboards:** Where are you leading your gamers? Where are they along the way? How many points

have they earned? Are there bottlenecks in the user experience? Dashboards track these and other metrics in the Engagement process.

- **Octalysis:** You should have a decent understanding of the Octalysis Framework to design and implement experiences that maximize user motivation.

Case Study: Gary Vaynerchuk

Gary Vaynerchuk, also known as Gary Vee, is a serial entrepreneur, venture capitalist, and social media influencer. With more than 13 million followers on Instagram, 8.5 million followers on Twitter, and 3.2 million subscribers on YouTube, Gary has mastered Engagement to a ridiculous degree. He uses his Community to share his thoughts on a variety of topics, including entrepreneurship, marketing, social media, and personal branding. He also uses his community to connect with other entrepreneurs and business leaders.

Gary uses relentless Experimentation and has built a global brand and following–his ecosystem is likely worth over a billion dollars. He is a strong advocate for relentless Experimentation and extensively leverages NFTs and gamification to build Community and Engagement. He believes these technologies have the potential to revolutionize the way we interact with each other online. Some of his initiatives include:

- **VeeFriends V1 NFTs:** VeeFriends V1 is the core collection of 236 hand-drawn concept characters that Gary has created. The characters have varying rarities that are represented by colors and textures which make up 10,300 NFTs. Each VeeFriend has its own unique personality trait, and over time, Gary and his team are building out backstories. This gives his audience a chance to peek behind the scenes into how everything is being built.; Gary sees them as "digital trading cards" that can be used to build relationships and access exclusive experiences.

- **Veefriends V2 NFTs**: This collection is an extension of the first, which contains 55,277 NFTs, including an additional 15 characters that he introduced. Instead of being hand-drawn, the characters in this collection are the fully fleshed-out cartoon version that Gary has been using in his content. Since its inception, he has been releasing animated shorts, theme songs, and memes to further spread awareness of his brand IP.
- **Burn Island:** Burn Island is a gamified platform that allows VeeFriends holders to burn their NFTs in exchange for rewards, such as NFTs, merchandise, and other benefits.
- **VeeCon:** VeeCon is an annual conference for VeeFriends holders. The conference features keynote speakers, panels, workshops, and other events. In 2022 and 2023, celebrities like Snoop Dogg, Pharrell Williams, Eric Thomas, Tom Bilyeu, and Deepak Chopra spoke to an audience of almost 7,000 attendees.
- **VeeFriends Discord:** The VeeFriends Discord server is a community forum to connect VeeFriends holders. The server boasts 350,000 members.
- **Flyfish Club:** An collection of 3,000 NFTs (worth about $10 million as of May 2023) that gets holders a restaurant membership and related activities.

The secret to Gary Vee's success? He day trades in the attention economy. He goes where the people are and over-indexes on those platforms with content.

As a final testament to the importance of Engagement, let's note that the Google Brain paper that started all the recent LLM AI craze was titled "Attention Is All You Need."

How to Get Started with Engagement

1. **Train up in Octalysis**: To get started with engagement, it is crucial to first understand the Octalysis framework, a comprehensive model for analyzing and designing engaging experiences. Train key team members in this methodology to ensure a shared understanding and effective implementation of engagement strategies.
2. **Run an Incentive Prize**: Running a contest within your organization can be a valuable approach to generate ideas and insights regarding the types of community engagement that have the potential to unlock the most value. Encourage employees to contribute their ideas, fostering a culture of innovation and collaboration.
3. **Apply Gamification**: Once the top ideas have been identified, consider gamifying them to enhance engagement and participation. Applying game mechanics and elements can make the engagement experience more interactive, motivating, and rewarding for community members, thus increasing their level of involvement.
4. **Launch an Incentive Prize**: To attract and amplify community engagement, launch an incentive prize within the broader crowd. By offering rewards or recognition to individuals who actively participate

and contribute to the community, you can incentivize and cultivate a vibrant and engaged user base.

5. **NFT Project**: In addition to traditional engagement strategies, consider exploring the world of Non-Fungible Tokens (NFTs) and launching an NFT project tailored for your most active users. NFTs can provide a unique and exclusive digital asset or experience to participants, creating a sense of ownership and exclusivity, thereby further deepening their engagement and loyalty.

• • •

This completes our close-up look at the external attributes of an Exponential Organization. In the next chapters, we will look at the internal attributes of a successful ExO, including Interfaces, Dashboards, and Social Networks.

Key Resources/Links where you can learn more

- Gaming NFT's changing the world of Gaming
    - https://www.techtimes.com/articles/ 265703/20210922/how-gamified-nfts-are- changing-the-future-of-gaming.htm
- Blockchain And Gamification—A Match Made in Heaven
    - https://bitcoinist.com/blockchain- gamification-match-made-heaven/
- Duolingo and Octalysis
    - https://raw.studio/blog/ how-duolingo-utilises-gamification/

- The Next Wave of NFTS Will Be Gamification and Play-To-Earn
  - https://medium.datadriveninvestor.com/the-next-wave-of-nfts-will-be-gamification-and-play-to-earn-6b823aa967da
- The Block: Samsung enters the metaverse, opening flagship 837 store in Decentraland
  - https://www.theblockcrypto.com/post/129380/samsung-metaverse-flagship-837-store-decentraland
- NFT Incubator to Merge With Crypto Venture Firm in $129M Deal - Blockworks
  - https://blockworks.co/nft-incubator-to-merge-with-crypto-vc/
- Cryptoeconomics - Wikiversity.
  - https://en.wikiversity.org/wiki/Cryptoeconomics
- The GaryVee Content Model
  - https://ccbc.org.br/wp-content/plugins/staff-listing/uploads/13c71c14ef351b5fb86444914671ac30.pdf
- 25 Gamification Statistics [2023]: Facts + Trends You Need To Know - Zippia
  - https://www.zippia.com/advice/gamification-statistics/
- The Basics of EXOS Token
  - https://www.youtube.com/playlist?list=PLThvGbBloMEmWDNncRQAG6Vq10Pxq4npa
- OpenExO 30-doubling challenge by ExO Angels
  - https://exoangels.com/30-doubling-challenge/
- Engagement - ExO Insight
  - https://insight.openexo.com/tag/engagement/

PART 3
IDEAS

10

Interfaces

Interfaces are the matching and filtering processes that allow an organization to translate an abundance of data into precise and meaningful information that can be acted upon.

—Exponential Organizations 2.0

The three things you'll learn in this chapter

- Interfaces allow an ExO to efficiently filter and manage the abundance generated from the SCALE attributes.
- Interfaces are the attributes via which an ExO can become a platform company.
- The biggest companies in the world have mastered Interfaces. This is not an accident: ExOs need Interfaces to achieve automation and, therefore, scale.

---

n the previous chapter on Engagement, we discussed the various techniques that an Exponential Organization can employ to bind Communities and Crowd closer to the enterprise. To achieve massive scale, however, Engagement (and the other SCALE attributes) can't be manual. They must be automated—leveraging the channels, rules, and Interface protocols of a powerful platform.

What are Interfaces?

In an ExO context, "Interfaces" refers to the automation of one or more SCALE attributes. Interfaces are the matching and filtering processes—using Artificial Intelligence and Algorithms, as well as automated workflows—that allow an organization to translate an abundance of data into precise and meaningful information that can be acted upon. Interfaces are the bridge between the external, SCALE drivers of exponential growth (the internal, IDEAS drivers for stabilization. An early example of interfaces are APIs, or application programming interfaces.

Case Study: Shopify

Canadian online commerce giant Shopify was founded in 2006 by two snowboarding enthusiasts. Originally an online snowboard shop, Shopify pivoted into e-commerce software when the founders couldn't find what they were looking for online: namely, a platform for users to sell goods while simultaneously growing their brand in the digital space.

At the heart of Shopify's success is its proprietary e-commerce platform for online stores and retail point-of-sale systems. The Shopify platform offers online retailers a suite of services, including payments, marketing, shipping, and customer-engagement tools. In other words, Shopify offers Interfaces for most aspects of its platform and offers that platform to any e-commerce enterprise. Any business can leverage those assets, including warehousing and distribution as a service.[43]

As of May 2023, sellers had created more than 4.4 million e-commerce stores in 175 countries on Shopify, with a total gross merchandise volume of more than $50 billion USD per quarter. The platform even boasts an app marketplace, which turns Shopify into a full ecosystem of third-party functions. Today, you can set up an e-commerce store on Shopify in fewer than 30 minutes.

Shopify has mastered Interfaces. By automating services on both the supply side and demand side of their e-commerce offerings, they can scale infinitely (and seem to be doing so).

Description of Interfaces

Many ExO attributes (e.g., Community or AI/Algorithms) are well understood by the business world. Interfaces, however, are one of the least documented—yet most important—business dynamics we have ever uncovered.

All platform businesses create value by facilitating exchanges between two or more interdependent groups, usually producers (supply side) and consumers (demand side). Platforms businesses use Interfaces to automate the supply side and/or the demand side. For example, on eBay, both the creation of an auction (supply side) and the selling of the item (demand side) are automated Interfaces that can be self-provisioned by the user. Providing your partners with a

---

[43]   "Shopify Fulfillment Network Is Building the Only End to End Shipping Solution.," Shopify, https://www.shopify.com/fulfillment.

user-friendly API allows others to easily build businesses on top of your services, thus turning you into a platform.

Interfaces serve as filtering and matching processes, enabling ExOs to connect with and manage their SCALE externalities. These processes often begin as manual and slowly become automated around the edges, eventually evolving into self-provisioning platforms that allow the ExO to scale. For instance, Google's AdWords has become a multi-billion dollar business, largely due to its self-provisioning nature. Interfaces like these help ExOs systematically and automatically filter and process outputs from external attributes (SCALE) and integrate them into the core organization. As a result, processes become more effective and efficient, reducing margins of error.

When a company grows exponentially, Interfaces become crucial for seamless scaling, particularly on a global level. Exponential Organizations have developed unique Interface processes to coordinate data and to oversee everything from prizes to personnel. Kaggle, for example, manages its million data scientists. The XPRIZE Foundation has mechanisms and dedicated teams for each prize. TED enforces strict guidelines for consistency in its franchised TEDx events. Uber has customary protocols for handling its army of drivers. Interface processes are often unique and proprietary to the organization that created them, representing a distinct type of intellectual property with considerable market value.

ExOs devote significant attention to Interfaces, employing human-centered design thinking to optimize them. As Interface processes evolve and become more powerful, they typically involve heavy instrumentation and metadata gathering, which feed the company's Dashboards. Ultimately, Interfaces often become the most distinguishing internal characteristics of a fully realized ExO. At peak productivity,

Interfaces enable an enterprise to manage its SCALE external attributes, especially Staff on Demand, Leveraged Assets, and Community and Crowd. Without effective Interfaces, an ExO cannot scale. For all these reasons, they are mission-critical.

One way to conceptualize Interfaces is to consider their role in managing abundance. While most processes focus on scarcity and efficiency, SCALE elements generate large result sets, necessitating Interfaces that are designed for filtering and matching. For example, the Apple App Store receives millions of submissions, requiring a very sophisticated Interface to manage, filter, categorize, and down-select all those entries.

Because good Interfaces are personalized, they enable a close relationship with individual users. Over time, they incorporate a select subset of user stories, not only enriching these relationships but enabling the quicker development of relationships with new users.

In fact, Interfaces facilitate beneficial interactions at scale and determine whether abundance and supercharged growth will overwhelm the ExO or enable it to successfully convert that abundance to value. They are the key to standardizing processes and accessing new information and resources, including Leveraged Assets and Staff on Demand.

APIs: The Beginnings of Interfaces

An API is a set of rules and protocols for building and interacting with software applications. It defines the kinds of calls or requests that can be made, how to make them, the data formats that should be used, and the conventions to follow. APIs essentially allow different software programs to communicate with each other. They serve as a contract between different software components, dictating how each component should interact with the others.

APIs make it easier for developers to integrate different software applications, services, and functionalities into new or existing systems, thus enabling seamless communication between various platforms and allowing for the creation of more powerful and feature-rich applications.

APIs provide pre-built functions and enable developers to build on top of existing platforms, services, and technologies. In these ways, they save developers time and effort while fostering innovation: developers can focus on creating unique features and experiences rather than building everything from scratch. These practices also help to establish standardized protocols and interfaces for communication between software applications, ensuring consistency and compatibility across different systems.

Here are some examples of leading companies using APIs:

- **Google**: Google provides APIs for many of its services, including Google Maps, Google Drive, and YouTube. These APIs allow developers to integrate Google services into their own applications—for example, embedding maps, accessing cloud storage, or playing YouTube videos within an app.
- **Facebook/Meta**: Facebook's Graph API allows developers to access and manipulate Facebook data, enabling the creation of third-party apps that integrate with Facebook's platform. This includes features like posting updates, retrieving user information, and managing Facebook Pages and Groups.
- **Amazon Web Services (AWS)**: AWS offers a wide range of APIs for its cloud-computing services,

allowing developers to build and manage their applications on Amazon's infrastructure. This includes APIs for storage, computing power, machine learning, and more.

- **Twitter**: Twitter's API allows developers to interact with the Twitter platform to post tweets, search for specific hashtags or users, and retrieve data related to a user's timeline.

- **Stripe**: Stripe provides a suite of APIs for online payment processing, allowing developers to easily integrate payment functionalities into their applications. This enables businesses to accept and manage payments without having to build their own payment infrastructure.

The Relationship between Interfaces and Platforms

Interfaces are the vehicle by which *companies* become *platforms*. The automation of supply and demand Interfaces, for example, created the Amazon Marketplace platform. Interfaces are vital to the design of the ExO process, allowing the inside of the organization to access the outside world and vice versa to create a platform and, ultimately, form a dedicated Community.

When an organization becomes a platform upon which users (entrepreneurs and businesses) build their business and livelihoods, then these users are incentivized to support, promote, and maximally utilize that organization. A great example is YouTube, which has become one of the most successful platforms in history. In 2022, YouTube had an average of 2.681 billion monthly active users and was valued at $23.89 billion, up from $17.29 billion in 2021. The typical compensation for YouTube content creators in the United States was approximately $4,616 per month in 2022.

Examples of Interfaces in ExOs

Interfaces reflect how an ExO exposes one of the SCALE attributes. Here's a chart of well-known ExOs and how they use Interfaces, as well as examples of other attributes incorporated into those Interfaces:

ExO	Interface	Description	Internal Usage	SCALE Attribute
Uber	Driver selection	System to allow users to find and choose drivers	Algorithm matches best/closest driver to user location	AI & Algorithms
Kaggle	Leaderboard rankings	Real-time score-board that shows the current rankings of a contest	Aggregate and compare results of all users in a contest	Engagement
Kaggle	User scanning	System to scan for relevant users for private contests	Cherry-pick the best users for special projects	Community & Crowd
Bitcoin	Mining	Downloadable open-source software running a Bitcoin node	Bitcoin nodes validate, broad-cast, process, and store BTC transactions	Community & Crowd
TED	Video transla-tion subtitles	Manage translations created by volunteers (via the vendor Dotsub)	Seamlessly integrate TED Talk translations	Community & Crowd
Stripe	Credit-card processing	Allow payment systems to be self-provisioned by any merchant	Integrates into websites seamlessly	Leveraged Assets
ChatGPT	LLM Access	Gives users ability to interact seamlessly with the model	LLM provides rich, precise answers with no human intervention	AI & Algorithms

ExO	Interface	Description	Internal Usage	SCALE Attribute
Waze	User gestures while driving	Users spot accidents, police-car sightings, etc.	Maps display resulting gestures for all users	Community & Crowd
Google	AdWords	User picks keywords to advertise against	Google places ads against search results	AI & Algorithms
GitHub	Version control system	Multiple coders update software sequentially and in parallel	Platform keeps all contributions in sync	Community & Crowd

Case Studies: Interfaces

- **Twilio** provides APIs to automate voice, text, and email as a service. Customers can build their own business around these APIs. Among these services, Twilio digitizes VoIP + text infrastructure, machine-to-machine communication, machine-to-people communication, and bridging analog to digital. As of May 2023, Twilio was worth $11 billion.
- **Solidity.** The protocols underlying blockchain implementations are good examples of decentralized Interfaces. Solidity, a scripting language, turns the Ethereum ecosystem into a decentralized application-development platform.
- **Google Adwords.** Developed nearly a quarter-century ago, Google Ads is an online advertising platform by which advertisers bid to display advertisements, service offerings, product listings, or videos to web users. Adwords has the capability to place ads either in Google search results or on non-search sites, including websites, videos, and mobile apps.

215

- **Coinbase,** the largest cryptocurrency exchange in the United States by trading volume, has no headquarters, and all employees work remotely. This unique organizational structure makes good Interfaces a necessity, as does the fact that Coinbase's core business is powered by a cryptocurrency exchange platform and used by more than 100 million customers.
- **Templafy**. Since 2014, this fast-growing business B2B SaaS company has established itself as a global powerhouse that helps clients process business content—including documents, presentations, and emails—and turn it into smart templates (i.e., Interfaces). Templafy serves more than 2.8 million users, including such enterprise customers as KPMG, IKEA, and BDO.
- Australia's **Canva,** whose MTP is "Empowering the world to design," is a free (for basic service) online design platform that makes it very easy for anyone to rapidly create quality designs, such as posters, flyers, presentations, documents, social media images, etc., through a library of thousands of graphical templates that can be accessed via a drag-and-drop Interface.
- A particularly innovative Interface, Amsterdam's **Miro** is a collaborative platform that helps people work together, from anywhere at any time, at scale, using virtual whiteboards. The company claims 35 million users, including 99% of the Fortune 500.

The Future of Interfaces

Going forward, we will see significant advancements in various Interface areas, including the following key developments:

- **DAOs**: The rise of decentralized autonomous organizations (DAOs) as a major organizational form will be driven by the increased automation capabilities of Web3 Interfaces (mostly via Smart Contracts). However, DAO governance will continue to be a problem.
- **NFT Platforms**: An explosion of Engagement-driven NFT platforms, powered via some of these Interfaces, will emerge to manage sophisticated virtual assets and worlds.
- **Supply Chain Automation**: Intelligent and AI-driven supply chains will become more prevalent, utilizing sensors and blockchain for efficiency and transparency.
- **Government Usage**: Increasingly, government functions will transform into Interfaces with open public datasets, enhancing accessibility, transparency, and accountability.
- **Books and Books**: Given the importance of this attribute for the scalability of any ExO, we expect books to be written on the topic of Interfaces.

Benefits of Interfaces

The benefits of interfaces, especially automated ones, are manifold. They are integral to the scalability of ExOs, acting as a bridge between external resources and internal operations while enhancing productivity. Interfaces, through APIs, boost efficiency, promote interoperability, and aid in data accessibility, ultimately leading to innovation, cost savings, a superior user experience, and greater customization options. Other Interfaces benefits include:

- **Scalability:** Automated interfaces allow ExOs to scale and take advantage of abundance. Further, they help funnel external abundance (e.g., Uber with its drivers; Airbnb with its property-owning "hosts").
- **Value Creation:** Interfaces serve as a bridge between external growth drivers and internal stabilizing factors. They transform external abundance into internal value.
- **Efficiency and automation:** APIs allow different software systems to communicate and interact with each other, enabling tasks to be executed automatically and more efficiently.
- **Integration and interoperability:** APIs allow different software programs to integrate and work together seamlessly in a common language.
- **Innovation and extended functionality:** APIs expose functionalities of other software systems, which can be leveraged to build new and innovative applications and can extend the functionality of existing systems.
- **Data accessibility:** APIs can provide access to data that can be used for analysis and decision-making. They allow data to be easily accessed and shared between systems, increasing its overall availability.
- **Cost savings:** APIs can help reduce development time and cost by reusing existing software functionalities rather than developing them from scratch.
- **User experience:** By enabling the integration of different software applications, APIs can help to create a seamless user experience across different platforms and services.

Challenges of Interfaces

As crucial as they are, Interfaces can also be challenging, as usability influences scalability and inept design can perpetuate inequality. Exponential Organizations require automated interfaces underpinned by AI and algorithms. Their implementation demands careful, strategic decisions and ample resources.

- **Focus on Human-Centric Design**: Usability leads to human-centric design. If an Interface is insufficiently usable, it won't scale.
- **Address Broken Interfaces**: Broken Interfaces can drive inequality and negative second-order effects (such as reinforcing negative feedback loops). It is crucial to identify and rectify these issues to avoid unintended consequences.
- **Choose Automation Wisely**: It can be difficult to choose what to automate and in what order. A strategic approach is necessary to prioritize automation efforts effectively.
- **Ensure External Abundance**: You must have abundance externally via one or more of the SCALE attributes. Otherwise, what are you scaling? What are you automating? What are you Interfacing?
- **Leverage Intelligence and Automation**: The success of an ExO depends on the intelligence and automation of its Interfaces. Over time, the best way to achieve a high degree of scalability and automation is via Algorithms and AI.

Requirements and Prerequisites for Interfaces

Interface requirements and prerequisites include:

- **Standardized processes:** An organization must have prescriptive and standardized processes to allow automation. This means clear agreement inside the ExO about what aspects are to be scaled.
- **Scalable externalities:** Automation via Interfaces assumes that the ExO has an abundance of data to automate. Implementing one or more of the SCALE attributes is critical to deliver that abundance.
- **AI and Algorithms (in most cases):** Effective Interfaces, backed by Algorithms, allow the ExO to manage interactions with clients, Crowd, and Community in a scalable but personalized manner.
- **Experimentation:** In an ideal world, Interfaces are designed with the capability to run experiments. Experimentation allows an ExO to iterate and improve on its Interfaces to find the best way to meet customers' needs.

Case study: Roblox

Roblox doesn't just let users play games: it lets them *create* them. Roblox enables creators to co-develop new video games and deploy them to its platform marketplace. A graphical user Interface (GUI) guides players and creators through the platform, providing information about characters, game mechanics, and a variety of other features. Roblox has more than 40 million games in its ecosystem. Fully 75% of young people in the US play and create on Roblox.

Roblox's expansive distribution is made possible by its powerful Interface, which includes accessing digital twins, generative AI automation (e.g., GPT4), and new AI models.

The video game industry is larger than the music and film industries combined, notes Oxford University robotics researcher—and OpenExO community member—Wolfgang Merkt. "Roblox democratizes not only the distribution but also the tools to co-create video games," he says. "It empowers its users to leverage their creativity in creating new games and thus creating loyal followings. Traditionally, game development is highly complicated and secretive, with established developer studios producing the key franchises in multi-year development cycles, often tied to new console releases. Roblox leverages Community and Crowd in the discovery and development of ideas."

How to Get Started with Interfaces

Automation is a key aspect of scaling your organization efficiently. It involves identifying elements of your SCALE attributes that can be automated, standardizing those elements to create replicable processes or Interfaces, and building those Interfaces using existing software or your organization's App team. Additionally, utilizing tools like AutoGPT can be beneficial in this effort.

- **Identify Automatable SCALE Attributes**: Identify the elements of your SCALE attributes that can be automated. This is the first step towards creating a more efficient and scalable organization.
- **Standardize Elements for Replicable Processes**: Determine whether you can standardize those elements to create replicable processes—or Interfaces.

Standardization is crucial for consistency and scalability.

- **Build Interfaces**: Build those Interfaces using existing software or via your organization's App team. Leverage available resources to develop the necessary Interfaces for automation.
- **Utilize AutoGPT**: Bonus: Use AutoGPT to help in this effort. AutoGPT can be a valuable tool in assisting with the automation process and enhancing overall efficiency.

Remember that Interfaces become platforms. And in Web3, they become protocols. Interfaces can stand on their own, but platforms need Interfaces to function properly.

● ● ●

In the dynamic business environment of an ExO, the SCALE attributes don't stand alone. Exponential Organizations need to know their efficiency and health in real-time—not just in intermittent snapshots but via the dynamic and continuous monitoring of the enterprise's key life signs. In the next chapter, we will look at how to accomplish this through Dashboards.

Key Resources/Links where you can learn more

- Roblox creation engine, Roblox Studio
  - https://www.roblox.com/create
- Unreal game creation engine
  - https://www.unrealengine.com
- Unity game creation engine
  - https://unity.com
- Figma—Interface design tool
  - https://www.figma.com/ui-design-tool
- Largest online store for PC games
  - https://store.steampowered.com
- Gucci builds a world inside Roblox
  - https://futureparty.com/stories/gucci-town-roblox/#
- Interfaces - ExO Insight
  - https://insight.openexo.com/tag/interfaces/

11

Dashboards

Dashboards are the internal and external presentation of the real-time information that ExOs need to operate.

—Exponential Organizations 2.0

The three things you'll learn in this chapter

- Engagement metrics are used for measuring ExOs externally, while Objectives and Key Results (OKRs) are critical for internal team and organizational execution.
- Dashboards and OKRs are important to enable a distributed leadership team to monitor and evaluate the health of a business; evaluate the results of experiments; and get everyone on the same page.

> • Metrics need to be in near real-time. If things are going wrong (or right) in an ExO, they are going exponentially wrong or right. Either way, you and your team need to know quickly.

In the previous chapter, we discussed the crucial role of Interfaces and Platforms in the operation and success of Exponential Organizations. But Interfaces and Platforms need to function properly, and proper function is possible only if an ExO can monitor those processes continuously and draw useful data out of them to improve operations. The best way to do that is via powerful Dashboards—the subject of this chapter.

What are Dashboards and OKRs?

Traditional business reports cover what happened in the past. Dashboards cover what's happening in real-time. Advanced Dashboards can predict what *should* happen and benchmark current events against those predictions.

Dashboards are the internal and external presentation of the real-time information that ExOs need to operate. They reflect essential company and employee metrics and allow for the implementation of short feedback loops. The phrase "what gets measured gets managed" is made manifest with Dashboards. In the case of ExOs, where growth is rapid, Dashboards are essential as they enable management decision-making to keep pace with the extreme rate of change.

There are two types of Dashboards: external and internal. Think of an automobile dashboard, which offers important operating data, from speed to oil pressure to available gasoline. An ExO dashboard, however, offers many, many more metrics.

External Dashboards typically present Engagement metrics for early-stage companies and dollar metrics for mature companies. External Dashboards are made up of company, team, and personal Objectives and Key Results (OKRs). This type of Dashboard uses "leaderboards" to drive Community behavior and Engagement. For example, Peloton created Community competitions using Dashboards that compared users' stats against their friends'. All digital gaming platforms are external Dashboards.

Internal Dashboards, exemplified by OKRs (Objectives and Key Results), are a collaborative goal-setting methodology for teams and individuals to set ambitious goals and track measurable progress in real time. Unlike key performance indicators (KPIs), which are measured at the end of a business cycle, OKRs provide continuous insights into performance. This methodology can be applied to various types of company operations and organizational levels, effectively aligning the entire enterprise on the path to achieving its goals.

Case Study: Amazon

Amazon uses a Dashboard to generate a Weekly Business Report that company leaders spend many hours analyzing. The genesis of this report dates to the very beginning of the company, when founder Jeff Bezos connected a digital bell to the company's servers and had the computer ring the bell every time a book was sold. The bell was great for morale, but the real reason behind it was that Bezos wanted to track sales.

Today, this feedback loop is the heart of Amazon's operations. The Weekly Business Report numbers in the hundreds of pages. It shows every imaginable metric regarding the company, with the most important and challenging information bannered at the top.

In light of this book's chapter on Experimentation, it's particularly interesting that Amazon executives use the report to monitor the progress of various experiments underway throughout the organization. Based on this information, they narrow down those experiments to one or two huge bets every year.

One of these big bets was Amazon Prime. It had seemed illogical (and like a money loser) at the time it was originally proposed. With free shipping included in the subscription, why wouldn't people just buy a toothbrush one day, toothpaste the next day, and floss the day after that? The fulfillment costs would be huge. But experiments showed that Amazon Prime members grouped much bigger purchases than non-members.

On another occasion, Amazon management considered whether to sell disposable diapers, which have almost no margin. To their surprise, they discovered that customers bought more diapers if they didn't have to go elsewhere to buy them. Our point? Assumptions can often be wrong; testing the product or service is the only way to really know what will work.

Once decisions are made about an experiment, Amazon tracks them constantly through Dashboards. Because of that, staff are guided by the Dashboard as part of their daily work.

Description of Dashboards and OKRs

Let's take a deeper look at both external and internal dashboards:

External Engagement Metrics

For an ExO, tracking the right metrics is paramount. By tracking these key external engagement and growth metrics, Exponential Organizations can confidently steer towards sustained success in rapidly changing business environments. The importance of metrics cannot be overstated: they are the beacons that guide organizations through the unchartered waters of exponential growth.

Here are some key engagement and growth metrics that ExOs track:

- **Monthly Recurring Revenue (MRR):** the amount of revenue a company expects to receive each month from its customers
- **Annual Recurring Revenue (ARR):** the total amount of recurring revenue a company expects to receive from its customers annually
- **Customer Acquisition Cost (CAC):** the cost a company incurs to acquire a new customer
- **Lifetime Value (LTV):** the total revenue a company can expect to receive from a single customer over the lifetime of their relationship with the company
- **Gross margin:** the percentage of revenue that a company retains after deducting the costs associated with producing and selling its products or services
- **Burn rate:** the rate at which a company is spending its cash reserves to finance its operations
- **Runway:** the length of time that a company can continue to operate with its current cash reserves, given its current burn rate

- **Net Promoter Score (NPS):** a measure of customer satisfaction and loyalty, based on how likely customers are to recommend a company's products or services to others
- **Churn:** the rate at which customers stop using a company's products or services over a given time period
- **Customer Lifetime Value to Customer Acquisition Cost (LTV:CAC) ratio:** measures the relationship between the lifetime value of a customer and the cost of acquiring that customer
- **Viral coefficient:** measures the rate at which a company's customers are bringing in new customers through word-of-mouth marketing
- **Customer Retention Cost (CRC):** measures the cost of retaining existing customers
- **Magic number:** a formula that helps companies determine the efficiency of their sales and marketing efforts by comparing their revenue growth to the cost of acquiring new customers

Objectives and Key Results (OKRs)

Business thinker and investor Robert Goldberg thinks of OKRs as a company's operating system. Goldberg has implemented OKRs in more than 40 companies with considerable success; he is probably the most practiced OKR guru in the world. He believes that OKRs are the key to a revival of America's declining Rust Belt companies. By looking beyond their day-to-day operations and setting Objectives and Key Results, even the most hidebound and traditional companies can break away from their normal operations and pursue the equivalent of MTPs. (Goldberg's work, "Reinventing American Exceptionalism", will be the subject of a future ExO book.)

- OKRs continuously ask, "Where do I want to go?" (Objective) and "How will I know I'm getting there?" (Key Results)
- OKRs are not determined top-down, but bottom-up.
- Objectives are the dream; Key Results are the success criteria of that dream (that is, they are a way to measure incremental progress toward the objective).
- Objectives are qualitative, and Key Results are quantitative.
- OKRs are not the same as employee evaluations— rather, they are about the company's goals and how each employee contributes to those goals.
- Instrumenting early and often is key to implementing Dashboards.
- Objectives are ambitious and should stretch those pursuing them.
- Five Objectives and four Key Results per Objective are optimal.
- Key results should see an achievement rate of not more than 60 to 70%. If results are higher, the bar has been set too low.

While the best Dashboards monitor continuously, the monitoring of OKRs is necessarily periodic and varies according to apparent need:

- **Frequency/cadence:** Cadence sets the frequency with which an enterprise establishes and reviews its Objectives and Key Results. Ideally, an ExO would pursue its OKRs at different cadences, which allows them to be addressed in turn and in detail. Most companies address their initial OKRs a year after implementation.

- **Transparency:** Google is a prime example of a company that has chosen to share its Dashboards with most of its employees, partly as a matter of trust but also as an incentive and motivator. This is probably the best approach for ExOs. Note, however, that some very successful ExOs have chosen the opposite path, largely to reduce peer pressure among employees who have not yet reached their full objectives.

- A company's **MTP,** which may be seen as the ultimate OKR, is established and inviolable. Like an OKR, it needs to be revisited regularly to determine if the enterprise is on track. That said, MTP is rarely fundamentally altered. Rather, the rest of the company's strategy and operations continuously align around it as external and internal conditions change.

Case Studies: Dashboards and OKRs

Many of the most notable companies in Silicon Valley use OKRs as their internal operating system. Along with Google and Intel, which pioneered the paradigm, these include LinkedIn, Airbnb, Dropbox, Spotify, Twitter, Uber, Netflix, and Oracle. And that's just a few. Google takes its OKR system to full throttle by making all the Os and KRs fully transparent. Any employee at Google can look up anyone else's targets and how they've performed. Other organizations utilizing OKRs include:

- **Clickup.** A cloud-based collaboration and project management tool that can be used by most businesses, no matter what their size or industry.

- **Klipfolio.** A Canadian, cloud-based Dashboard company that enables users to build real-time business Dashboards, access them from several devices, and share them instantly with colleagues. Users can connect to multiple data services, automate data retrieval, and manipulate and visualize that data.
- **Tableau.** This self-described "world's leading analytics platform," purchased by SalesForce in 2019, specializes in visualization techniques for exploring and analyzing relational databases, online analytical processing cubes, cloud databases, and spreadsheets to generate data visualizations.[44]
- **WeWork.** In one of the biggest business catastrophes in decades, WeWork made the critical mistake of hyper-scaling before getting its unit metrics right. Their Dashboards didn't highlight this important information—and the company scaled its losses in its global quest for growth.
- **The Trading Desk.** This is a US-based multinational company that uses real-time programmatic marketing automation technologies, products, and services to personalize digital content for users. "Programmatic" marketing is an automated, real-time process that enables instant decision-making based on known user data points, making possible a highly

[44] "Relational Database," Wikipedia, August 12, 2023, https://en.wikipedia.org/wiki/Relational_database.
"OLAP Cube," Wikipedia, July 25, 2023, https://en.wikipedia.org/wiki/OLAP_cube.
"Cloud Database," Wikipedia, July 22, 2023, https://en.wikipedia.org/wiki/Cloud_database.
"Spreadsheet," Wikipedia, August 23, 2023, https://en.wikipedia.org/wiki/Spreadsheet.

personalized consumer experience. The Trading Desks offers a self-service publishing platform for brands and advertisers, as well as a platform for advanced analytics.

- **eHang.** This Chinese company aims to make safe, autonomous, eco-friendly air mobility accessible to everyone. eHang's command-and-control center features the ultimate Dashboard: a visualized platform that displays the real-time flight data and status of every eHang aerial vehicle, including battery level, flight altitude, speed, altitude, and position, as well as real-time audiovisual communication between passengers and ground personnel.
- **Strava.** This is a "quantified-self Dashboard" that enables users to link various Dashboards to track physical exercise. Strava is, essentially, a DaaS (Dashboard as a Service) that uses GPS data and integrates systems, including Garmin and Fitbit, to monitor distance, time, speed, and other metrics on a sophisticated Dashboard. Users can join incentive programs and compete against themselves or other athletes. Many Olympians are on Strava, and users can follow them on the Dashboard.
- **TensorBoard.** This is a common machine-learning Dashboard for monitoring training progress and improving model performance. The TensorBoard toolkit displays a Dashboard where logs can be visualized as graphs, images, histograms, embeddings, texts, and more. TensorBoard also tracks information gradients, losses, metrics, and intermediate outputs. Its competitor, **Weight and Biases,** features experiment tracking, dataset versioning, and model management.

Future of Dashboards

Future Dashboards will look very different from today's. Today, 70% of the world's sensors are currently not networked. Therefore, their data is wasted. "Connected sensors" (i.e., the Internet of Things (IoT)) is an important enabling trend to roll out Dashboards to more "traditional" processes. In 2014, only 2% of the Fortune 500 used OKRs. Today, we estimate that percentage has doubled to just around 4%: big companies have a long way to go. Therein lies an enormous business opportunity for someone who can address this enormous unmet need.

So, where might future ExOs take Dashboards?

- **Automation.** Dashboards will become increasingly automated, with AIs driving most of the content and tracking, using their innate intelligence to identify the most important parameters and metrics and emphasizing those for audiences' attention.
- **AI Mapping of MTP.** AIs will create Dashboards for most organizations by mapping the MTP onto actionable metrics.
- **Data Relevance.** AI will use ubiquitous sensors, public data sets, and Dashboards that will advise companies about market trends.
- **Focus on future issue alerts and prevention.** AI-enabled Dashboards will focus on probabilistic risk analysis, elevating potential future concerns, alerting management about issues, and suggesting solutions to prevent failures before they happen.

Ultimately, as the speed of ExO operations continues to accelerate, we anticipate that there will be no more five-year

Strategic Plans with quarterly or annual KPIs. Instead, a company will have an MTP and a one-year operating plan, monitored by real-time Dashboards that will continuously assess whether it's on track.

Benefits of Dashboards

Dashboards play a crucial role in empowering Exponential Organizations by providing valuable insights and facilitating effective decision-making. Here are some key benefits that Dashboards offer to ExOs:

- **Alignment of teams.** Dashboards serve as a powerful tool for aligning teams within an ExO. By presenting a clear and comprehensive view of organizational goals and objectives, Dashboards enable teams to understand their roles in achieving these targets. This alignment fosters collaboration, improves communication, and ensures that everyone is working towards a common purpose.
- **Tracking critical growth drivers.** Real-time tracking of critical growth drivers is essential for ExOs to stay on top of their performance and make necessary adjustments. Dashboards provide a visual representation of key metrics, enabling ExOs to monitor progress, identify trends, and promptly address any areas that require attention. This agile approach to tracking growth empowers ExOs to adapt their strategies and make informed decisions based on up-to-date data.
- **Enabling experiments.** Dashboards act as catalysts for innovation and Experimentation within ExOs. By offering a quick view of critical metrics, they

enable organizations to assess the impact of different experiments and initiatives. This real-time feedback allows ExOs to quickly identify new opportunities, optimize processes, and drive continuous improvement. Dashboards provide the necessary visibility to support a culture of exploration and enable ExOs to embrace change and adapt their strategies proactively.

- **Minimizing errors.** Dashboards provide short feedback loops that are instrumental in minimizing errors and enhancing operational efficiency. By monitoring key performance indicators (KPIs) in real-time, ExOs can quickly identify any deviations from desired outcomes and take corrective actions promptly. This proactive approach helps prevent potential errors from escalating and ensures that operations remain streamlined and effective.

- **Transparent leadership accountability.** Dashboards can promote transparency within an ExO by making leadership accountable to users. When leaders share Dashboards openly, they demonstrate a commitment to transparency and foster trust with stakeholders. This level of transparency holds leaders responsible for their decisions and actions, creating an environment of openness and accountability.

- **OKRs as a control framework.** Objectives and Key Results provide a valuable control framework for managing fast growth and aligning teams toward common goals. Dashboards serve as a visual representation of OKRs, allowing ExOs to track progress and assess the performance of individual teams and the organization as a whole. This control framework helps ExOs stay focused, prioritize initiatives, and ensure that efforts are aligned with strategic objectives.

Challenges of Dashboards

While Dashboards offer numerous benefits, they also present challenges and considerations for an ExO. Some of the challenges include:

- **Metrics overload.** A Dashboard with too many metrics can be as challenging as a Dashboard with too few. It's critical to pay attention to the most important—typically less than a dozen—top-level numbers at first glance and then be able to drill into greater specifics as needed. In other words, it's crucial to track the right metrics and not too many in order to avoid a glut of superfluous data.
- **Vanity metrics.** It's easy to default to using vanity metrics instead of real value metrics, which can give the illusion of growth and success.
- **Data validity.** Can you rely on the validity of data, and what are your sources? How do you get real-time, up-to-date data to populate your Dashboard?
- **Experimentation.** How will you identify and run experiments to get the data you need?
- **Frequent updates.** ExOs need to update Dashboards frequently, especially before data collection and visualization are fully automated.
- **Dealing with uncomfortable data.** Can you act ruthlessly on the data you receive, especially if and when it goes against expectations? Corporate culture acceptance and wise use of Dashboards can also be a challenge for ExOs.

Requirements and Prerequisites

To successfully implement Dashboards, an organization must consider the following requirements and prerequisites:

- **MTP.** As usual, an MTP is critical to guide the content of Dashboards and assess whether the organization is on track.
- **AI and Algorithms.** As Dashboards become increasingly automated, Artificial Intelligence becomes increasingly necessary as a real-time steering mechanism.
- **Cultural acceptance and appreciation of OKRs.** At the individual, team, and organizational levels, OKRs are crucial to keep the organization on track.
- **Integration with other software**: Most software, such as SAP or Salesforce, requires a separate Dashboard to capture insights and integrate data from various company management programs.

Case Study: eBay

In 2012, online auctioneer eBay was in deep trouble. It had lost market share to Amazon and others. Its stock price was down 80% over a two-year period. Searching for reasons why eBay's CEO did something that seemed ridiculous. He looked at the company's recent acquisitions and selected the craziest CEO among them. Then he told that CEO to form a team, go off-site as far away as possible for several weeks, and come up with a strategy. "When you come back," he said, "we'll implement it."

The team did it. They went to Australia for three weeks, looked at a lot of data, came back, and made one change:

they turned the eBay homepage from a search box into a deal-finder page. They then created a Dashboard that internally tracked data from the new page. The Dashboard provided real-time data about how users were interacting with the site, allowing eBay to immediately optimize its offerings per user.

The result was astounding. Combined with some of the CEO's other efforts, this initiative helped increase eBay's market cap by $50 billion—the result of learning from data as opposed to staying tied to the process-driven status quo. This success story underscores the power of data-driven decision-making and the value of embracing innovative strategies in the face of stiff competition. It's a testament to eBay's adaptability and willingness to learn, adapt, and evolve—a crucial trait for any organization aspiring to maintain a competitive edge in the fast-paced world of e-commerce.

How to Get Started with OKRs and Dashboards

Objectives and Key Results, along with Dashboards, can be incredibly useful tools to help align your team and visualize your progress. Here's a sequential guide to help your company get started:

1. **Educate your team.** Begin by explaining the concept of OKRs and the benefits of Dashboards to your team. Make sure everyone understands the purpose, importance, and means by which these tools can contribute to the company's success.
2. **Identify your objectives.** Objectives are high-level organizational goals. Start by identifying your company's aims and a specific timeframe related to your

MTP and Moonshots. Objectives should be qualitative, ambitious, and inspiring.

3. **Define key results.** For each objective, define between two and five key results. These are specific, measurable outcomes that indicate progress toward the objective. Remember, Key Results should be quantifiable and achievable and lead to objective grading.

4. **Align OKRs.** Ensure that the OKRs of different departments or individuals within the organization align with the company's overall OKRs. This will ensure everyone is working towards the same overarching goals.

5. **Set up your dashboard.** Choose a platform or software that suits your needs for a Dashboard. This could be a business intelligence tool, a project-management system, or even a shared spreadsheet, depending on the complexity of your needs and the size of your team.

6. **Integrate data sources.** Connect relevant data sources to your Dashboard. These might include financial systems, customer-relationship-management systems, project-management tools, and other data sources relevant to your key results.

7. **Design dashboard layout.** Decide on the layout and visualization types (i.e., graphs, charts, or tables) that will best represent your OKRs. Aim for clarity and simplicity.

8. **Train your team.** Provide training and support to your team on how to use and update the Dashboard. This will ensure that everyone can actively engage with the tool.

9. **Regularly review and update your OKRs and Dashboard.** This will keep your team focused and

informed about progress. Typically, OKRs are set quarterly and reviewed weekly or monthly.

10. **Iterate and improve.** Based on the insights gained from regular reviews, adjust your OKRs and refine your Dashboard as necessary. Remember, Dashboards are flexible tools designed to adapt to an ExO's evolving business needs.

Implementing OKRs and Dashboards is a collaborative and iterative process. It encourages open communication, transparency, and a data-driven culture within the organization.

• • •

One of the best features of Dashboards is that they allow you to test new scenarios and operations and quickly see the results—some of which may transform your company. We'll look at that process in the next chapter: Experimentation.

Key Resources/Links where you can learn more

- *Measure What Matters: OKRs: The Simple Idea that Drives 10x Growth*, by John Doerr
  - https://www.amazon.com/ Measure-What-Matters-Simple-Drives/ dp/024134848X/ref=asc_df_024134848X/?
- Measure What Matters OKR Starter Kit by John Doerr and Coda
  - https://www.whatmatters.com/faqs/ best-free-okr-tools-software

- Dashboards—ExO Insight
  - https://insight.openexo.com/tag/dashboards/

Companies that provide drag and drop Dashboard builders

- Tableau / ArcGIS
- Snowflake (and other...)—streaming of data (Apache Kafka)
- Big Tech company platform offerings e.g., Microsoft: Azure
  - https://docs.microsoft.com/en-us/azure/azure-portal/azure-portal-Dashboards
- PowerBI
- Google Fusion Tables, Google Studio
- AWS Redshift + (streaming data analysis tools)
- DashboardFox
- Domo

Open-source tools:
- E.g., for Python: ...(Plotly Dash)
- R-Studio which has a web export (R Shiny)
- Redash
  - https://redash.io/

12

Experimentation

Iteration/experimentation is the only way.

—*Exponential Organizations*, First Edition

The three things you'll learn in this chapter

- A culture of Experimentation is fundamental to being an Exponential Organization. The top companies in the world are ruthless experimenters.
- Constant Experimentation keeps a team closely mapped to external realities—which is especially important in a volatile, rapidly changing world.
- Ideas can come from anywhere (and the best ones often do). That's why it's important to open up the Experimentation process to everyone.

ExOs are perpetually experimenting, constantly trying something new. Traditional companies see Experimentation as a side activity, a novelty, something to do when the enterprise is doing well and cash is flowing. That is a huge mistake, especially in modern life, when change is fast and continuous, markets are volatile, and radical shifts in technology and customer demand are regular occurrences. As Amazon's Jeff Bezos has said, "Our success is a function of the number of experiments we run per year, per month, and per day." In this chapter, we'll look more closely at what true Experimentation means and how to achieve it. What is Experimentation?

Definition of Experimentation

Experimentation is the means by which EXOs make data-driven decisions. Each experiment creates a set of learnings that can be used to improve a product, service, and/or process or test a new product or service. Experimentation thrives inside a culture of imagination and risk-taking and enables significant breakthroughs and non-linear growth. Historically, most decisions inside an organization were made by experts and consultants based on their "experience" or "intuition." Often, such decisions were made while flying the banner of "slow and steady wins the race."

Moonshots are the ultimate form of Experimentation, wherein an ExO, directionally inspired by its MTP, converts a sequence of successful experiments into large, funded initiatives with an audacious endpoint. As the name suggests, Moonshots carry considerable expense and risk, but they also represent tremendous potential payoffs, propelling the company that much closer to realizing its MTP.

As Peter often says, "The day before a major breakthrough, it's a crazy idea." If you're not experimenting, then you are an incremental innovation company and not an ExO.

Case Study: Jeff Holden and Amazon

Peter's friend Jeff Holden is a renowned innovator and past XPRIZE board member. His illustrious career is marked by key roles at Amazon, Uber, and his current venture, Atomic Machines. As chief product officer at both Amazon and Uber, he spearheaded the creation of Amazon Prime and popular Uber services like Uber Eats and Uber Pool (now UberX Share). He has a wealth of experience in disruptive innovations, which he distilled down to four key lessons when Peter sought his advice.

Jeff's first directive is to design your company as a potent experimental engine from the beginning. In an era where change is the only constant, continuous innovation and Experimentation are crucial for survival and hyper-growth. Jeff incorporated this ideology at Amazon, Groupon, and Uber.

Integrating this experimental engine isn't an effortless task, and it often requires a cultural transformation in established companies. It also requires a commitment to ceaselessly test bold ideas, new business models, products, and processes. This principle was evident in Amazon's early days when a comprehensive experimental platform was made available to almost everyone.

This openness led to an onslaught of experiments, many of which proved futile. As Jeff explains, Amazon ran countless experiments out of sheer curiosity, despite their costs and inefficiencies. Eventually, Amazon formed an Experiments Group. Before executing an experiment, its hypothesis and potential value to the company had to be convincingly presented.

Proper interpretation of experimental results is Jeff's second key lesson. Like Uber, which runs thousands of monthly experiments and bases decisions on statistical significance, knowing the difference between significant and insignificant results is crucial. At Uber, only about 20 to 30% of experiments are successful, but all provide valuable insights. Jeff's advice? Ignore the external noise, stay focused, and continue to build.

In his third directive, Jeff provides two key pointers about constructing a team and a company: nurture an experimental ethos within the organization and hire individuals familiar with Experimentation and the data-informed mindset.

Finally, Jeff emphasizes the importance of comfort with being misunderstood. Strong experimental cultures often invite misunderstanding from external observers. Jeff cites Amazon Prime, which was initially met with skepticism but now has over 50 million members, as an example: "Amazon Prime could have been one of those catastrophic failures," says Jeff. "We tried auctions, and that failed, and we tried zShops and that failed. But we just kept going, and we finally cracked it. Then, when we launched it to the world, the response was: 'You guys are insane! This is like, super risky. You're going to blow up with all this margin from shipping.' Bezos, characteristically, replied, 'Yeah, I kind of figured this would be misunderstood.'"

Description of Experimentation

Experimentation is a fundamental characteristic of nature and, indeed, of evolution. All organizations need to change in order to thrive and grow. Change, further, happens only via continuous adaptation … and that adaptation occurs only through Experimentation.

The classic modern example of Experimentation is A/B testing a website: that is, putting out two versions of a page to two different viewing audiences to see which version performs better. Other types of testing approaches include randomization, causal inference, and counterfactual testing. Since our 2014 book, the power of Experimentation has increased tremendously due to the availability of data, the automation of testing models, and a plethora of tools to help track experiments.

As Jeff Holden described his Experimentation process to Peter, we extracted several key themes:

1. **Passion.** "To be experimental, you must first be deeply passionate about the subject, to the point that it consumes you, that you are willing to invest yourself completely in your search for the best solution. There have been times in my career when people call me first at my office at 11 PM because they assume I'll be there. And they're right."

2. **Culture.** History has shown repeatedly that great products and inventions come from companies that have a culture of innovation and Experimentation.

3. **Intelligent failure.** Innovative companies aren't forgiving of failure; they are forgiving of the *right kind of failure*: the failure that comes after an incredible, intelligent effort. In these companies, bad failures are punished as a waste of time, people, and resources. Innovative companies, on the other hand, embrace "failure [that] is always advancing our understanding."

4. **Ideas.** A seemingly great idea may prove impractical, while an apparent clunker may prove the most

viable once it's been tweaked. It's crucial to keep an open mind about ideas: to avoid the tendency to fall in love and stick too long with an unworkable idea or, conversely, to give up on an ugly idea too early. Often the problem with a seemingly "bad" idea is not intrinsic but a prejudice—stemming, perhaps, from envy that it was another person's idea. Cultivate intense honesty and patience when it comes to generating and refining ideas.

5. **First principles.** The very best ideas are grounded in first principles: foundational assumptions or propositions that cannot be broken down or deduced from other assumptions or propositions. First principles thinking requires tremendous amounts of research and investigation, and ideas built upon first principles are often unstoppable. "Once you are convinced that something is possible—even if it is assumed to be impossible—you can't be knocked off your perch; your conclusions are unassailable," says Holden. First-principles thinking is how seemingly crazy ideas—like rebuilding the economy from molecules and competing with physical stores with virtual alternatives—get funded and attract the best talent. That's because facts built on first principles can't be dismissed. Holden points to Elon Musk as the master of using first principles to come up with ideas, like the Hyperloop, that others have dismissed out of hand.

6. **Volume.** Great experimenters come up with dozens, even hundreds, of related ideas and then narrow them down. Amazon and Uber, says Holden, ran thousands of experiments each year. "Every company should have that number." What's more, even

rejected experiments may hold viable and valuable kernels; amalgamated, they may result in the best idea yet.

7. **Iteration.** Before he finally created the incandescent light bulb, Thomas Edison was asked if he was doomed to failure. The great inventor replied that he hadn't failed—rather, he'd found 10,000 ways the lightbulb didn't work. Testing new ideas requires an experimental model that uses previous results to modify the original idea, improving each subsequent iteration. Repeat until you run out of incremental improvements—and you likely have found your product or service.

Experimentation: Lessons from the Trenches

Peter and Salim have thought deeply about the role of Experimentation in modern business—and especially in Exponential Organizations. Here are some of their observations and conclusions:

A to B, then to C

A key insight from the Lean Startup movement is that if you are at point A, you cannot see point C, so focus on getting from A to B. Once you're at B, then you can see point C and plot a course toward it. For example, if you're building a product with 15 features, don't build them all. Build the two that will get you market traction and feedback from users, then plan the implementation of the rest. This is also known as the MVP or Minimum Viable Product. Experimentation serves as the tool of choice when organizations have a clear destination in mind but lack a predefined roadmap to reach it. By embracing Experimentation, companies open themselves up to agile and iterative processes that enable them to navigate uncertainty and adapt to changing circumstances.

Imagination and Experimentation, not Expertise and Experience

A prevailing myth that must be debunked is that an expert holds the key to guaranteed success. As Peter often says, "The expert will tell you how *not* to do something." An ExO acknowledges that expertise alone is not sufficient and that relentless Experimentation is essential for progress. By shifting the focus from seeking expert opinions to creating a culture of learning and Experimentation, organizations can tap into the collective intelligence of their teams and communities to explore new frontiers. Peter and Salim interviewed Sebastian Thrun of Udacity about this topic. Sebastian said, "When hiring, I look for imagination, not experience."

Secrecy

Unless Experimentation is the default policy throughout an organization, secrecy is critical when conducting experiments. Smart organizations often operate in stealth mode to protect against larger market consequences and media exposure when shutting down unsuccessful projects. This freedom to fail in private allows them to experiment more boldly, explore unconventional ideas, and iterate without fear of external judgment.

A Culture of Learning

An ExO is the embodiment of a "learning organization." Creating a culture that encourages taking risks is vital for unleashing the full potential of Experimentation within an organization. By instilling a sense of psychological safety and removing the fear of failure, teams become more inclined to explore uncharted territories. The best ExOs go beyond mere lip service and establish reward mechanisms, including the use of crypto rewards, to incentivize and recognize successful experiments conducted within the community. Top ExOs give awards and recognition to team members who take big operational risks.

Big Companies Can Also Experiment

Large, mature organizations often face challenges when it comes to adopting a culture of Experimentation: namely, higher costs, regulatory barriers, and a fear of failure. Double that for government departments. However, some multinational corporations (MNCs) have recognized the value of running experiments in smaller markets to mitigate these challenges and test ideas more efficiently. This approach allows them to reduce costs, gather valuable insights, and make informed decisions before scaling globally.

Living on the Edge

While the heading sounds dangerous, it's actually the opposite. By constantly experimenting, organizations stay closer to market realities. This is especially important in volatile and uncertain times. Their constant learning delivers an agility that enables them to remain responsive to market shifts and customer demands. By embracing Experimentation as a core attribute, ExOs ensure that they are constantly learning and evolving, positioning themselves as frontrunners in their industries.

Case Studies: Experimentation

- **Zoho.** Founded in 1996, this Indian platform company currently boasts more than 60 million satisfied customers. Zoho led the charge in enabling a swift corporate response to the pandemic and the subsequent work-from-home revolution, testing several options and eventually offering free subscriptions to its millions of SMB and enterprise clients.
- **Atlassian.** This Australian software titan is a complete project-management, bug-tracking, and all-around IT-management platform. Its Confluence team-management platform has a built-in template for experiments to be planned, executed, and tracked. Atlassian is already used by more than 160,000 organizations, including companies as diverse as Carfax and Domino's Pizza.
- **Hootsuite.** Founded in 2008, Canada's Hootsuite offers an all-in-one Software as a Service (SaaS) solution that empowers customers to strategically grow their brands, businesses, and customer relationships with social media. Hootsuite's platform enables customers to manage all their social media channels from one place, allowing them to create and schedule posts to multiple networks simultaneously, monitor posts, manage and respond to incoming messages from customers, track and manage brand mentions and market activity, easily create and manage advertising campaigns, and measure and analyze users' performance on social media.
- **Zoom.** Eric Yuan was one of the first 20 employees of WebEx, eventually becoming vice president of engineering. In 2007, WebEx was acquired by Cisco,

and Yuan became Cisco's corporate VP of engineering. Yuan soon realized that Cisco had a problem: the WebEx product. "I knew WebEx customers were not happy, and I understood why," Yuan says. "The solution was very old, the architecture was very old, and it didn't support video very well ... I tried to convince others [at WebEx] to build a new solution and to start over, but nobody listened." When Cisco wouldn't let Yuan experiment on a new product, he did it himself. He founded his own company, Zoom, building iteration and Experimentation deep into the culture. Zoom had a strong start: by 2019, 10 million people participated in its meetings each day, generating enough revenue for the company to go public. And then came the global COVID lockdown. By April 2020, Zoom's daily meeting participants had jumped to 300 million. Zoom became a key feature of global business life—all because Eric Yuan decided to experiment at precisely the right moment in history.

The Future of Experimentation

In today's dynamic business landscape, adaptability and innovation are crucial, and Experimentation is a tool of transformative potential. Experimentation goes beyond mere testing to cultivate a mindset of discovery, reshaping ExOs from the inside out. Its multifaceted benefits include fostering a culture of learning, promoting efficiency, and enabling customer-focused development. Here's how this process can redefine an ExO's future:

- **The emergence of organizational structures.**
  The first revolution in Experimentation lies in
  the transformation of organizational structures.
  Beyond products, services, and business models,
  Experimentation is seeping into the foundations
  of organizations themselves. In the coming years,
  we'll witness a Cambrian explosion of new organizational models, such as decentralized autonomous
  organizations (DAOs), redefining the boundaries of
  corporate structure.
- **Experimentation in monetary systems: The crypto
  factor.** The advent of cryptocurrencies like Bitcoin
  marks a significant shift in our monetary systems. We
  are experiencing the first wave of innovation in these
  systems in decades, with thousands of experiments
  testing different facets of money, stores of value, and
  mediums of exchange. The culmination of these trials will radically reshape today's fiat currencies.
- **AI-driven Experimentation: The next big leap.**
  The power of Artificial Intelligence is driving a
  revolution in Experimentation. As evident in the
  biomedical world, AI and computation enable us to
  run a massive number of parallel experiments, iterate, and then run them again. This capability will
  span all industries, heralding the age of automated
  Experimentation. AI will streamline experiment
  design, implementation, and analysis, accelerating
  the process while reducing human error.
- **Predictive experimentation: Harnessing the
  power of LLMs and big data.** The future of
  Experimentation also lies in predictive capabilities.
  Leveraging large language models (LLMs) and big
  data, organizations will optimize experiments using

predictive modeling. This shift will enable businesses to hypothesize outcomes even before the tests are conducted, paving the way for unprecedented efficiencies in innovation.

- **A global surge in startups.** According to Eric Ries, the author of *Lean Startup*, "a startup is an experiment looking for a business model." As technology becomes increasingly accessible and affordable, we will witness a global surge in experiments, leading to a radical increase in startups. This democratization of technology will fuel the entrepreneurial spirit worldwide, creating a vibrant ecosystem for innovation and progress.

Benefits of Experimentation

In an era marked by change and complexity, Exponential Organizations must harness the transformative power of Experimentation. This attribute is about more than just trial and error; it's about driving innovation, enhancing performance, and embracing the unknown. Experimentation offers multi-dimensional benefits:

- **Discovery of opportunities and talent.** Lean startup thinking allows for the discovery of unknown opportunities and untapped organizational talent.
- **Agility and competitiveness.** This approach reinforces the agility that leads to Exponential breakthroughs, keeping an organization competitive.
- **Minimized risk.** Experimentation minimizes bad investments by keeping failure at the experimental rather than the operational levels.

- **Culture of responsiveness and learning.** Experimentation establishes a culture of responsiveness, constant learning, productive risk, and questioning bias.
- **Maximization of serendipity.** It allows the team to "tinker," as Apple co-founder Steve Wozniak suggests, thereby maximizing serendipity.
- **Evidence-based decision-making.** Data Rules. Experimental data and evidentiary results eliminate politics and internal resentments.
- **Faster time to market.** By focusing on building a minimum viable product (MVP), organizations can bring products to market quicker, gather customer feedback, and make necessary improvements.
- **Cost efficiency.** Experimentation promotes the efficient use of resources, saving organizations money by avoiding investment in undesired features or products.
- **Innovation and customer-centricity.** This type of thinking encourages innovation and ensures customer-centric product development through regular feedback loops.
- **Organizational learning and employee empowerment.** Embracing failure as an opportunity to learn fosters continuous learning within the organization and empowers employees.

Challenges of Experimentation

While the benefits of Experimentation are compelling, establishing a culture of trial and error is not without significant challenges. Balancing innovation with risk management, the acceptance of failure, and the effective execution of experiments are complex tasks. Let's delve into the intricacies of these challenges.

- **Tolerance for failure.** Colleagues, managers, and boards may struggle to accept failure, often perceiving it as a defeat rather than a learning opportunity.
- **Public perception.** If failed experiments are publicized, they may be misconstrued as signs of the company's incompetence rather than its commitment to learning and growth.
- **Legacy constraints.** Introducing Experimentation in legacy organizations, particularly public companies or governments, can be extremely challenging. In such settings, attempts to experiment can potentially hinder career progression.
- **The art of selection.** Selecting the right experiments to conduct remains a complex task. This challenge reflects the larger issue of posing the right question or prompt, especially when working with large language models (LLMs) like ChatGPT or Bard.
- **Engaging management.** Encouraging the management team to constantly run experiments instead of rushing towards conclusions requires fostering a learning-focused and curiosity-driven culture.
- **Termination timing.** Determining the right time to conclude an experiment is complex. The balance between achieving set goals and optimizing resources is delicate, with the risk of either inconclusive results or missed opportunities. If you end the experiment too early, what are you leaving on the table?

Requirements and Prerequisites of Experimentation

Several key enablers of Experimentation must be considered if an ExO is to fully implement this attribute:

- **MTP.** We'll say it again: A company's MTP must guide all Experimentation. Otherwise, there's no guidance for asking the right questions.
- **Company culture.** Cultivate an environment that accepts the right kind of failure, recognizing that it contributes to experience and gathers all learnings. Experimentation requires a CEO and a board of directors (supporting the CEO) who understand and support a culture of Experimentation, the associated risks, and the potential for sequential (small) failures along the way to success.
- **Dashboards.** It is critical to track experiments via Dashboards to measure outcomes.
- **Autonomy** is a critical enabler of Experimentation. General Electric famously trained 60,000 managers in lean startup thinking—the biggest corporate training exercise in the history of business. And the initiative mostly failed because they didn't implement autonomy alongside it. (Nor did they operate under the guidance of an MTP.) Experimentation inside an organization cannot survive without Autonomy (more on this in the following chapter).
- **Time and money.** Experimentation requires sufficient timespans and budgets. Often, business leaders get frustrated after the first cycle or two and shut down the project, leaving great ideas an iteration or two away from fruition. Today, as the cost of experimenting drops, time will be the gating factor.

Case Study: Astro Teller and Managing Experimentation

Astro Teller, the chief executive of Google X and a celebrated speaker on the company "Moonshots," is known for his innovative approach to Experimentation. Moonshots, the ultimate form of Experimentation, involve ExOs converting successful experiments into large, funded initiatives within the guidelines of their MTP. These projects carry significant expense and risk but also offer tremendous potential payoffs and propel the company closer towards the realization of its MTP.

The following three principles, Astro explains, describe a good experiment:

1. Any experiment where you already know the outcome is a BAD experiment.
2. Any experiment when the outcome will not change what you are doing is also a BAD experiment.
3. Everything else (especially where the input and output are quantifiable) is a GOOD experiment.

Seems simple enough, right? You must ask questions to which you don't currently know the answers and whose answers, if you discovered them, would change the way you operate.

If you already know the answers, or if you're testing an insignificant detail that doesn't matter, you'll just be wasting time and money. To get good questions and therefore good experiments, you must create a culture that incentivizes asking good questions and designing good experiments.

Astro describes a very unique approach to doing just this: "At X, we set up a 'Get Weirder Award.' The whole point of the Get Weirder Award was to focus the team on experiments and to drive home the need to think in terms of experiments." Teams would be challenged to ask "weird" questions: to put forth crazy ideas around framing problems differently, and to design experiments that push the limits. Critically, Astro gives out the Get Weirder Award only *after* the experiments are run. "If you give out the award after they've run the experiment, independent of the results, then people start to really feel that you don't actually care about the outcome. You care about the quality of the question."

In this way, X constantly (and viscerally) reinforced the asking of good questions. Accordingly, they've built a culture around celebrating the questions themselves.

Recently, when Teller was addressing Peter's Abundance360 Summit, he explained further how he helps his teams at X conduct more effective and meaningful experiments in a three-step process:

1. He asks his team to bring him a list of proposed experiments in order of their perceived importance. Astro reviews that list and says, "Humor me and reorder your list so the items at the top are the ones that would teach us the most in this project."
2. When the team returns with their reordered list of experiments/action items, Astro instructs them to "Go do the top two things on your Learning List."
3. Once the team returns, he asks them to create a new list in order of importance. Chances are the new list won't look anything like the original list. This is why Teller emphasizes doing things in learning order.

How to Start Building a Culture of Experimentation

If you're a startup, it's relatively trivial to implement an experimental culture. This task, however, becomes much more difficult as organizations get bigger. As we've mentioned, large organizations are geared toward efficiency and predictability, which are antithetical to experiments that are counter to both those objectives. Here are some steps to integrate this Experimentation into an organization.

- Appoint a team "head of experiments" to educate the team on the qualities of a good experiment and, in turn, prompt continuous Experimentation.
- Award those teams that run experiments and learn, whether they succeed or fail.
- Elevate the Experimentation conversation to your weekly or monthly Executive Staff meeting. Have your teams report on the experiments they ran and what they learned. Again reward the effort, but don't penalize the failures.
- Encourage your management team to ask great questions. This is an analog of the MTP. ExOs think big in almost everything they do—and never more so when experimenting with new products, markets, technologies, organizations, customer experiences, and employee culture. Formulating great questions is an art form. It also takes courage. But somewhere out there is that one question that can lead to a billion-dollar opportunity for your company.
- Utilize generative AI as a thought partner to recommend experiments you should be running, how to design them, and what parameters to measure.
- Run an incentive prize (or series of prizes) in your company to canvas crazy ideas. As described in Peter's book *BOLD*, MIT's Michael Schrage said, "The best way to become innovative is to innovate more." Schrage suggests running a 5x5x5 design competition within companies to encourage such innovation:

- Step 1: Within your company or group, organize a minimum of 5 teams of 5 people each. The teams should have a diverse makeup of executives, engineers, marketing members, executive assistants, customers, and suppliers.
- Step 2: Give each team a period of 5 days to come up with a portfolio of 5 "business experiments" that should take no longer than 5 weeks to run and cost no more than $5,000 to conduct. Each experiment should have a business case that explains how running that experiment will give tremendous insight into a possible savings or growth of $5 million for the firm. Tell the teams that you're not looking for incremental improvement but significant changes that are exponential in nature.
- Step 3: Run the 5-week experiments and have each team report on their outcome. If one or two of the experiments yields significant results, invest in those ideas to develop new products or services.

• • •

As we've noted, a successful corporate culture of Experimentation requires a strong element of Autonomy. We'll investigate Autonomy in the next chapter.

Key Resources/Links where you can learn more

- Why These Tech Companies Keep Running Thousands Of Failed Experiments
  - https://www.fastcompany.com/3063846/why-these-tech-companies-keep-runnin g-thousands-of-failed
- Testing Business Ideas - Innovation Process to Reduce Risks
  - https://www.strategyzer.com/books/testing-business-ideas-david-j-bland
- Udacity - How to Build a Start-Up
  - https://www.udacity.com/course/how-to-build-a-startup — ep245
- Brilliant! Wisdom from Astro Teller of Alphabet's Moonshot Factory
  - https://insight.openexo.com/brilliant-wisdom-from-astro-teller-o f-alphabets-moonshot-factory/
- Experimentation - ExO Insight
  - https://insight.openexo.com/tag/experimentation/

13

Autonomy

Autonomy can be a powerful motivator in the age of the
Exponential Organization.

—*Exponential Organizations*, First Edition

The three things you'll learn in this chapter

- Decentralizing decision-making maximizes agility by empowering team members up and down the org chart and bridging into Community, which then enables scale.
- Autonomy is tricky to implement—especially in existing organizations. A powerful, pervasive, and fully accepted corporate MTP is required to guide autonomous team members.
- Decentralized autonomous organizations (DAOs) are the full embodiment of Autonomy. DAOs will soon become commonplace; governance is their biggest current impediment.

As Dashboards provide greater insight into company operations, they reduce the need for direct management and thus enable greater Autonomy. Greater Autonomy, in turn, allows for more freedom, the spontaneous formation of teams, and, inevitably, greater creativity and productivity. In this chapter, we'll look at the fundamental role of Autonomy in the Exponential Organization. In a remote-working, post-COVID world, Autonomy has eclipsed almost every other ExO attribute in terms of importance, not least because it is nearly impossible to impose traditional managerial control over a widely scattered, decentralized workforce.

What is Autonomy?

Autonomy is an organizational approach characterized by self-organized, multidisciplinary teams that operate with decentralized authority and, ideally, self-select their work—all in service of hitting OKRs and the company's MTP and Moonshot(s). This approach stands in stark contrast to the traditional hierarchical workplace. Autonomous ExOs are flatter, populated by highly motivated self-starters who are empowered to innovate.

Case Study: Bitcoin

Bitcoin may be the most talked-about financial construct on the planet—with good reason. Built on several generations of digital money, Bitcoin pioneered a true global, peer-to-peer digital currency. It is all but synonymous with blockchain technology. Bitcoin is also an almost perfect embodiment of an ExO. Indeed, all it lacks is an explicit MTP. But if it had one, it would likely be "A global, peer-to-peer, 21st-century monetary system." Still, Bitcoin encompasses the remaining nine ExO attributes, with Autonomy ranked highest:

1. **Staff on Demand** via open source. Note that, as a peak Autonomous organization, Bitcoin has no core organization. In fact, we predict DAOs will eventually replace Staff on Demand.
2. **Community and Crowd.** In fact, Bitcoin exists only as Community and Crowd.
3. **Algorithms and Artificial Intelligence.** Proof-of-work algorithms are the heart of Bitcoin, along with Merkle Hash trees.
4. **Leveraged Assets.** Bitcoin piggybacks on others' computations.
5. **Engagement.** Bitcoin mining is fully gamified, with a feedback loop to keep Engagement high and to create reward structures for miners.
6. **Interfaces** are part of Bitcoin's protocol. The protocol is the interface.
7. **Dashboards.** Bitcoin's blockchain is public, transparent, and analyzable by anyone.
8. **Experimentation.** Thousands of developers have built new ideas on Bitcoin.
9. **Autonomy.** Bitcoin is so decentralized there's not even a core organization. The entire effort is just a protocol.
10. **Social Technologies.** With its public blockchain and transparent wallets, Bitcoin resides entirely in social space.

Description: Autonomy

Our own bodies are a perfect illustration of autonomy. We are made up of some 40 trillion cells, each of which runs millions of autonomous functions that operate without our awareness. These functions are based on protocols, resulting in enormous scale and near-infinite complexity.

Autonomy is the culmination of the modern "fail fast" philosophy, which contrasts with the traditional "be better" point of view. An autonomous company trusts its employees to organize themselves into teams and provides them with the necessary tools and resources to pursue their goals and define their destinies, all in service of the company's MTP.

Some teams may fail but without recriminations. Learnings are documented. Many teams will succeed, driving the company to become smarter, more innovative, and agile in identifying new opportunities and emerging competitive threats.

The more autonomous a company, the greater its agility: reaction and learning times are shortened, expertise is more accessible, and decision-making is closer to the customer, allowing for increased accountability at the edge. Morale improves as the organization builds trusting relationships with employees, who spontaneously create teams, forming a "hive mind" that facilitates the emergence of collective intelligence. This increased capacity enables organizations to scale.

Sangeet Paul Chowdry, co-author of *Platform Revolution: How Networked Markets Are Transforming the Economy and How to Make Them Work for You,* has observed the transition from operating companies to platforms, protocols, and ecosystems built around those protocols. Open-source projects serve as a prime example of this evolution.

Companies that embrace this approach foster an innovative, collaborative work environment, ultimately leading to greater adaptability and success. As organizational design expert Steve Denning puts it, new hierarchies form that are competence-based and rely on peer accountability, reflecting a shift in the role of the manager rather than its abolition. This new model enables companies to harness the full potential of their employees and respond swiftly to the ever-changing demands of the digital age.

Case Studies: Autonomy

- **Valve Software,** a game company, has 330 staffers but no traditional management structure, reporting lines, job descriptions, or regular meetings. Instead, the company hires talented, innovative self-starters who decide which projects they want to join. New hires also are encouraged to start new projects so long as they fit the company's MTP. The organization operates under the philosophy of "permissionless innovation": relying on small, independent, multidisciplinary teams. It's working well: Valve has a higher revenue-per-employee ratio than any other gaming company.
- **Buurtzoorg,** Dutch for "neighborhood care," is a Dutch home-care organization that has attracted international attention for its innovative use of independent nurse teams in delivering relatively low-cost care.
- **SpaceX.** In a break with tradition for a science company, SpaceX demands that every requirement must have an individual's name associated with it, not a department's. Why? Because, after many years,

an organization often ends up with a long list of requirements, some of which are no longer valid. When a team member goes back to check on why that requirement was put in place, it's important to know whom, specifically, to ask. One challenge that SpaceX faced was that sometimes that person was no longer with the company, and the department had no idea why the requirement was put in place.

- **WordBlu** is a consulting firm that specializes in transitioning leaders and companies around the world from hierarchical to democratic leadership. The company's MTP is "Freedom at Work." To support its mission, WordBlu creates a yearly list of global freedom-centered organizations and advocates for more freedom and autonomy in the workplace.

- **ING Group.** This giant international banking and financial services corporation, headquartered in Amsterdam, has assets of more than $1 trillion and 53 million clients in 40 countries. In 2020, in an extraordinary move, ING's global headquarters underwent a complete transformation towards more autonomous ways of working. The company fired all its employees, who could then reapply for jobs in the new structure. In the process, nearly one-third of its workforce quit—and ING discovered that it could achieve the same business results with just the remaining two-thirds.

- **Haier.** This appliance manufacturer implemented the "Rendanheyi" model in 2005, flattening the hierarchical organization and eventually removing all mid-layer departments. Along the way, 12,000 middle-level managers had to become entrepreneurs or leave. Meanwhile, the company's 80,000 employees formed into thousands of micro-enterprises (MEs), each composed of 10 or fewer people. (This is an old example, but ask any MBA university today how to produce 55 million fridges and ovens, and they'll design an incredibly centralized (and inflexible) structure.)

- **Cryptocurrencies.** Also known as Layer One blockchains, each major cryptocurrency publishes a set of tools on how to interface with that blockchain, plus some documentation. This approach has led to blockchains like Cardano and Solana being worth billions of dollars by allowing complete autonomy to their community. In 2022, we learned that Cardano's ecosystem was largely designed using the ExO framework. One of the more recent and exciting protocols is Casper, where the founders have laid down a very long-term token release structure and demonstrated a commitment to systemic change. Casper stands out as specifically designed to cater to the evolving needs of enterprise customers. With its use of familiar programming languages, the ability to upgrade in the future, and the flexibility to accommodate fully private, fully public, and hybrid instances, Casper offers a comprehensive and user-friendly platform.

The Future of Autonomy

As we shift from top-down, traditional organizations to ExO-style, decentralized structures, Autonomy will see some major transformations:

- **Human-AI collaboration.** AI will increasingly partner with human team members in decentralized organizations, enhancing productivity and decision-making.

- **Nonprofits and the public sector as DAOs.** Many nonprofit and public-sector organizations will transition to DAOs, leveraging their inherent transparency and community-driven nature.
- **Participatory budgeting.** Decentralized organizations will utilize participatory budgeting, allowing groups to vote on resource allocation and fostering a sense of ownership.
- **DAOs replacing Staff on Demand.** We'll see the integration of temporary or contract-based staff into decentralized, member-based organizations.
- **Widespread use of technology.** Blockchain technology, generative AI, smart contracts, and decentralized systems will underpin transparent, trust-based environments that enable equitable decision-making and efficient collaboration.
- **Customizable career paths.** Employees will have greater flexibility to shape their careers, explore new opportunities, and develop diverse skill sets within their organizations.
- **Emphasis on learning and development.** Continuous learning and skill development will be crucial, requiring organizations to invest in training programs that support employee growth and adaptability.
- **Focus on organizational culture.** Companies will prioritize fostering a positive, collaborative, and supportive culture that values employee autonomy and nurtures innovation.
- **Ethical considerations.** The rise of autonomous organizations will necessitate addressing ethical

concerns, such as equitable decision-making, privacy, and data security, through guidelines and policies.

Benefits of Autonomy

In an era of rapid digital transformation and persistent disruptions, organizations must adapt their decision-making processes to remain nimble and responsive. Adopting a decentralized decision-making framework provides several benefits:

- **Increased agility.** Autonomy, a cornerstone of decentralized decision-making, greatly enhances organizational agility. As disruptions such as COVID-19 continue to reshape business landscapes, it's crucial for organizations to adapt swiftly and efficiently. By decentralizing authority, businesses can make quicker, more responsive decisions tailored to their unique context and challenges.
- **More accountability.** The decentralization of decision-making can also bring decisions closer to the customer, leading to increased accountability. Teams directly interfacing with customers possess a deep understanding of customer needs and preferences. Entrusting these teams with decision-making powers empowers them to make more informed choices, bolstering both the quality of service and accountability.
- **Speed of learning.** Another key benefit is improved reaction and learning times. In a decentralized framework, decision-making processes are distributed, reducing bottlenecks and expediting response times. Further, this structure allows for rapid feedback and learning, enhancing the organization's ability to iterate and innovate.

- **Better morale.** Decentralized decision-making also boosts morale by fostering a sense of trust and purpose within the organization. Employees, feeling valued and trusted, are more likely to take responsibility for their roles and display a heightened commitment to their work. This not only enhances job satisfaction but also fuels the drive toward achieving organizational objectives.
- **Accessibility to expertise.** In this framework, organizations gain greater accessibility to expertise within the team. Decentralization enables those with specialized knowledge and skills to contribute effectively to decision-making processes, leading to better-informed and more nuanced decisions.
- **Hive mind.** Finally, a decentralized framework can facilitate the emergence of a hive mind and collective intelligence. By drawing on the diverse perspectives and insights of its members, the organization can unlock innovative solutions and strategies that may not emerge in a centralized decision-making structure. This collective intelligence offers a competitive edge, propelling the organization toward growth and success.

Challenges of Autonomy

The principal challenge to implementing Autonomy lies in trying to implement it into legacy organizations. But there are several others. For example:

- **Trust and Autonomy:** Autonomy demands a high degree of trust, which is very difficult for legacy organizations that are designed to mistrust their people.

- **Risk of Duplication**: Conversely, without centralized control, an autonomous organization risks significant duplication of effort and internal competition.
- **Governance Challenges**: Because an autonomous organization is composed of independent individuals and teams in scattered locations, governance can pose major challenges.
- **Team Dissolution**: After a newly formed team has achieved its goals, getting them to voluntarily shut down can be a challenge.
- **Ambiguity in Job Responsibility**: Autonomous organizations, by definition, get things done by being more flexible and less defined. However, this flexibility often leads to nebulous job descriptions, resulting in ambiguity in job responsibility and a lack of clarity around roles.
- **Informal Hierarchy**: Humans naturally gravitate towards structure or hierarchy. When that hierarchy isn't there, they will often create one informally, with leadership awarded to those with stronger personalities, more charisma, higher social class, or the loudest voices.
- **Management in a Bossless Workplace**: As Google learned soon after its founding, with a flat organizational structure, most employees will report directly to the boss. Even in a "bossless workplace," employees will still look to the ostensible leader for answers on more complex issues. With a flood of questioning employees, management becomes impossible.
- **Limited Promotion Opportunities**: Fewer management layers mean fewer promotion opportunities. As a result, some employees may feel like there's a ceiling on their chances for career advancement and move

somewhere where those opportunities still exist. The solution? Compensate for the lack of advancement with alternative opportunities, such as a different compensation model, a custom career development plan, or added benefits.

Requirements and Prerequisites of Autonomy

Harnessing the power of Autonomy in organizations requires the adoption of several key attributes, the most important of which is the MTP. A strong MTP is mandatory in an ExO—it helps keep autonomous teams pointed in the right direction. Other prerequisites include:

- **Dashboards.** These are particularly vital for decentralized teams. Dashboards facilitate real-time tracking of team progress and initiative implementation, thereby providing a comprehensive overview of organizational operations. Dashboards not only streamline task management; they also enhance transparency, enabling teams to identify bottlenecks, optimize workflows, and align their efforts toward shared objectives.
- **Hiring self-starters.** Hiring self-starters can significantly maximize the potential of autonomous teams. Self-starters are proactive, inherently motivated, and display a high degree of initiative, driving the team forward even in the absence of immediate supervision. Their energy and drive can inspire others, fostering a culture of proactive problem-solving and creativity that spurs the overall productivity of the organization.
- **Dynamic culture.** A strong and dynamic culture serves as a unifying force between autonomous teams.

It ensures a sense of cohesion and collaboration, even when teams operate independently. This type of culture values open communication, mutual respect, and shared goals, which enable different teams to work together seamlessly and efficiently toward the organization's objectives.

- **Engagement.** The gamification of different organizational goals can effectively engage employees and enhance their performance. By transforming mundane tasks into engaging challenges, gamification taps into the competitive spirit of the workforce, stimulating creativity, innovation, and enthusiasm. This strategy not only boosts motivation but also fosters a sense of achievement, encouraging continuous improvement and higher productivity.

- **ExO mindset and leadership.** The right culture is critical for the success of Autonomy within an organization. It can be challenging for traditional leadership to relinquish control. A corporate culture that thrives on Autonomy, however, coupled with a leadership team that supports this attribute, can usher in transformational changes. An ExO-minded leadership fosters trust, encourages risk-taking, and empowers teams, thereby promoting a culture of innovation, adaptability, and sustainable growth.

Closing Story: Decentralized Autonomous Organizations (DAOs)

A DAO is Autonomy taken to the fullest extent. DAOs are decentralized autonomous organizations: entities created according to rules encoded in a transparent computer program and controlled by the organization's members. In other words, DAOs have no central leadership but are run by their members. Anyone can launch any model into the decentralized environment, letting the marketplace decide who will participate. Even their finances and rules are maintained on a blockchain. DAOs function, essentially, as co-ops running on a blockchain with smart contracts—Interfaces—codifying their internal operating rules. These interface-enabled DAOs are the reason why the Web3 world can scale so quickly.

Because anyone can participate, DAOs can recruit the most interested and talented parties. Consider Braintrust, which bills itself as "the first user-owned talent network." Users join Braintrust by creating a Braintrust profile listing their background and experience. Upon approval, members are invited to add a portfolio and information about their skill sets and work history. In theory, becoming a member of the Braintrust DAO accelerates your career as you get matched to jobs with the world's most innovative companies. Meanwhile, the site lets you set your own rates and get 100% of the fee. Clients pay a 10% platform fee, on top of the freelancer's rate, to Braintrust. Freelancers set their own payment terms.

Braintrust is a glimpse of how near-perfect Autonomy can be brought to the jobs market by giving job searchers complete control over the process. In a gig economy, where freelancers will begin to dominate the marketplace, ExOs will need to become skilled at navigating and taking advantage of the Braintrusts of the world to locate and recruit the kind of top talent they will need to succeed.

DeFi (or "decentralized finance") is one of the most interesting subspecies of DAOs. DeFi is an umbrella term for financial services on public blockchains, usually founded on

Ethereum. As with most crypto, DeFi is global, peer-to-peer, pseudonymous, and open to all.

Consumers can use DeFi for most traditional banking services and functions: borrowing, lending, earning interest, trading derivatives and assets, and even buying insurance. DeFi, however, is much, much faster than traditional banking—not least because it doesn't require paperwork. Examples of DeFi entities on Ethereum include:

- **Uniswap,** the largest decentralized exchange on Ethereum
- **Maker,** the governance mechanism for the Dai stablecoin, and
- **Aave,** a lending platform to trustlessly lend and borrow major assets.

"Grants" DAOs are designed to fund new ventures, typically in the DeFi space. They include:

- **Gitcoin,** which funds developers of open-source applications
- **MolochDAO,** which provides a transparent and efficient funding mechanism for Ethereum projects
- **"Collector" DAOs** that pool funds to purchase collectors' items such as NFTs, artwork, and music
- **Flamingo,** which focuses on purchasing NFTs for investment, and
- **PleasrDAO,** an omnibus DAO that pools funds to buy any type of collectible or artwork.

"Social" DAOs often require membership fees, paid in DAO tokens. Social DAOs are often famous and exclusive and are typically based on common interests. Two examples are:

- **Friends with Benefits,** a very exclusive DAO largely composed of Web3 artists and followers.
- **Bored Ape Yacht Club,** a DAO popular with celebrities. Membership requires you to own a unique "Bored Ape" NFT.

Autonomy: How to Get Started

Perhaps the most important consideration in implementing Autonomy is: *don't do it in existing organizations.* Zappos tried for three years to implement Autonomy and failed. Do it in new ExOs off the edge of the mothership.

- **Use your MTP.** As noted earlier, the Massive Transformative Purpose is the single most important factor in an ExO for galvanizing the organization and its stakeholders and for aligning them in the pursuit of a common goal with a common purpose. More than anything, the MTP will keep autonomous teams moving in the same direction. Autonomous teams are especially powerful at determining and then pursuing out-of-the-box Moonshots.
- **Take advantage of Staff on Demand.** The gig economy is key to greater Autonomy because the presence of outside "employees"—especially remote staffers— reinforces more flexible and adaptive teams. Teams can augment their internal skillset with the best outside talent, making them even more capable of operating independently.
- **Use the power of Dashboards.** A common management concern about increased employee Autonomy is that independent teams will go rogue and create organizational chaos. With new generations

of Dashboards and sensor technology, that fear is largely misplaced as the use of OKRs usually keeps everyone aligned.

- **Decentralize.** Breaking up the enterprise into smaller and more functional pieces is the heart of both decentralization and Autonomy. That said, decentralization can be particularly terrifying for large companies—even though Alfred Sloan pioneered the concept nearly a century ago at mighty General Motors. But the success of companies such as Finland's Supercell and Sweden's Spotify suggests that this model can not only work but can even become a key competitive advantage.
- **Reinforce agility.** One of the core elements of an agile framework is autonomous, self-organizing teams, each with its own unique ability to adapt according to evolving circumstances. When ExOs allow for Autonomy, they simultaneously allow for a range of approaches to change, from radical to conservative, thus increasing the odds of surviving that change.
- **Alter your perspective.** Teach employees, wherever they are in the organization, to think and act like owners: to treat their work and their decision-making as their own property for which they are fully responsible. At the top of the organization, act as if you are the owner of that organization, not merely a caretaking executive. And, like a founder, trust in your employees to "own" their duties and to make decisions in the best interests of the company.
- **Link to Algorithms and Artificial Intelligence.** Blockchain and smart contracts can be used to create fully decentralized autonomous organizations,

replacing the traditional bureaucratic "glue" with organic networks.

In his 2014 book *Reinventing Organizations,* Frederic Laloux profiled 12 pioneering organizations (including Patagonia, WL Gore, Holocracy, and Morning Star) who were reinventing themselves using radically new management practices and principles, self-management, and the precursor of MTP. He noted that these organizations operated largely without organizational charts, management hierarchies, quarterly goals, or other traditional management strategies. Instead, they were characterized by self-managed teams, intuitive reasoning, and decentralized decision-making. In other words, they were Autonomous.

• • •

We have now explored nine attributes of the Exponential Organization. Next, we'll investigate the glue that binds together all the stakeholders—company, supply chain, distribution chain, Community, Crowd, and shareholders: Social Technologies.

Key Resources/Links where you can learn more

- ING's agile transformation | McKinsey
    - o https://www.mckinsey.com/indus-tries/financial-services/our-insights/ings-agile-transformation
- List of the latest WorldBlu Certified Freedom-Centered Organizations
    - o https://www.worldblu.com/certified
- Valve Employee Handbook
    - o https://archive.org/details/ValveEmployeeHandbook
- Reinventing Organizations by Frederic Laloux
    - o https://www.reinventingorganizations.com
- Autonomy: ExO Insight
    - o https://insight.openexo.com/tag/autonomy/

14

Social Technologies

Social Technologies accelerate conversations and, therefore,
learning cycles.

—*Exponential Organizations 2.0*

The three things you'll learn in this chapter

- Social Technologies increasingly extend from the internet to the metaverse (that is, into a digital world that users will "inhabit" and interact in as they do the natural world).
- Social Technologies act as the nervous system of the modern ExO, collecting data from the edges of the Community, disseminating new ideas and innovations, and building greater cohesiveness among all the players in the organization.
- New crypto and Web3 technologies have begun to integrate identity and cryptoeconomics into the social conversation.

What are Social Technologies?

Social Technologies encourage and optimize peer-to-peer, collaborative interaction in an ExO. Social Technologies encompass communication tools (i.e., social messaging and discussion forums, like Zoom, Slack, Notion, Google Docs, etc.), collaboration tools (such as cloud-based document management for sharing and real-time editing), and workflow tools (to manage tasks and activity streams).

Case Study: Tony Robbins and the Pandemic

Amidst the chaos of the global pandemic, large events and conferences suffered a near-complete shutdown. One individual who managed to successfully adapt to those trying times was the legendary motivational speaker and author Tony Robbins.

Robbins is renowned for his energetic, large-scale events that often draw tens of thousands of participants from all over the globe. The onset of COVID-19 completely shut down the possibility of such gatherings. In typical fashion, undeterred by the circumstances, Robbins sought to translate the unique energy of his live events into a digital space, thereby redefining the concept of peer-to-peer communication in the era of virtual interactions.

Robbins and his team designed a custom-built studio featuring a wall of screens known as the "Zoom wall." This allowed Robbins to see and interact with thousands of participants in real-time during his events. This innovative setup not only maintained the visual element of communication but also facilitated peer-to-peer interaction among participants, a crucial feature of his pre-pandemic live events.

Robbins's approach transformed conventional, webinar-style presentations into engaging, dynamic experiences. This innovative platform facilitated real-time feedback, lively discussions, and open sharing of experiences, replicating the vibrant energy of a live audience. It allowed attendees to be more than just passive viewers, encouraging them to actively participate in discussions, share insights, and connect with others, thus fostering a sense of community.

Virtual breakout rooms were utilized for smaller group discussions and one-on-one interactions, thereby ensuring personal connections were not lost in the virtual setting. Attendees could still network, support each other, and develop relationships, much like they would have at a physical event.

Robbins's digital revolution did not stop at communication. He recognized the value of physical movement in maintaining energy levels and engagement. Therefore, he regularly integrated activities to keep the virtual audience moving and engaged.

The success of Robbins's approach during the pandemic highlights the power of innovation in overcoming adversity. He not only adapted to the situation but also significantly evolved the concept of peer-to-peer communication in the virtual space, setting a precedent. In essence, Robbins managed to transform a difficult pandemic into an opportunity for reinvention and growth, preserving the sense of community and connection that lies at the heart of his events.

Description: The Elements of Social

According to J.P. Rangaswami, former chief scientist at Salesforce, an advancing business has three key objectives: first, reduce the time between obtaining information and making decisions. Second, migrate from seeking out information to having information flow through to you. And third, leverage the Community to build out ideas. Implemented properly, Social Technologies can help an enterprise achieve all three of these goals.

Social Technologies create transparency and connectedness. They accelerate conversations and, therefore, learning cycles. Most importantly, they move a company toward zero latency—a state in which the time between idea, acceptance, and implementation all but disappears, providing a significant return on investment.

Prior to the COVID pandemic, most CIOs were attempting to prohibit social tools, deeming them too unruly to manage. However, the pandemic forced them to reconsider and embrace these tools. Consequently, the tools themselves have evolved and become more potent. Further, the growth of internal social networks has continued unabated.

Importantly, Social Technologies should not be confused or conflated with social media. While corporate social networks may use popular social media applications, Social Technologies as an attribute is characterized by peer-to-peer communication and collaboration, not simply friendly social contact. "Social Technologies," says systems architect and ExO ambassador Diego Soroa, "enhances team creativity—even in the face of, or because of, a shift to remote work, which has created more diverse networks of contacts and accelerated new ways of thinking and interacting, despite declines in in-person communication."

Social Technologies enable the "real-time enterprise," meaning an organization that operates with low latency. They promote peer-to-peer communication, break down hierarchical barriers, and enhance collaboration, thereby fostering a sense of community and shared purpose within organizations. Here are some examples:

- **Social Networking Platforms.** Tools like LinkedIn, Facebook, and Twitter allow employees to connect, share ideas, and collaborate, providing a platform for a more inclusive and participatory form of communication. Moreover, platforms like Yammer and Slack offer dedicated spaces for project coordination, resource sharing, and real-time interaction, facilitating more efficient teamwork and problem-solving.
- **Collaboration and project management tools.** Applications like Trello, Asana, and Jira provide platforms for team coordination, project management, and task tracking. They encourage transparency, foster responsibility, and enable better project execution through shared timelines, goals, and feedback.
- **File sharing and document collaboration.** Technologies such as Google Docs and Dropbox facilitate real-time collaboration on documents, spreadsheets, and presentations. They allow multiple users to edit and comment simultaneously, promoting an exchange of ideas, facilitating knowledge sharing, and reducing duplication of effort.
- **Video Conferencing tools.** With the rise of remote work, platforms like Zoom, Microsoft Teams, and Google Meet have become indispensable for maintaining communication. They enable face-to-face interaction, making team meetings, brainstorming sessions, and presentations more personal and interactive.
- **Enterprise social networks (ESNs).** ESNs like Chatter (Salesforce) or Connections (IBM) provide an internal platform for employees to engage in social interaction, knowledge sharing, and collaborative problem-solving. They enhance connectivity,

foster a sense of community, and can boost innovation and productivity.

- **Wikis and intranets.** These tools are great for accumulating, preserving, and distributing institutional knowledge. They promote a culture of learning and information-sharing, helping to onboard new staff and keeping everyone on the same page.
- **Social learning platforms.** Tools like Degreed, Coursera for Business, or LinkedIn Learning offer opportunities for peer-to-peer learning, skill sharing, and professional development, thereby boosting employee engagement and productivity.

In addition, two major new dimensions have joined Social Technologies.

The first is crypto economics and Web3 tokens. These are revolutionizing organizational structures by fostering decentralized, trustless, and incentivized collaboration. They reward participants in decentralized networks for their contributions. They function not just as a medium of exchange but also as a mechanism for aligning the interests of various stakeholders. For instance, blockchain-based projects often issue native tokens that give holders governance rights, encouraging active participation in decision-making processes and fostering a sense of collective ownership. They also allow an organization to seamlessly extend social technologies into the Community and even the Crowd.

Second is generative AI, which will revolutionize Social Technologies by automating and enhancing various tasks. Generative AI will generate insightful data analysis, draft reports or emails, offer personalized content recommendations, and even aid in decision-making processes, thus freeing up time for employees to engage in higher-value interactions. Further, with capabilities like natural language processing, it can stimulate and moderate brainstorming sessions, contribute innovative ideas, and serve as an impartial mediator in discussions, eliminating biases and promoting inclusivity. Moreover, it can provide personalized learning and development resources, encouraging continuous growth within teams.

Case Studies and Tools

- **Canva,** a collaborative graphics tool, is currently valued at $40 billion and was co-founded by a teenager. As opposed to using social collaboration, the company creates an environment *for* social collaboration. As OpenExO's Sophie Krantz has written, Canva "is building a strategic network of investors and advisors before they are needed. These investors are positioned to provide investment in future funding rounds and enable a funding pipeline to be developed. Beyond this, these strategic investors and advisors are also positioned to provide valuable introductions, insights, and influence, all of which open important doors for future growth." Canva is predicted to play a key role in powering the next generation of DAOs.
- **Whatsapp** currently reaches about 2 billion people worldwide and is the most-used mobile messenger app in the world.[45] During the pandemic, WhatsApp became the go-to platform for communications by

---

[45] "Two Billion Users -- Connecting the World Privately," WhatsApp.com, February 12, 2020, https://blog.whatsapp.com/two-billion-users-connecting-the-world-privately/?lang=en.

companies, governments, non-profits, and international organizations. By 2020, these institutions had sent more than 4 billion messages, often to remote and low-income communities. Whatsapp recently added Community functionality to its product.

- **Miro Boards.** An estimated 35 million users (including 99% of the Fortune 500) depend upon Silicon Valley's Miro to provide virtual whiteboards for real-time and asynchronous collaborative brainstorming and note-taking. Team participants can be co-located, distributed, or fully remote.

- **Slack.** The granddaddy of internal social tools (it was bought by Salesforce in 2021 for a staggering $27.7 billion), Slack provides a messaging platform designed specifically for workplaces. Slack offers several distinctive apps, notably chat rooms organized by topics and direct messaging. Slack is used by 12 million people daily through more than 2,000 integrations into other applications. Seventy-nine percent of business customers say that Slack improves their workplace, while teams say that productivity grows by more than 30%.

- San Francisco's **Asana** is a web and mobile work management platform that has created a software-as-service platform. It is designed to help teams organize, track, and manage their work. Teams using Asana can develop projects, manage tasks, assign work, communicate about tasks, and specify deadlines. The product also includes a wide range of supporting apps—and can even track a company's progress on moonshots and toward its MTP.

- **Notion** is a versatile and all-in-one productivity platform that is perfect for collaboration, as it allows teams to create, share, and manage a wide variety of content, including notes, databases, calendars, and project boards. By consolidating multiple tools into a single, user-friendly interface, Notion enables seamless communication and organization among team members, streamlines workflows, and enhances overall efficiency. Its customizable templates and rich integrations with other popular apps make it an ideal choice for teams seeking to boost their productivity and collaborative efforts. With a recent valuation of more than $10 billion and a user base exceeding 20 million, Notion has demonstrated its significant impact on the productivity and collaboration landscape.

The Future of Social Technologies

Social Technologies will become more immersive, faster, and more intelligent, supercharged by AR/VR, metaverse, and AI technologies. Here's a glimpse of what we can expect:

- **Persistence of Remote Working**: Remote working and distributed global teams will remain fundamental to the working life, signifying a long-term shift in work dynamics.
- **Expanded Corporate Social Networks**: Corporate social networks will not be confined within a company but will create peer-to-peer connections across the entire Community, fostering broader collaboration.
- **Immersive Virtual Experiences**: Today's text-only social technologies will soon give way to immersive virtual experiences where workers meet as avatars in virtual reality, with AI present as non-player

characters (NPCs), extending conversations from text to full emotional engagement.
- **Virtual Rooms as the Norm**: Hanging out in virtual rooms with colleagues will continue to be standard, allowing for the return of informal "water-cooler" conversations.
- **Accelerated Virtual Innovation**: The speed of collaborative virtual innovation will surpass that of collaborative in-person innovation, highlighting the efficiency of virtual collaboration.
- **AI as Personal Assistants**: AIs will become personal assistants and expert co-pilots for executives, analyzing conversations to extract key points and eventually becoming ongoing partners in conversations. AI-based digital twins will emerge to shadow, support, and enhance their human counterparts, representing them in less important meetings and reporting back outcomes.
- **Metaverse Meetings**: Zoom-type calls will evolve into metaverse meetings using avatars, VR headsets, and other devices, creating a more immersive and interactive experience.
- **Metaverse Collaboration**: Collaboration environments in the metaverse will explode, with Vatom being a key leader in this emerging field. Communities will gather in virtual worlds such as Decentraland and Sandbox, marking the rise of the spatial web as the future of social technologies.
- **Virtual Reality Disrupting Reality**: Soon, the resolution on a screen will exceed the resolution of the human eye, leading to a point where virtual reality will disrupt reality itself.

Benefits of Social Technologies

Adopting Social Technologies can catalyze transformative change for ExOs, fostering collaboration, boosting speed, and promoting a culture of innovation. Here's how these technologies can enhance an organization's dynamics and output:

- **Increased value.** Empirical evidence suggests that peer-to-peer communication and collaboration bring much more value than traditional top-down, command-and-control communication patterns.
- **Empowering small teams.** Social Technologies excel at enabling small, particularly autonomous, teams by providing them with platforms for effective collaboration and shared decision-making.
- **Enhanced speed.** These tools facilitate swift Experimentation cycles and communications and, consequently, more rapid decision-making processes.
- **Global team-building.** ExOs can leverage Social Technologies to assemble top-tier talent from around the globe, thus expanding their capabilities and reach.
- **Efficient use of time.** By reducing the time spent on formal, structured meetings, these technologies enable more focus on strategic tasks and creative thinking.
- **Fostering informal interactions.** Virtual meeting rooms promote more casual social interactions, which can lead to faster and more innovative decision-making.
- **Enabling small teams.** The real-time and convenient nature of these tools allows smaller teams to

thrive by staying in closer contact without the delay and bureaucracy of organizing larger, structured meetings.

- **Customized collaboration spaces.** The latest virtual and custom web platforms provide teams with personalized digital spaces designed to nurture collaboration, exploration, and brainstorming.

Challenges of Social Technologies

Social Technologies are transformative tools. Implementing them, however, presents its own set of challenges, particularly in larger organizations:

- **Privacy and accessibility.** Storing and archiving communications generated through Social Technologies can create significant privacy concerns and accessibility issues. Ensuring security and ease of access requires careful consideration and robust systems.
- **Integration with legacy organizations.** Larger, traditionally structured organizations often operate on a top-down basis. Social Technologies, which promote horizontal communication, can disrupt these established patterns, making integration a challenging process.
- **Message distortion.** Corporate social networks are prone to the "broken-telephone syndrome," where the original message can become distorted as it passes through a vast network of employees. Ensuring message integrity is vital for effective communication.
- **Message Fragmentation.** In a digital environment with diverse platforms like WhatsApp, Slack, or email, messages can become fragmented.

Coordinating employees around a single initiative or message can become increasingly complex.

- **Platform confusion.** With numerous communication channels like LinkedIn, Slack, Discord, Instagram, or direct messaging, employees may struggle to remember which platform a message originated from. LinkedIn? Slack? Discord? Instagram? Was it an IM? A DM? This can result in missed or misunderstood messages, making a comprehensive platform strategy essential.A key takeaway: to be effective with Social Technologies, consider choosing one or two channels exclusively so as not to drown in a tsunami of channels.

Requirements and Prerequisites for Social Technologies

Harnessing the power of Social Technologies can be transformative for an Exponential Organization. These tools can amplify peer-to-peer communication, foster collaboration, and boost overall productivity and innovation. To fully capitalize on their potential, an ExO must consider some key requirements and prerequisites:

- **Artificial Intelligence and Algorithms.** Employing AI and Algorithms can facilitate detailed analysis of social streams, highlighting important conversations and directing them to appropriate channels. This allows for real-time feedback and identification of key themes, shifts in opinions, and potential areas for image enhancement.
- **Dashboards** play a critical role in tracking and analyzing metrics related to various interactions. With real-time oversight, Dashboards empower

organizations to make swift changes and adjustments as necessary, allowing them to stay adaptive and responsive.

- **Engagement** is a crucial aspect of Social Technology utilization. Approaches such as gamification, incentive prizes, and cryptoeconomics can significantly amplify social engagement. By making participation enjoyable and rewarding, organizations can increase loyalty, foster collaboration, and uncover valuable insights.

- **Autonomy** and social peer-to-peer collaboration share a symbiotic relationship. While Social Technologies amplify peer-to-peer communication—moving beyond top-down directives—they also enable Autonomy by fostering a culture of shared responsibility and collaborative problem-solving.

Case Study: Spotify

Spotify, the global music streaming giant, has been at the forefront of implementing Social Technologies as a key driver of collaboration and project management; they have been a significant driver of its growth. One of Spotify's most talked-about methodologies is its use of "squads," "tribes," "chapters," and "guilds" for team organization, an approach that is inherently collaborative. This agile methodology breaks down traditional silos and facilitates cross-functional collaboration, innovation, and faster decision-making. It encourages each "squad" to work like an independent startup, with the Autonomy to make decisions and iterate quickly.

In terms of collaboration software, Spotify uses Jira by Atlassian extensively. Jira helps them manage projects and track issues. Each "squad" can manage their backlog, sprints, and releases on Jira, providing transparency and enabling smooth coordination across teams. This means that any member of a squad can easily see the status of a task, who's responsible for it, and what the next steps are, which drastically cuts down on inefficiencies and speeds up decision-making.

Alongside Jira, Spotify also uses tools like Google Workspace for real-time document collaboration and Slack for communication. These platforms allow for immediate, cross-team communication, contributing to the company's culture of open dialogue and knowledge sharing. This has been particularly crucial for Spotify, given that its global workforce is distributed across different time zones.

Further, Spotify has its own internal, peer-to-peer knowledge-sharing platform called "Spotify Rhythm." This platform allows employees to share updates, insights, and learnings with the rest of the company. It's this kind of internal communication that keeps everyone aligned with the company's goals and contributes to a sense of shared purpose.

There are only two primary music-streaming platforms in the world. The first is Apple Music, which brings enormous size. The second, Spotify, competes toe to toe with Apple not in terms of size and scale but via exceptional peer-to-peer collaboration and teamwork.

Case Study: Discord

We usually end each chapter with one case study. However, Discord's over the last two years is worthy of documenting. Discord is a VoIP and instant-messaging social platform that enables users to talk over voice, video, and text. It is a pioneering Social Technology for a new form of internal/external social networking.

Discord was established in 2015 by Jason Citron and Stanislav Vishnevskiy and initially targeted the gaming community. It swiftly gained popularity by addressing the need for a lightweight, voice-focused chat app, offering features like low latency, high-quality audio, and the capacity to create and join servers. Its user base has since expanded beyond gaming to serve communities, including artists, entrepreneurs, and musicians.

Central to Discord's success are its community focus, ease of use, and wide range of features, with its vibrant global community acting as a growth driver. By 2021, the platform had 300 million users, with daily engagement reaching four hours for some. People send almost a billion messages per day on Discord, contributing to the company's estimated worth of $15 billion.

The rise of remote work, the rapid growth of the gaming industry, and the burgeoning NFT and crypto markets are key factors behind Discord's continued growth. As a central hub for NFT and crypto projects, Discord has solidified its place as an integral communications platform in these communities.

Discord is the appropriate capstone case study in our discussion of ExO attributes because it is ideally positioned to lead the business world into the metaverse. Further, because it's popular with younger generations, it will likely be paradigmatic as a collaboration tool for years to come. With its commitment to Community and simplicity, and its feature-rich offerings, Discord is poised for sustained growth and influence, especially in the Web3 community.

How to Get Started with Social Technologies

Here are some steps you can take to implement Social Technologies into your ExO:

- **Employee input.** Let your employees vote on what aspects of their interactions and collaborations they want to automate. This approach not only creates a sense of ownership and buy-in but also ensures that the technologies you implement are solving real problems that your team faces.
- **Tool selection.** Pick two tools and get started. It's better to start with a few tools that your team can get comfortable with rather than overwhelming them with too many at once. Starting with a few tools also allows for easier troubleshooting and adjustments as your team adapts.
- **Virtual reality.** Join an emerging VR platform and watch the ecosystem evolve. This not only gives you firsthand experience with this cutting-edge technology but also provides insights into how it might one day be used within your own organization.
- **NFT projects.** Pick an NFT project you find exciting and join its Discord channel. This can provide insight into how these new types of communities operate and evolve. Better yet, consider launching an internal NFT collection to spark creativity, engagement, and a sense of ownership among your team.
- **Remote work experiment.** As a bonus project, have everyone work from home for two weeks. Measure output carefully during this period and compare it to in-office output. This exercise can provide valuable insights into the effect of remote work on

productivity within your team and can inform future decisions around flexible work arrangements.

Social Technologies as an Organizing Force

Social Technologies may be the ultimate gravitational force holding together the Exponential Organization. They serve as connective tissue, keeping the many diverse parts of the enterprise tightly bound to its MTP and ensuring cohesion even during the most challenging times. They enable management to keep watch on the health of the organization and its employees, keeping problems from emerging into the open when they are too late to remedy.

Using Social Technologies won't make your company an ExO—but *not* using them will keep you from becoming one.

Key Resources/Links where you can learn more

- Collaborative Software
  - https://en.wikipedia.org/wiki/Collaborative_software
- *How Discord, Born From an Obscure Game, Became a Social Hub for Young People*
  - https://www.nytimes.com/2021/12/29/business/discord-server-social-media.html
- Discord Is the World's Most Important Financial Messenger, and a Hotbed for Scammers
  - https://www.vice.com/en/article/n7n848/discord-is-the-worlds-most-importan t-financial-messenger-and-a-hotbed-for-scammers
- Frame VR virtual platform
  - https://learn.framevr.io
- Vatom
  - https://www.vatom.com/
- Social — ExO Insight
  - https://insight.openexo.com/tag/social/

15

Lessons Learned: Implications of ExOs

While the notion of an Exponential Organization may seem revolutionary to most people even today, in fact, many of its characteristics have long shown up in certain corners of the business world—most notably, Hollywood.

Why did Hollywood, 3,000 miles away from both the acting world of Broadway and the banking center of New York City, become the world capital of the film industry by the end of the 1920s? Because the West Coast was far removed from the traditional culture of the East, and with its almost unlimited cheap real estate, natural light, and pliant local government, the early film barons were free to do almost anything they wanted, including writing their own rules.

The result was the *studio system*, in which early filmmakers set out to own the entirety of their assets and their workforces, from the sets to the studios to the employees.

Even actors were contracted to single studios, and distribution was exclusive to the theaters owned by that studio.

By the 1960s, the studio system was all but dismantled due to anti-trust and other factors. It was replaced by a system that was almost its exact opposite.

Today, Hollywood operates in exactly the same loosely coupled, networked environment of an ExO ecosystem. Each participant, from the writer and actor to the director and camera grip, manages their own career. Meanwhile, agents at every level help find and connect scripts with talent, production companies, and equipment.

Currently, when a film is created, a swarm of independent entities come together for the duration of the production, operating on 24/7 schedules and in close collaboration. Once the film is finished, sets are broken down for reuse, equipment is reassigned, and all the actors, grips, and production assistants disband and scatter to pursue their next projects, which often start the very next day.

Hollywood didn't plan this metamorphosis. Rather, it evolved into an ExO-like ecosystem because it is the nature of film to be a series of discrete projects. This made Hollywood a pioneer in the virtualization of enterprises. Today, with new social and communications technologies, it is in the vanguard of the rise of the Exponential Organization.

The high-tech startup ecosystem of Silicon Valley is another example of this model: entrepreneurs, employees, scientists, marketers, patent lawyers, angel investors, venture capitalists, and even customers all operate within a small geographic region of the San Francisco Bay Area. Wall Street is a similar ecosystem. Many similar ecosystems are emerging around the world

Leveraged by new generations of technology that, according to Moore's Law, have emerged every few years, the infrastructure is now in place for many industries to move to this framework. And they *will* move and quickly—not only because it confers an enormous competitive advantage but also because the system rewards first movers.

In this chapter, we'll examine in depth some of the implications of the ExO model and ecosystem. In fact, we've identified *eighteen* key dynamics at play. Nine were documented in the original book. In this version, naturally, we've naturally doubled that to 18. Let's look at each of them in turn:

Condensed Implications from the Original ExO Book

1. Information Accelerates Everything

Everywhere you look, a new information paradigm is accelerating the metabolism of products, companies, and industries. In industry after industry, the development cycle for products and services grows ever shorter. And, like the shift from film photography to digital photography, once you change the process from a material, mechanical basis to a digital and informational one, the match is lit for an explosive acceleration of the market.

How explosive? In 1995, 710 million rolls of film were developed at thousands of processing centers. By 2005, nearly 200 billion digital photographs, the equivalent of about eight *billion* rolls, had been snapped, edited, stored, and displayed in ways that were unimaginable just a decade earlier. Today, web users upload almost five billion photographs *per day* to sites such as Snapchat, Facebook, and Instagram.[46]

---

[46] Matic Broz, "How Many Photos Are There? (Statistics & Trends in 2023)," Photutorial, August 25, 2023, https://photutorial.com/photos-statistics/.

As we saw in Chapter 1, a similar shift from analog to digital is occurring in multiple core technologies with multiplier effects at their intersections. This process of dematerializing or "virtualizing" one industry after another is advancing exponentially, at multiples, as data about different components or processes is systematically analyzed and automated by software.

2. Drive to Demonetization

One of the most important—and least celebrated—achievements of the internet is that it has cut the marginal cost of marketing and sales to nearly *zero*.

By this, we mean that with the web, it became possible to promote a product worldwide for a tiny fraction of what it cost just a few decades earlier. It is precisely this advantage that has allowed businesses such as Amazon, Alibaba, and eBay to scale with extraordinary speed to become some of the world's biggest companies.

What's important to understand is that in the age of the Exponential Organization, the exponential cost drops not only for sales and demand generation but also for the cost side, with a radical drop in the cost of supply. For example, the use of crowdsourcing and community ideation by companies like Xiaomi, GitHub, or Reddit means their product development costs approach zero.

What we're now seeing with ExOs—and this is tremendously important—is that *the marginal cost of supply goes to zero.*

A case in point: it costs Uber a pittance to add an additional car and driver to its fleet. For Airbnb, the marginal cost of adding a room to its inventory is near zero—not so for Hyatt or Hilton, who have to build an entire hotel. ExOs are able to scale their businesses with near 100% variable costs, even in traditionally capital expenditure–heavy industries.

This advantage seems obvious when it comes to information-based or information-enabled sectors. But remember: *every* industry is becoming information-based, either by being digitized or by using information to identify under-utilized assets (e.g., collaborative consumption).

In their book *Abundance*, Peter Diamandis and Steven Kotler argue that as technology brings us a world of abundance, access will triumph over ownership. They argue that technology is a "resource-liberating force" that makes available resources accessible at increasingly lower costs. By comparison, scarcity of supply or resources tends to keep costs high and stimulates ownership over access.

In traditional industries that can be fully information-enabled, new competition has produced staggering revenue drops for old companies. The business models for music, newspapers, and book publishing, for example, have all suffered through this transformation, and today these business models look almost nothing like they did ten years ago. The newspapers that have survived have largely shifted their revenue efforts to their web pages; the albums and CDs of the music industry of old have since dematerialized into Spotify playlists; and many of today's bestsellers enjoy most of their profits from e-book sales.

We believe the next industries to fall will be education, automotive, and energy. Take cars. Trends today indicate that the younger generation doesn't want to own cars. Many teenagers aren't even getting driver's licenses. By 2018, Tesla cars in autopilot driving mode had fewer accidents than human drivers driving the same distance. There's obviously some catching up to do by the insurance and regulatory side. Clearly an autonomous taxi model of payment per kilometer is coming.

Demonetization does not have to be at the product level.It can also destroy demand. At the 2016 Rio Olympic Games, for example, major construction companies started planning for the needed 60,000 hotel rooms (Where would they place new hotels? Who needed to be bribed? Etc.) And then, instead, Rio decided it had no space for a bunch of new hotels and partnered with Airbnb instead. That's 60,000 unbuilt hotel rooms.

3. Disruption is the New Norm

In his influential bestseller *The Innovator's Dilemma*, Clayton Christensen (may he rest in peace) pointed out that disruptive innovation rarely comes from the status quo. That is, established industry players are rarely structured or prepared to counter disruption when eventually it appears. The newspaper industry is a perfect example.

Today, the outsider has all the advantages. With no legacy systems to worry about, as well as the ability to enjoy low overhead and take advantage of the democratization of information and—more important—technology, the newcomer can move quickly and with a minimum of expense. Thus, new actors and entrants are well-equipped to attack almost any market and profit margin, including yours.

Indeed, change happens so fast these days that you now must *assume* that someone will disrupt you, and often from a direction you least expect. As Steve Forbes sees it, "You have to disrupt yourself or others will do it for you." This applies to every market, geography, and industry.

This pattern will take longer to impact older, capital-intensive industries such as oil and gas, mining, and construction. But have no doubt: disruption is coming. Consider that solar energy, which is powered by information technology, has been doubling in its price performance every 22 months (and has been doing so for 40 years!). In 2016, it reached grid parity in the US. In 2020, it became cheaper to build and operate a solar farm than to continue operating a comparable fossil-fuel facility.

Think about that: the capital and operating expenses of solar are now cheaper than the operating expenses alone of fossil fuels. The market share of solar and wind in global electricity generation grew at a compound average annual growth rate of 15% from 2015 to 2020. If exponential growth continues at this rate, solar and wind bills reach 45% of electricity generation by 2030 and 100% by 2033.

Here's a concrete example of the exponential growth of solar as a percentage of energy generated in the Netherlands:

- in 2012: 0.2%
- in 2014: 0.7%
- in 2016: 1.4%
- in 2018: 3.3%
- in 2020: 7%
- in 2022: 14% → A doubling every two years

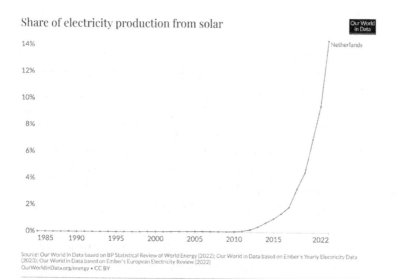

Share of electricity production from solar

Netherlands

14%

12%

10%

8%

6%

4%

2%

0%

1985   1990   1995   2000   2005   2010   2015   2022

Source: Our World In Data based on BP Statistical Review of World Energy (2022); Our World In Data based on Ember's Yearly Electricity Data (2023); Our World In Data based on Ember's European Electricity Review (2022)
OurWorldInData.org/energy • CC BY

Meanwhile, other traditional industries, including real estate, automotive, and manufacturing, are already succumbing to this new zeitgeist. Who would ever have predicted that, in just three years, a Silicon Valley team of mostly electrical and software engineers at Tesla would have created what is arguably the safest car ever built? That car would, within ten years, turn founder Elon Musk into one of the world's wealthiest (if not *the* wealthiest) individuals.

We see six sequential steps around disruptive innovation:

1. The domain, product, or service becomes partially or fully digitized (information-enabled)—for example, Teslas are updated by wireless software upgrades.
2. Marginal cost of supply drops exponentially—for example, the price of taking and uploading digital photos—and the product/service is demonetized.

3. Access to the product/service—for example, Bard and ChatGPT—is democratized.
4. Hobbyists form an open-source community, as we've seen with the massive generative AI community.
5. Technologies converge in new combinations, and new business models are birthed—for example, Web3/Metaverse combining blockchain, AI, and VR.
6. New products/services and business models—for example, the Khan Academy (with KhanAmigo)—that are orders of magnitude better and cheaper than their predecessors and thus disrupt the status quo.

We are seeing this set of steps play out in drones, DNA sequencing, 3D printing, sensors, robotics, and, certainly, bitcoin. In each domain, an open-source, networked community has sprung up, delivering an accelerated stream of innovation exactly in line with the steps above.

Further, while a dozen technologies are accelerating on their own in doubling patterns, their intersections add a whole other multiplier to this phenomenon. Take cryptography and computation: individually, each is accelerating. Put them together, and entire categories of blockchain, cryptocurrencies, and NFTs emerge.

Democratized, accelerating technologies, combined with the power of community and engagement techniques like cryptoeconomics, are converting Christensen's *Innovator's Dilemma* into an unstoppable force.

If we take healthcare as an example, Michael Friebe PhD, an OpenExO Ambassador based in Germany maintains that exponential technologies will transform the current "sick care" business model to "prevention and prediction". It will be exceedingly difficult for the encumbents to adopt these new approaches.

As a final example: in 2002, the BMW M5 E39 was the fastest sedan ever built. Twenty years later, the Lucid Air (Dream edition) is faster than the 2002 BMW, uses one-eighth of the energy, and generates three times the power for roughly the same cost. That's a 24x price-performance increase in two decades.

4. Beware the "Expert"

Ask Peter what an expert is, and he'll tell you, "An expert is somebody who tells you exactly why something can *not* be done." During these Exponential times, this has never been more true. History has shown that the best inventions or solutions rarely come from existing experts in the field; they almost always come from outsiders. It wasn't the horse-and-buggy producers who created the car. The icebox providers didn't create the refrigerator. Almost all innovation has come from thinkers who aren't domain experts, who bring a fresh perspective and don't know what can't be accomplished.

When Kaggle runs a competition, the first responders are typically experts in a particular domain who say, "We know this industry, we've done this before, and we'll figure it out." And just as inevitably, within two weeks, complete newcomers to the field trounce the experts' best results. Kaggle has run more than 200 such competitions. Incredibly, the winner has never come from the same industry as the data.

So, if experts are suspect, to whom should we turn instead? As we've already noted, everything is measurable. And the newest profession making those measurements is the data scientist. Andrew McAfee calls this new breed of data experts "geeks." He also sees the HiPPO, or "highest paid person's opinion," as the natural enemy of geeks. That's because HiPPOs still base their opinions largely on intuition. We don't believe that this is a contest that should be won completely by one side or the other. Instead, we think that when it comes to ExOs, both groups will co-exist—but with a proviso: the role of HiPPOs (or experts) will change. They will continue to be the best people to ask questions and identify key challenges, but the geeks will then mine the data to provide the solutions.

5. Death to the Five-Year Plan

One of the hallmarks of large companies (and especially governments) is the presence of strategy departments that formulate and publish five-year plans. In Japan, incredibly, they favor ten-year plans — as if they can look that far into the future of a rapidly changing world.

These multi-year strategies are supposed to outline and discipline a company's long-term vision and goals. In fact, the primary function of many corporate development departments is simply to fill in the details of that vision and provide specifics on planning, purchasing, HR, and operations.

A few decades ago, it was feasible (and important) to plan ahead that far. Companies made strategic investments by looking ahead a decade or more, and the five-year plan served as the central document outlining the implementation details of those even longer-term strategic bets. However, the world is changing so quickly that today's five-year plans have a high probability of offering the *wrong* advice for tomorrow. In an exponential world, the five-year plan is not only obsolete, it is seriously counterproductive—and the advent of ExOs signals its death.

Consider TED and its launch of TEDx events. Imagine if Chris Anderson had stood up in early 2009 and said, "Okay, folks, let's do this TEDx thing. We want to have 9,000 such events in five years." He would have instantly lost the buy-in of his team because 9,000 events would, at that moment, have sounded both insane and impossible.

Now, imagine if Anderson had asked Lara Stein, the guiding light for the TEDx brand, to actually develop a five-year plan for TEDx. A very aggressive plan by Stein might have looked like this:

Number of events per quarter

Year	Q1	Q2	Q3	Q4	Total	Comment
2009	2	8	20	40	70	Start slowly to test and learn
2010	60	30*	80	100	270	* Slower in the summer
2011	120	100	140	160	520	Steady improvement
2012	180	150	190	200	720	Starting to reach saturation
2013	200	180	220	250	850	Some variations drive increase
					2,430	Total TEDx events over five years

Even that sounds crazy: almost 2,500 events in five years? No way. In linear thinking, that goal is clearly a stretch, what James Collins and Jerry Porras termed a BHAG (Big Hairy Audacious Goal) in their 1994 classic, *Built to Last: Successful Habits of Visionary Companies.*

Yet as we now know, TED achieved much, much more. Today, more than 3,000 TEDx events take place each year! Consider the following: Had Anderson and Stein presented even the 2,500-event goal, they would have either likely triggered a mutiny among the team or have left a lot on the table. Instead, they simply plunged in and let the Community set the pace for TEDx. Indeed, Anderson, Stein, and the team had no idea they could maintain such a torrid pace until they actually did so.

In short, a five-year plan is a suicidal practice for an ExO. If it doesn't send the company racing off in the wrong direction, it can present an inaccurate picture of what lies ahead, even in the right direction.

The only solution is to establish a big vision (i.e., an MTP), put an ExO structure into place, implement a one-year plan (at most), and watch it all scale while course-correcting in real-time. That's exactly what TED did, and that's what the winning companies of the future will do as well.

In an ExO world, purpose trumps strategy, and execution beats planning. Replacing five-year plans with these new, real-time elements can be scary but also liberating, and the rewards for those willing to stay on the ride will be both decisive and astonishing. Besides, being eaten alive by an upstart competitor is anything but fun.

6. Smaller Beats Bigger

Early on in this book, we talked about Coase's Law: that larger companies do better because they aggregate assets under one roof and, as a result, enjoy lower transaction costs. We declared it dead because the information revolution plus the ExO movement has negated the need to aggregate assets in the first place. Yet business schools still focus on the management and organization of extremely large corporations (there is still no MBA program in the world that can teach you how to build AirBnB). The same big-company focus is true for consulting firms—and Wall Street has gotten rich trading the stock of giant companies, which often merge to create even more gigantic organizations.

In the coming years, adaptability and agility will increasingly eclipse size and scale. We've already discussed Airbnb, which by leveraging its users' existing assets, has achieved a valuation greater than the Hyatt Hotels chain worldwide.

Similarly, Lending Club, Bitcoin, Kickstarter, and RobinHood are forcing a radical rethinking of banking and venture capital. (No retail outlets are involved in these new financial tech startups. If you look at the new DeFi, or Decentralized Finance, world closely, you can see that retail banking will be severely threatened by the end of the decade.)

As Peter has often noted, one key advantage of a small team is that it has much less to lose than a large established organization and can therefore take on much bigger risks. As an example, we saw Vitalik Buterin and his seven co-founders create Ethereum, which peaked at a value of over half a trillion dollars. We'll suggest that 99% of banking and finance executives would never have taken on the associated risk of failure and are utterly unable to digest the speed and magnitude of the value created.

In his May 2023 newsletter, Sriram Krishnan, a partner at Andreessen Horowitz, wrote:

> The significance of smart people in small teams working on ambitious projects cannot be overstated.
>
> OpenAI is a case in point. Even with over 300 employees, OpenAI continues to operate with the agility and spirit of a very small startup. Upon speaking to several folks who are familiar with OpenAI, I am genuinely impressed by the achievements they have accomplished with projects like DALL-E and ChatGPT, despite having a relatively small team of project contributors.

ChatGPT originated as a side project from a team of 2–4 individuals. Even after the initial launch, ChatGPT only required the continuous efforts of 4–5 individuals to ensure its ongoing maintenance and enhancement until recently when the team grew. One person spearheaded the development and subsequent launch of PlugIns.

DALL-E was brought to life by 2–3 individuals who were working on a side project. This side project eventually paved the way for the creation of DALL-E.

Even if these numbers are directionally correct, I am told that this was how OpenAI operated: small teams and individuals are given the opportunity to build and have an impact.

One might wonder what the long-term defensibility and moat are. There are ongoing debates. But there is one thing we know for sure: these folks can execute.

How big can an ExO get? We hear this fundamental question regularly. The last few years have given us a clear indication that, when successful, ExOs will build on the leverage created by their externalities and turn into platforms that then turn into ecosystems. They will wire themselves into the infrastructure and start enabling other ExOs to emerge from and operate off of those platforms.

Perhaps the earliest example of this platform/ecosystem model was Google. Its search prowess allowed it to scale quickly. Once the company hit critical mass, the AdWords platform enabled self-provisioning advertising platforms from which other companies could grow. Google, in turn, took its share by taxing that growth. When the company got too big, it broke itself into smaller, integrated pieces and today we have Alphabet.

Facebook was also successful at becoming a platform, relying on its extraordinary market penetration and knowledge about its users to spawn such ExOs as Zynga and acquisitions like Instagram and WhatsApp. Amazon is another success story, as is Apple's App Store ecosystem, which is probably the clearest example of an ExO product becoming an ecosystem. It's one big coral reef.

MySpace and Friendster, on the other hand, failed to become platforms, as did Yahoo, Nokia, and Blackberry. All of those companies are dead.

For example, as Uber scales, it is helping its drivers buy cars. Uber today is a platform with a critical mass of drivers, which allows it to move horizontally and offer new services: postal, gift, grocery, and food delivery, as well as limousine and even medical services.

Now that the information asteroid of digitization, dematerialization, demonetization, and democratization has hit, the global economy has changed forever. The era of traditional, hierarchical market domination by old-breed (aka "dinosaur") companies is coming to an end. As one can see from the many examples in this book, the world now belongs to smarter, smaller, and faster-moving enterprises. This is certainly true now for information-based industries, and it will soon be true for more traditional industries as well. In the Fortune 100 Analysis of the top 10 ExOs vs. the bottom 10 ExOs, notice how much better the top 10 did during the pandemic. This same transformation will occur in non-profits and, finally, public-sector organizations. Who knows? We might finally see the advent of small government.

7. Rent, Don't Own

An important mechanism empowering individuals and small teams everywhere is variable cost access to technology, tools, and personnel.

Emblematic of this new reality is cloud computing, which offers the ability to store and manage massive amounts of information with unlimited processing, all on a cost-per-use basis requiring no upfront or capital investments. The cloud also puts small companies on the same footing as—or even gives them an advantage over—big companies, which are burdened by expensive internal IT operations. In addition, the growing body of innovative Big Data analytical tools will give all companies, big and small, an unprecedented understanding of their markets and customers.

Fablabs are small-scale workshops with equipment like 3D printers, CNC machines, and tools with which one can fabricate almost anything. Nearly 2,000 such facilities currently operate globally, giving any individual or small team the ability to rent equipment and be as capital-empowered as an established corporation. The popular payment system Square was prototyped at a fablab.

First computing, then tools and manufacturing. Today, that same rent-not-own philosophy even encompasses employees. Individual "temps" are nothing new, of course, but the concept now includes groups of temporary workers. Organizations can rent staff on demand from Gigwalk and other companies when a large amount of work needs to be done quickly, relieving them of the traditional, nightmarish practice of serial hiring and firing. In this instance, there is no distinction between "rented" staff and the ExO attribute of Staff on Demand.

Be it facilities, equipment, computing, or people, the concept of renting rather than owning is a major factor contributing to an ExO's agility and flexibility, and thus its success. This, too, can be seen as the culmination of a long-term trend. Over the decades, business owners have steadily moved from viewing business through the lens of a balance sheet to instead focusing on P&L—that is, emphasizing the primacy of profits over ownership. Much of this movement has grown out of the realization that the ownership of assets, even if mission-critical, is better handled by experts. ExOs focus only on those areas where you can add the most value, and outsource everything else.

Apple essentially rents capabilities from Foxconn to manufacture its products. And Alibaba, the Chinese e-commerce giant, allows an ExO to outsource itsentire manufacturing cycle.

8. Trust Beats Control and Open Beats Closed

As we saw with Valve Software, autonomy can be a powerful motivator in the age of the Exponential Organization. The millennial generation is naturally independent, digitally native, and resistant to top-down control and hierarchies. To take full advantage of this new workforce and hang on to top talent, companies must embrace an open environment.

Google has done just that. As we outlined earlier, its Objectives and Key Results (OKR) system is fully transparent across the company. Any Googler can look up the OKRs of other colleagues and teams to see what they're trying to achieve and how successful they've been. Such transparency takes a considerable amount of cultural and organizational courage, but Google has found that the openness it engenders is worth the discomfort.

The control frameworks used by traditional organizations were devised because the longer (and slower) feedback loops between management and teams required considerable oversight and intervention. Over the last few years, however, a new wave of collaborative tools has emerged to allow an organization to monitor each of its teams with little oversight and maximum autonomy. ExOs are learning to harness these capabilities and deliver self-management— often with extraordinary outcomes—by tracking data on a real-time basis. The most famous example of this is Slack, but another excellent example is Teamly, which combines project management, OKRs, and performance reviews with the power of an internal social network.

Another key reason that ExOs are implementing trust frameworks is that in an increasingly volatile world, predictable processes and steady, stable environments are now all but extinct. Anything predictable has been or will be automated by AI or robots, leaving the human worker to handle exceptional situations. As a result, the very nature of work is changing—and it will require more initiative and creativity from every team member. At the same time, team members often wish their organizations placed more trust in them. It is important to understand that open trust frameworks cannot be implemented in isolation or simply by fiat. Rather, they are an important consequence of implementing Autonomy, Dashboards, and/or Experimentation.

ExO community member Jerry Michalski, best known for Jerry's Brain,[47] summarizes this concept wonderfully: "Scarcity equals abundance minus trust." As we enter an abundance economy, we must figure out how to scale trust. (Hint: Web3 does just that.)

9. Everything is Measurable, and Anything is Knowable

The first accelerometers (devices used to measure motion in three dimensions) were the size of a shoebox and weighed about two pounds. Today's models measure just two

---

[47] Jerry's Brain, http://www.jerrysbrain.com/.

millimeters across, weigh almost nothing, cost about 35 cents, and are found in every smartphone on the planet.

Welcome to the sensor revolution, one of the most important and least celebrated technological revolutions of our time. A BMW automobile today has more than 2,000 sensors, tracking everything from tire pressure and fuel levels to transmission performance and sudden stops. The modern aircraft engine has as many as 3,000 sensors, measuring billions of data points per voyage.

The world's more than 8 billion mobile phones, most equipped with high-resolution cameras, can record anything and everything in real time, from a baby's first words to the events on the ground in Ukraine. Like it or not, we are hurtling towards a world of radical transparency—and losing much of our privacy to the trillions of sensors recording our every move. Beyond Verbal, an Israeli company, can analyze the tonal variations of a 10-second clip of your voice against 400 measurables to determine your mood and underlying attitude with 85% accuracy.

Add drones, which cost less than $100 a pop and can be flown at a variety of altitudes, their five-gigapixel cameras capturing everything in the landscape below. Finally, consider the several nanosatellite companies launching mesh configurations of hundreds of satellites into low-Earth orbit, which will provide real-time video and images anywhere on the planet. Given the staggering pace of technological innovation, the possibilities are endless.

On a much more intimate level, the human body has approximately 40 trillion cells operating as an ecosystem of unimaginable complexity. For all that intricacy, however, we usually track our health using just three basic metrics: temperature, blood pressure, and pulse rate. Imagine if we could measure *each one* of those 40 trillion cells—and not with just three metrics, but with a hundred? What would happen if we could track the levels of thousands of proteins in our bloodstream, organs, and tissues and correlate those levels in real time with our health, energy levels, and mental alertness? What incredible insights would we glean from analyzing these mountains of data, correlating cause and effect?

Another technology, laser spectroscopy, is currently being used to analyze food and drink for allergens, toxins, vitamins, minerals, and calories. Companies already exploring this technology's capabilities include Apple, SCiO by Consumer Physics, TellSpec, Vessyl, and Airo Health. Before long, laser spectroscopy will be used as a medical and wellness indicator, as well as to measure and track everything in our bodies, including biomarkers, diseases, viruses, and bacteria. For example, Yonatan Adiri, founder of OwnHealth, and Jon Carter, CEO of Vessel Health, both use the cloud to analyze smartphone photographs of urine test strips in order to diagnose many medical conditions.[48]

ExOs are taking advantage of this accelerating trend in two important ways: by creating new business models on existing data streams and by adding new data streams to old paradigms. As these and hundreds of other examples suggest, we are moving toward a world in which everything will be measured, and anything can be knowable, both in the world around us and within our bodies. Only enterprises that plan for this new reality will have a chance at long-term success.

---

[48] http://en.wikipedia.org/wiki/Urine_test_strip

Updated ExO Implications 2.0

10. Everything Will Be AI Enabled

Artificial intelligence will soon be embedded into every device, system, and industry, automating and optimizing them all. Along the way, almost every process will be automated and optimized.

To date, we've automated almost all manufacturing with algorithms and AI. And that's only part of the story: literally every month sees yet another domain of modern life—from credit-card fraud detection to electronic commerce recommendation systems—automating in some manner. One of the most common experiences of life today is the replacement of human operators by automated "intelligent" systems that are, in many cases, able to anticipate our needs.

But that, of course, is only the beginning. Soon, we will automate entire organizations. Everything—from strategic planning to sales, from business decisions to marketing, and almost everything in between—will be run by new generations of ever-more powerful and human-like algorithms and AI. Even what many consider the last bastion of unique human capabilities, namely creativity, is increasingly being done better, cheaper, and faster by AI. During the decade ahead, every human profession will have an "AI co-pilot" to help us to do more, faster and more accurately. In the decade that follows, expect to see a wide range of autonomous AIs independently handling services ranging from legal and architectural design to drug discovery and medical services.

If you haven't started your AI transformation, please begin now—you cannot gamble on having extra time. You need to start working towards becoming a fully AI-driven company, right now. What does that mean? It means experimenting with the leading technologies, algorithms, and systems and working to incorporate them into your business operations model. As Peter says, "At the end of this decade, there will be two kinds of companies, those that fully utilize AI, and those that are out of business."

According to Google's Bard AI, here are the leading AI platforms in 2023:

- Google AI Platform (Bard)
- Amazon SageMaker
- Microsoft Azure Machine Learning
- IBM Watson Studio
- TensorFlow
- OpenVINO
- Azure OpenAI
- Google Vertex AI
- HuggingFace
- ChatGPT/GPT-4 (OpenAI)
- Caffe

The more you think about it, the more you'll discover ways for AI to be utilized in your organization. And if you can think of those ways, be sure that somebody out there is already coming up with the algorithm to make your ideas reality.

Speaking of R&D: why can't AI come up with hypotheses and then run its own experiments—a thousand times a day? How fast can your current human scientists perform the same task with the same precision? Wouldn't you prefer to save them for really intractable problems that require impressive leaps of imagination?

AI eventually transforms the way your companies are structured. We've talked in this book about smart contracts and Decentralized Autonomous Organizations (DAOs), and how many organizations (especially in the public sector) will eventually become DAOs and be managed automatically by smart contracts. That will only be possible with AI, especially when all of the employees, suppliers, and customers operate under their own, individualized smart contracts.

Imagine a world where your network always knows the status of your people on a project, suppliers' delivery dates for parts, and customer usage of your products.

If a lot of this is new—even mind-boggling—you aren't alone. Most people, even very forward-thinking people in the business world, have little idea how far the AI revolution is going to go. Indeed, it will extend into human interaction and judgments. Now that you do understand, you have the opportunity to beat the competition to this new reality.

Why do you want to get there first? Because decentralized systems *scale*. And interfaces to that system will enable anybody to come, self-provision, and temporarily (or permanently) join the company or your community. And that, we believe, will become the operational nature of the ExO of the future.

11. Decentralization and DAOs

Several of the ExO attributes, particularly Autonomy, point to a more decentralized future for organizational design. Combining ExO attributes—MTP plus Community and Crowd, Autonomy, Interfaces, and Dashboards—enables and drives the creation of Decentralized Autonomous

Organizations. Decentralized systems scale naturally, enabled by Interfaces. Known as "Smart Contracts" in the Web3 world, these Interfaces allow anyone to self-provision to membership of a DAO.

We believe that MTP-centric DAOs will be the organizational form of the 2030s. For the first time in human history, ExOs will provide a global organizational structure to tackle grand challenges like the United Nations' Sustainable Development Goals. The enormous challenge to this development—one that will take a few years to sort out—is governance. As Austin Hill, founder of Blockstream, puts it, "DAO governance? Take the antics at an annual public company shareholders' meeting and grow it to internet scale."

12. ExOs Create Serendipity and Flow States

Ask any successful Silicon Valley founder in an authentic moment why their company popped above the competition. Most of the time, the answer you'll get is, "Luck." Just like being "discovered" in Hollywood or in the music business, luck is a tremendous, perhaps essential, factor in the success of a startup. To be sure, you must work hard, and you must be talented, but for that final push, Lady Luck often plays a part. The Roman philosopher Seneca defined luck as "where opportunity meets preparation."

ExOs maximize both opportunity and preparation. Thus, they maximize luck and serendipity. An MTP drives passion and grit. Experimentation takes the organization into uncharted territory and pushes and tests new premises. Autonomy gives team members the freedom to try (and fail). AI and Algorithms can analyze vast amounts of data and identify patterns and trends that could indicate new business opportunities.

The various ExO attributes lead to increased collaboration and cross-functional teamwork, as different parts of the organization are able to work together more closely and share information more easily. This fosters a culture of innovation and creativity, which can lead to more serendipitous discoveries.

When individuals and teams feel empowered to take risks and try new things, they are more likely to discover new ideas and opportunities that may not have been uncovered otherwise.

The decentralized nature of an ExO and its Community allows it to tap into a wide range of diverse perspectives and ideas, increasing the likelihood of making non-linear discoveries.

Eric Yuan, CEO of Zoom, struggled for years to get major traction for his company. Then the pandemic hit, and instantly millions of customers signed up. Luckily, Eric was prepared for the incredible demand that resulted and was able to scale his offering as needed. Zoom is one of the key ExOs that allowed the world to minimize the impact of COVID-19.

Steven Kotler is famous for researching and expanding the thinking around Flow States in individuals. Moving from the individual to the organizational level, ExOs create flow states in organizations. Salim often talks about Serendipity and Luck as a measurable outcomes of being in Flow.

13. Cryptoeconomics and Web3

In the 1970s, the US dollar floated off the Gold Standard. Since then, national (aka fiat) currencies are not based on assets but on debt. Debt-based systems are wonderful for expanding the economy because borrowing money increases money's velocity. However, debt-based systems rely on inflationary prices. A business can borrow $1 million, and as long as the economy grows, that same $1 million ten years later is easier to pay back. However, this all crashes if you have a deflationary economy. And what the governments didn't realize back in the 1970s was that technology is deflationary. A $1,000 TV today will be worth $500 in a year, following Moore's Law. A debt-based system is not compatible with technology deflation.

Canadian entrepreneur Jeff Booth, author of *The Price of Tomorrow*, has pointed out this weakness. "We live in a world of abundance, bounded by a financial system built on scarcity."

In a staggering observation, Jeff observes that, over the past few decades, every $1 increase in global GDP has come with an increase of $4 in debt. In other words, for decades now, we have been growing the global economy by borrowing from the future. Needless to say, this is not sustainable. And, Booth adds, this is not soft debt, like the kind you can write off with refinancing or bankruptcy. No, this is real, hard debt, the kind you can't write off. It must be paid back. But because governments are short-term thinkers, they are kicking that can down the road—and printing more money instead.

That's why Booth is excited about Bitcoin. "Bitcoin," he says, "gives you money velocity without debt."

With crypto, we now have a debt-free engine that, combined with Web3, smart contracts, and gamification, provides a new, truly democratic, financial and regulatory regime that will dominate human engagement over the next decades.

More recently, MicroStrategy CEO and Bitcoin proponent Michael Saylor (who is also Peter's fraternity brother), announced a product to deliver a Bitcoin wallet and Lightning address to every corporate account holder, enabling the quick and easy deployment of Bitcoin rewards (in the form of Sats, or Satoshis) to employees, customers, prospects, and partners. He calls the system and the methodology "MicroStrategy Lightening Rewards," a mechanism to pay for good behavior and incentivize customers' attention.

14. Technological Socialism

Don't let the title of this section scare you. "Technological socialism" is a term coined by Dr. Harry Kloor, an American scientist, filmmaker, and entrepreneur. In traditional Socialism, the "state," or the government, takes care of its citizens, providing everyone access to infrastructure and services ranging from healthcare and education to security and transportation. The inevitable problems traditional socialism faces are, first, corruption and, second, inefficiency.

However, consider that an app like Uber is actually a socialist ideal: the sharing of assets amongst people. The same applies to YouTube for entertainment and the Khan Academy for education. The difference is that an algorithm—rather than a centralized, inefficient government—matches supply and demand..

Technological Socialism refers to a future in which technology, not the government, manages the commons and serves the citizenry.

Indeed, once you learn to recognize it, you'll notice that technological socialism is emerging around us, making once expensive and scarce services available to everyone. The gig economy itself can actually be seen as a socialist endeavor, as it enables the sharing of work amongst a large group of people.

This technological ("enabled") socialism works because algorithms do the heavy lifting of hyper efficiently matching supply and demand, without the interference of human bias and corruption, and at superhuman speeds. The last is important because one of the biggest arguments against traditional socialism (as opposed to a market economy) is that a centralized system is incapable of dealing with billions of transactions per day or distributing resources fairly and effectively.

Apply this model to widely distributed, essential resources such as energy, healthcare, etc., and a whole new model for society emerges. The weakness of centralization is overcome because decision-making is distributed and networked across hundreds of thousands of sensor-equipped nodes located at the sites of production and consumption.

Technology holds the enormous opportunity not only to meet our every need but also to distribute resources most effectively to maximize happiness and productivity in society. This is what the ongoing convergence of AI, sensors, and networks will deliver. ExOs will be the how. We will be able to achieve a "small S" socialism without the materialistic soul, the obsession with class struggle, and all of those other concepts that set "big S" socialism on the wrong path.

15. Data Driven Leadership

Twentieth-century leadership, like the thousand years of leadership before it, was driven from domain expertise. People were put into positions of leadership because, starting with a relevant education, they had significant experience in that field, leading to a deep intuition.

Thus, if you were the supply chain head for all of BMW, it was because you had run the company's supply chain operation for one of its divisions (e.g., the Americas), and before that, perhaps a supply chain department for one specific car model.

In other words, you had basically grown up through the ranks of that one specialty. And now you run the supply chain globally because you know which manufacturer can deliver components on time, and which supplier has the highest component reliability—and which suppliers are waiting in the wings if those companies fail.

In the hyper-fast exponential economy, however, those rules have changed. There is little time for gut decisions and leadership based on years of experience. The modern leader needs to be *evidentiary*. That is, he or she needs to be more data-driven to find the optimal decision, more willing to use the power of technology under the umbrella of a company's MTP for high-speed Experimentation, and have a perpetually updated domain knowledge that is purpose-, not relationship-driven.

In an increasingly accelerating, globalized, and competitive world, successful leaders will make decisions based on data gathered from all sources possible, ranging from their in-house experiments to customer feedback and the Internet of Things.

The leader's mindset will be key.. Specifically, do they have an abundance, exponential, moonshot, and purpose-driven mindset that allows them to react quickly to challenges and opportunities?

For that reason, the most successful leadership will depend upon imagining meaningful experiments, asking deep and useful questions, and then figuring out how and where to get the data to answer those questions. As Peter frequently says, "In the coming future, it's not what you know, but rather *the quality of the questions you ask* that will be most important."

It follows that, in the future, almost all leadership decisions will be data-driven and evidentiary to deal with an increasingly volatile world. We have already seen this with the Internet. A marketing specialist with 20 years of experience find their skills not just useless in this new world, but worse than useless because they're trying to bring old paradigms to a new gunfight.

So, what does data driven leadership mean in practice?

It means regularly running A/B tests in all of your digital interactions, whether on your website to measure clickthroughs or on your consumer app to measure attention.

16. Transformation of the C-Suite

Two transformations will occur for every C-suite that aspires to be an ExO (which means all companies).

- **COO > CXO.** The rise of Autonomy will mean a reduced role for the operational aspects of a company and its COO. The role of the COO will transform into the CXO, or Chief Exponential Officer. She will be charged with relentlessly implementing all Exponential attributes.
- **Chief AI Officer.** As we mentioned in the AI and Algorithms chapter, every ExO will need a Chief AI Officer in charge of monitoring the latest emerging companies, apps, and AI strategies, and determining which are of the greatest value to different parts of the company. The Chief AI Officer builds partnerships, acquired licenses, and trains employees. She also advises on how and where to flow in AI at every level of the ExO.

17. Unbundling and Rebundling

Twentieth-century organizations were centered largely around profits, government agencies, or nation-centric NGOs. Twenty-first-century organizations will be centered around Sustainable Development Goals in pursuit of Global Grand Opportunities.

To accomplish that, traditional organizations will need to unbundle the existing "stacked" structures of their organizational charts. They will instead need to rebundle themselves around MTPs and global challenges.

Consider the recent history of the banking industry. As FinTech expert Chris Skinner notes, banking until recently meant a one-stop shopping solution. The typical bank offered everything from investing to private wealth management to savings, checking, and home mortgages.

This model, dominant for centuries, is breaking up. New technology start-ups began to appear on the scene around the turn of the century. Consumers could go to PayPal to make payments, to mortgage.com to finance a home, and to Quickbooks for a small business loan. Today, the once monolithic banking industry has fragmented into thousands of companies. Banking has become unbundled. And customers can now *re*bundle them: creating customized packages of services to fit their specific needs for specific projects.

Organizations in many other industries have been similarly traditionally bundled. Think of a single organization with multiple operations: HR, legal, finance, sales and marketing, and so forth. This historic organizational scheme may seem inevitable, but that's what we thought about banking. The fact is, in the future, as we move to an abundance economy and profit-driven organizations become less necessary, we'll unbundle those anachronistic structures too—and rebundle them to fit our new interests, such as SDGs.

Of course, those rebundled pieces will be largely AI-driven, enabling hyper-rapid scaling. You won't be surprised to learn that the companies best suited today to lead the move to unbundled/rebundled enterprises are ExOs—and they will do so with the help of their Communities.

18. Government Departments as ExOs

Salim has joked for years that "exponential government" is an oxymoron. Peter's face always grimaces when he talks about the 11 years it took to get FAA clearance for Zero-G flights. Indeed, a government is about as sluggish as any organization can get. But this is all changing, and very quickly. We will explore this much more in our third book of this series, but let's give it a quick look here:

- **MTP.** The purpose of government, to serve the people, is a natural MTP.
- **Staff on Demand or Community and Crowd.** Well, that's easy because it's the citizenry.
- **Algorithms and AI.** With the data available in the public sector, this is a rich area to explore.

We could continue, but you get the idea. It turns out that the 2014 ExO book is being used by dozens of governments. We mentioned earlier how Nishan Degnarain, a key advisor to the Mauritius government, designed the Ministry of Oceans on the ExO model. Why? According to Nishan, "The water borders of Mauritius are over two million square kilometers. It was impossible to cover that area with a traditional linear model. The ExO model was mandatory."

In 2014, Salim was invited to address the US Republican National Leadership Conference. After some back-and-forth, the title of the talk was settled: "How to drop the cost of government 10 times in 10 years." With today's technologies and techniques, it's eminently possible.

Perhaps the best example of an Exponential service in government comes from India, which has deployed UPI: the Unified Payments Interface. UPI is an alternative payment system that is secure, reliable, and interoperable among different payment companies. This technology is being adopted by many countries as it works well for a large population and has an open protocol. UPI aims to create a neutral, low-cost, and accessible marketplace and commerce platform. UPI already processes more than $100 USD billion a month and is used by hundreds of millions of people.

We expect to see hundreds of examples of public-sector ExOs in the near future. The use of the ExO model by governments might have the biggest global impact of all.

• • •

Now that we've examined the attributes and implications of ExOs, we turn to the exceedingly important topic of building an ExO and implementing these ideas. From the start, we have been committed to making this book not just an intellectual exercise in documenting this new phenomenon but also a prescriptive guide to implementing the ExO model.

16

Building an ExO

From the dawn of the internet, we've seen continuous and fundamental changes in how businesses are built and scaled. In particular, the earliest playbooks for building a hyper-growth company emerged during the dot-com boom of 1995 to 2001. Those narratives gained a new chapter in 2005 with the rise of social media. Then, 2008 saw yet another chapter thanks to the widespread availability of low-cost cloud computing and the launch of the iPhone.

Today, we are witnessing an accelerated transformation of the business world with the rise of the Exponential Organization. Driven by the convergence of exponential technologies, ExOs allow us to organize ourselves in new ways to tap into this information-enabled world.

Case Study: Thrasio

Carlos Cashman, a Boston-based entrepreneur, was running OrionCKB—an online marketing agency—when he and his co-founder Josh Silberstein noticed that e-commerce companies were being built by smaller and smaller teams of entrepreneurs building small e-commerce companies.

When Cashman and Silberstein examined the e-commerce companies they were promoting, they realized that many of the companies, while solid business ideas, lacked the critical mass needed for success on the web. So, together they formulated the idea to systematically buy the companies they thought most promising and then promote them on the Amazon Marketplace.

Along the way, they discovered AI software that could analyze products listed on the Amazon Marketplace and predict their future sales. The team then saw an exponential trend: 35 such businesses were sold in 2017, and that number doubled a year later.

In mid-2018, Cashman and Silberstein bought their first company, raising "friends & family" money to do so. By the end of that year, they had acquired seven businesses and crossed $1m in pro-forma sales. In 2019, they acquired over 40 companies. At an Amazon Marketplace conference, they put up a sign reading "We buy $1M businesses"... and had people lined up around the block. In 2020 the company, Thrasio, quintupled its revenue run rate. By the end of 2021, Thrasio's pro-forma revenues were more than $1 billion, with more than 200 brands and thousands of products.

How big is the opportunity Cashman and his team uncovered? On the Amazon Marketplace in 2021, third-party sellers sold $400 billion of products. More than 60 thousand were enjoying sales greater than $1 million per year.

Using this unique data-driven analytical approach, Thrasio crossed the one-billion-dollar revenue run rate—*less than three years after its launch.* It is a 21st-century CPG company (Consumer Packaged Goods) like Unilever or P&G. Thrasio has created an entirely new industry, is completely data-driven, and thus extremely low risk, at least on the market side. At startup events around the world, new startups are already saying, "We are the Thrasio of X."

Ignition

With Thrasio pointing the way, it is now time to discuss how to build an Exponential Organization. One caveat, however: This is not meant to be an exhaustive startup manual. Rather, we'll discuss the elements relevant to building an ExO that is leveraged by information and is highly scalable, either as a pure startup or from within an existing enterprise.

(A quick but relevant side note here: We strongly recommend, as an accompaniment to this chapter, reading *The Lean Startup* by Eric Ries. [1] We'll be referring to it frequently. In fact, the best definition we've found for a startup comes from Ries: "A startup is a human institution designed to deliver a new product or service under conditions of extreme uncertainty.")

Other books we highly recommend for exponential entrepreneurs include:

- *Zero to One - Peter Thiel and Blake Masters*
- *Startup Owners Manual - Bob Dorf and Steve Blank*
- *The Art of the Impossible - Steven Kotler*
- *BOLD: How to Go Big, Create Wealth and Impact the World - Peter Diamandis and Steven Kotler*

This is the best time in the history of business to build a new enterprise. The confluence of breakthrough technologies, acceptance (and even celebration) of entrepreneurship, different crowdsourcing options, crowdfunding opportunities, and legacy markets ripe for disruption have combined to create a compelling (and unprecedented) scenario for new company creation. Furthermore, traditional risk areas have been mitigated like never before. Continuing our earlier asteroid/dinosaur analogy: the asteroid has struck, the dinosaurs are teetering, and the conditions are ripe for a new category of small, furry mammal to thrive. A Commercial Cambrian Explosion, if you will.

When assessing a startup for funding, investors typically categorize three major risk areas:

- **Technology Risk:** Can you build the tech and make it work?
- **Market Risk:** Will people buy the product for your target price? Is there a need and product/market fit?
- **Execution/Team Risk:** Is the team able to function and pivot as needed?

The challenge facing every startup lies in discovering how to de-risk each of these areas—and, in the process, find a business model right for the chosen problem space. Nothing is more important. Let's look at each of these three risk areas in turn.

Technology Risk

In 1995, it cost about $15 million to build a software startup based in Silicon Valley. That money mostly went to building

server stacks, purchasing software, and hiring staff to configure and manage all of that technology, purchase bandwidth,
and write new code.

By 2005, the cost of all this had dropped to about $4
million. Servers were cheaper, and software—now often
open-sourced—was easier to develop and configure. Most
hard costs became focused on marketing and sales.

Today, with well-established capabilities, such as cloud
computing and social media, that same effort averages about
$12,000.[49] The technology risk that was once enormous (par-
ticularly in software) has been reduced over the last twenty
years by more than a thousand times. Most of the remaining
risk involves mere scalability issues.

A case in point: the rise of standardized web services.
These allow complex software functionality to be integrated
into a startup merely at the press of a button. Examples
include Google's Prediction API for predictive analytics and AlchemyAPI's deep learning software for pattern
recognition.

To illustrate the sheer magnitude and pervasiveness of
this reduced technology risk, consider hardware startups.
A new wave of large companies in Shenzhen, China (e.g.,
Foxconn, Flex, PCH International), as well as open-source
hardware platforms such as Arduino, Raspberry Pi, and 3D
printers, now allows anyone to design a hardware product
and quickly prototype and build it.

Liam Casey, the CEO of PCH, has aggressively turned
his company into a platform upon which anyone can create
the equivalent of an App Store for hardware startups. Brady

---

[49]   SaaS Academy, "5 Overlooked SAAS Startup Costs," SaaS Academy
       Training Courses to Scale Your SaaS Business, https://www.saas-
       academy.com/blog/saas-startup-costs.

Forrest, formerly head of Highway1, a PCH incubator, put it simply: "We want hardware to be as easy as software." Indeed, hardware is increasingly dissolving into software.

According to entrepreneur Chris Dixon, the most important change for entrepreneurs today versus a decade ago is the ratio of "reach to capital"—that is, how efficiently investment money can be used. Today, the reach of a startup is 100x larger, while the capital needed is one-tenth that of a decade ago—a thousandfold improvement in just a decade. One simple example is the cost of genome sequencing. In 2001, $100 million of capital would purchase you the sequencing of one single genome. Today as the cost of sequencing is approaching $100 per sequence, $100 million of capital would deliver you 1 million genome sequences.

The result is that technology risk, particularly for largely information-based or information-enabled businesses, has all but evaporated. (Needless to say, if instead, you want to build a supertanker, you will still need some capital.)

Market Risk

As to whether anyone will buy your product, we turn once again to Steve Blank, who famously said, "No business plan survives first contact with the customer." Historically, one had to first commission classic market research, fully build the product or service, hire an expensive salesforce, and then spend time and money marketing the idea—all before ever really knowing the answer to the question: Will it sell?

The Internet took a giant bite out of that paradigm, and the emergence of social media took another. Starting in the 2000s, startups could test the market ahead of time like never before. They did so by leveraging A/B testing, Google AdWords campaigns, social media, and landing pages.

Suddenly, an idea could be largely validated before product engineering even began.

Newer concepts, such as Minimum Viable Product and Product/Market Fit, furthered decreased Market Risk.

Today, the epitome of market validation is crowdfunding. Fundraising sites such as Kickstarter and Indiegogo allow users to pre-purchase a product. If enough people pre-purchase, the website releases money to the developer. This democratization of the fundraising process makes crowdfunding very compelling.

Execution/Team Risk

Of the three major risk areas, execution/team risk remains the only real issue in building a company. In particular, how will the enterprise organize itself to maximize performance? Can it find the right talent to execute its goals? Can it properly leverage technology and information to create a unique and sustainable advantage and business model?

Answering these questions correctly is the key to building a successful Exponential Organization. For this reason, we need to look more closely at each of the steps in building a powerful and effective ExO.

Lee's Unicorns

In 2013, Aileen Lee published an extensive overview in *TechCrunch* of US-based software startups with a market value of more than $1 billion—a group of companies she called "Unicorns."

These days, the concept of a Unicorn is more expansive. But Lee's findings are even more relevant for classic vertical markets and sectors as well. While we recommend reading her entire article, Lee's key findings as they pertain to ExOs are as follows:

- It takes more than seven years, on average, before a "liquidity event."
- Inexperienced twenty-something founders are outliers. Companies with well-educated thirty-something co-founders with a history together tend to be most successful.
- The idea of a "big pivot" to a different product after startup seems to occur rarely. Most successful Unicorns stick to their original vision (i.e., their founding MTP).

We have found a strong correlation between ExOs and Lee's Unicorns. In fact, using our diagnostic, most of Lee's Unicorns score well above the ExO threshold score. Their relatively young age means these Unicorn companies have been leveraging new information streams, have a low cost of supply, and embrace community—and thus can scale. Most have achieved their current heights by following some combination of the 12 steps described in the next section.

The 12 Steps of Starting a Successful EXO

The following steps provide a tried-and-true process for building an ExO. While we have updated some of the details, the sequence of steps has proved exceptionally powerful over the years. Perhaps for the first time in business history, we have a prescriptive path to building purpose-driven, scalable organizations.

Step 1: Select an MTP (Massive Transformative Purpose)

We have already covered this extensively in Chapter 4, but it is worth revisiting, as this is the most fundamental and foundational aspect of a startup.

Following up on Simon Sinek's "Why?" question: it is critical that you are excited and utterly passionate about the problem space you plan to attack. So, begin by asking this question: What is the biggest problem you would like to see solved? Only after you identify that problem space can you come up with an MTP to solve it. Even as a child, Elon Musk, perhaps the world's most celebrated entrepreneur today, had a burning desire to address energy, transportation, and space travel at a global level. His companies (SolarCity, Tesla, SpaceX) are each addressing those spaces. Each has a Massive Transformative Purpose.

The act of finding an MTP can be seen as the consequence of asking yourself the following series of questions:

- What do I deeply care about? What problem do I want to solve? What amazing thing do I want to create?
- What am I meant to do? At the end of my life, what will I be most proud to have achieved?
- What would I do if I could never fail?
- What would I do if I received a billion dollars today and had to spend it on making the world a better place?

Keep in mind that MTP is not only about you as an entrepreneur and your goals. It is also about your employees. PayPal co-founder Peter Thiel poses the following question to test if a startup has an MTP that will attract not only friends but also employees who share your motivation: "Why would the 20th employee join your startup without the perks, [such as] a co-founder title or stock [options]?" At some point in the company's future, most of your employees will not be high-ranking nor own much company stock. What will keep them engaged in their jobs and loyal to the company? It must be the MTP; they must buy the dream.

Accordingly, you should gauge your MTP against each of the acronym's letters: Is it truly Massive? Would others characterize it as Transformative? Is it intrinsically Purposeful?

A profit motive alone is insufficient to build an ExO—or, frankly, any startup. Rather, it's the burning passion to solve an obsessive, complex problem that keeps an entrepreneur pushing forward through the ebullience and despair that is the story of every startup. Chip Conley, an expert at building purpose-driven companies such as Airbnb, frequently references Kahlil Gibran: "Work is love made visible. The goal is not to live forever; the goal is to create something that will."

An MTP doesn't necessarily have to be, to continue the metaphor, a Mars-shot. It also can be transformational for a vertical industry or for a region. An example is Grab's MTP: "Empowering Southeast Asia with technology." With this guiding MTP, Grab has become the biggest Unicorn in that part of the world.

Another example is Infarm. Its MTP is "Feeding the Cities of Tomorrow." Infarm is the world's fastest-growing urban farming company, offering an Agriculture-as-a-Service business model. The company provides modular units that grow food on supermarket aisles and inside restaurants. Infarm uses 95% less water, 90% less transportation, and zero chemical pesticide compared to soil-based agriculture. Moreover, the electricity used throughout the Infarm network comes from renewable energy. To date, the Infarm network has saved more than 40,000,000 liters of water and 50,000 square meters of land.

Step 2: Join or Create Relevant MTP Communities

The collaborative power of communities is critical to any ExO. Your MTP is the starting point for galvanizing a community—better yet, building your own community around your MTP.

If you do not have the resources to build a community, then, whatever your passion (let's say you dream of curing cancer), there already are communities out there filled with other passionate, purpose-driven people devoted to the same crusade. For example, some of the many communities devoted to cancer or heart disease research include TEDMED, Health Foo, DIYbio, GET (Genes/Environments/Traits), WIRED Health, Sensored, Stream Health, Life Itself, and NextMed.

The rise of the Quantified Self (QS) movement is a great example of a community with an MTP. Beginning with just a handful of cities with a few thousand members, today, there are thousands of QS meetup groups worldwide with more than 100,000 members. Or consider Livekindly.com. It is a plant-based food community that aims to change the global food system.

If you think your problem space doesn't have community support, take a look at www.meetup.com. Meetup's mission is to revitalize local communities and help people around the world organize. The company believes that people can change the world by organizing themselves into groups that are powerful enough to make a difference. Founded by Scott Heiferman, Meetup helps convene more than 150,000 interest-based groups—made up of about ten million members—in 197 countries around the world. Given those numbers, the odds are pretty good that a passionate and purpose-driven community concerned with your problem space already exists in your own country.

Note, however, in any community-driven startup, there will be tension between the good of the community and the good of the company. For Chris Anderson, the choice is easy: "Are you primarily a community, or are you primarily a company? The reason you must ask yourself this is because, sooner or later, the two will come in conflict. We [DIY Drones] are primarily a community. Every day, we make decisions that disadvantage the company to bring advantage to the community."

Anderson says that his choice to opt for the good of the community came from Matt Mullenweg, the CEO of WordPress. According to Mullenweg, "Whenever this moment comes up, always bet on the community because that's the difference between long-term thinking and short-term thinking."

The lesson is: If you get the community right, opportunities will arise. If you get the community wrong, the engine of innovation dissolves, and you won't even have a company anymore.

Step 3: Compose a Team

While the founding team in any startup is important, given the rapid scaling of an ExO company—with its very small footprint in terms of resources—the careful composition of its founding team is especially critical.

The key to putting together a successful ExO founding team is that everyone must share a passion for the MTP. Ben Horowitz, a co-founder of Andreessen-Horowitz, one of the world's most successful VCs, noted the importance of shared passion in his recent book, *The Hard Thing About Hard Things: Building a Business When There Are No Easy Answers*: "If founders are in a startup for the wrong reasons (money, ego), it often degenerates into a nasty situation."

The following roles are critical if a founding ExO team is to deliver diverse backgrounds, independent thought, and complementary skills:

- **Visionary/Dreamer:** This individual's primary role is devising and revising the company's story. The founder with the strongest vision for the company comes up with the MTP—then holds the organization to it. This role will drive future hires in marketing and sales.
- **User Experience Design:** This role focuses on users' needs and ensures that every contact with users is as intuitive, simple, and clear as possible.
- **Programming/Engineering:** This person is responsible for bringing together the various technologies required to build the product or service.
- **Finance/Business:** The business function assesses the viability and profitability of the organization, is the cornerstone of interactions with investors, and manages the all-important burn rate.

In *The Innovator's DNA: Mastering the Five Skills of Disruptive Innovators*, co-author Clayton Christensen approaches the skill portfolio question slightly differently, identifying two distinct sets of skills:

- **Discovery Skills:** The ability to generate ideas—to associate, question, observe, network and experiment.

- **Delivery Skills:** The ability to execute ideas—to analyze, plan, implement, follow through, and be detail-oriented.

These are just two of many ways to put a founding team together. Whatever the approach, however, founders must intrinsically be motivated self-starters. Most of all, in the face of rapid growth and change, founding team members must have complete trust in one another's judgment. Let's also remember the leverage brought by ChatGPT and similar tools

Consider the PayPal story. Peter Thiel told his co-founders (Elon Musk, Reid Hoffman, Luke Nosek, Max Levchin, and Chad Hurley) that they all should work together as friends rather than more formally as employees. That concept famously cascaded into their hiring process—the company regularly sourced employees from amongst the friends of their current employees. Not only was PayPal very successful as a company (it was sold to eBay for $1.2 billion in 2002), but the friendships that grew out of it were equally successful. The original team is now known as the "PayPal Mafia," and its members have helped one another on subsequent startups, including Tesla, YouTube, SpaceX, LinkedIn, Yelp, Yammer, and Palantir—companies that today have a total market cap approaching two trillion dollars.

The pace of growth of an ExO places an extra emphasis on a fully synergistic core team. As Arianna Huffington says, "I would rather have somebody much less brilliant and who's a team player, who's straightforward, than somebody who is very brilliant and toxic to the organization."

Step 4: Breakthrough Idea

This next step is a big one: finding your breakthrough, disruptive idea.

It is essential to leverage technology or information in some way to massively transform the status quo. And when we say massively transform, we really do mean it. ExOs are not about incremental improvement in a marketplace. They are about breakthrough impact. According to Marc Andreessen, "Most entrepreneurs prefer failing conventionally rather than succeeding unconventionally." Don't be one of them.

Remember, the two key success factors for an ExO idea are:

- First, a minimum 10x improvement over the status quo.
- Second, leverage information to radically cut the cost of marginal supply (i.e., the cost to expand the supply side of the business should be minimal).

So, where do you look to find your disruptive or breakthrough idea? There are a multitude of approaches to consider.

1. Address your MTP by Applying Converging Exponential Technologies to a new marketplace or service area.

Let's look at an analogy from the turn of the 20th century, the application of electricity to common products. In 1882, Thomas Edison founded the Edison Electric Illuminating Company of New York to bring electric light to parts of Manhattan. But progress was slow. Most Americans would still light their homes with gaslight and candles for another fifty years. Only in 1925 did half of all homes in the U.S. have electric power. And as that revolution materialized, it became common for the disruption of products, services, and industries to occur as entrepreneurs electrified everything. Beyond electrifying lighting, they electrified clothes-washing machines, dish-washing machines, and hand-held drills and saws. The dominant business model was simple: "Add electric motors to replace human labor."

These days, we are seeing a wave of disruptions and breakthroughs as entrepreneurs apply multiple converging exponential technologies into existing slow-to-change markets. During 2023, the application of Generative AI to every field is birthing tens of thousands of startups. In addition, DeFi is attacking financing and banking, Web3 is hitting the future of gaming and education, and a combination of AI, Sensors, networks, and biotech is re-inventing healthcare.

Remember, your breakthrough business idea doesn't need to be a new technology; it can be a new business model. In fact, most of the most exciting companies of the coming decade are going to come from business model innovations rather than new technologies, as will be discussed below in Step-6.

2. Look at the coming disruptive meta-trends and see if your MTP fits inside one of them.

At the start of this book, we looked at the top 10 technological metatrends that are coming as a result of converging exponentials. To refresh your memory, here's a quick list:

1. The Rise of AI & Intelligence.
2. AI, Robotic & Human Collaboration.

3. Global gigabit connectivity (ground & space-based) connecting everyone and everything, everywhere, at an ultra-low cost.
4. Web3 & Metaverse transforming retail, education, and human interactions.
5. Autonomous vehicles and flying cars (eVTOL) redefining human travel, making it increasingly faster and cheaper.
6. CRISPR, Gene Therapy & Increasing Healthspan (20+ years).
7. Extending the human healthspan by 10-20+ years.
8. Cellular agriculture & vertical farming providing cheaper, healthier, high-quality food grown locally.
9. Energy becoming globally abundant, cheap, and renewable.
10. Sustainability and the Environment.

Another fertile area to find your MTP is to search within the context of the UN Sustainable Development Goals (SDGs) & the Grand Global Challenges.

The idea of delaying your "breakthrough idea" until the fourth step of the process may seem counterintuitive to many entrepreneurs... After all, isn't it the case that most legends hold that startups begin with an explosive new idea that's then applied to a problem space? We firmly believe, however, that it is far better to start with a passion to solve a particular problem rather than to start with an idea or a technology.

There are two reasons for this. First, by focusing on the problem space, you are not tied to one particular idea or solution—and thus, you won't end up trying to shoehorn a technology into a problem space where it might not be a good fit. Silicon Valley is littered with the carcasses of companies with great technologies searching for a problem to solve. Second, there is no shortage of great ideas or promising new technologies. After all, everybody in a place like Silicon Valley has an idea for a new tech business.

Instead, the key to success is relentless execution, hence the need for passion and an MTP. Your goal is to be so enamored with solving a problem that you refuse to give up on your purpose. To demonstrate, consider the number of times the founders of the following companies pitched investors before finally succeeding:

Company	Number of Investor Pitches before Getting Funded
Skype	40
Cisco	76
Pandora	300
Google	350

What if Larry Page and Sergey Brin had stopped pitching investors after 340 attempts? The world would be a very different place today. Just as intriguing: what magical technologies and businesses don't exist today because the founders gave up one investor pitch too soon?

We've said this already, but it can't be emphasized enough: *Entrepreneurial success rarely comes from the idea. The idea is the easy part!* Instead, it comes from the founding team's never-say-die attitude and relentless execution. Those who really want something will find options. Those who just 'kind of' want it will find reasons and excuses. This has been the case since Hewlett and Packard started their business in that now-famous Palo Alto dirt-floor garage—where, don't forget, they began with a passion and not a product. In the end, only raw, unbridled passion can solve an important problem and overcome the endless hurdles that present themselves.

PayPal co-founder Peter Thiel builds on this with a profound question for startup founders: "Tell me something you believe is true but [that] you have a hard time trying to convince others [of]." This is about conviction and passion on the one hand and radical, unconventional, breakthrough ideas on the other. As Peter Diamandis is fond of saying, "The day before something is truly a breakthrough, it's a crazy idea."

To illustrate: Salim once asked Elon Musk about his Hyperloop concept: "Elon, I have a background in physics, and it seems impossible to accelerate humans to 6,000 kilometers an hour and then decelerate them to zero in such a short space of time. That might kill a human being. Have you thought about that?"

Musk's answer? "Yes, it's an issue."

To a true entrepreneur, there are no impossibilities, just barriers to overcome. (And yes, it turned out there is a solution to that particular hyperloop physics problem—quite an easy one, in fact—via fluid dynamics.)

It is critical in an ExO for the founder to be a newcomer to that domain. As Peter Diamandis notes in one of his Peter's Laws: "An expert is someone who can tell you exactly how it cannot be done." Note that Elon Musk had no traditional education or previous work experience in the Space, Energy, or Automotive sectors when he set out on his corporate ventures. Yet, starting with first principle thinking, a few textbooks, and smart hires in his companies, has created market-leading companies in each of these areas. Likewise, the eight co-founders of Ethereum had no background in cryptocurrencies.

Step 5: Build a Business Model Canvas and ExO Canvas

Once a core idea or breakthrough has been identified, the next step is to elaborate on *how to get it to market*. Our suggested tool for this is the Business Model Canvas (BMC), which was created by Alexander Osterwalder[u] and has been popularized by the Lean Startup model. As shown below, you begin the process by diagramming the various components of the model like value propositions, customer segments, etc. [A warning: At this early stage, it is important that the BMC be simple and not overthought. Experimentation will then help navigate the best path and provide the next level of fidelity.]

After the BMC, it's important to fill out the ExO Canvas. This starts with stating your MTP and listing the information streams that can be leveraged. Then you document how you would apply each of the SCALE and IDEAS attributes. Finally, you list the implementation steps.

Massive Transformative Purpose (MTP)			
Information	Staff on Demand	Interfaces	Implementation
	Community	Dashboards	
	Algorithms & Artificial Intelligence	Experiments	
	Leveraged Assets	Autonomy	
	Engagement	Social Technologies	
ExO Canvas			

Step 6: Find a Business Model

It is important to understand that if you're going to achieve a 10x improvement, there's a strong likelihood that your company will require a completely new business model. As Peter has noted, the most exciting aspect of converging exponential technologies is how they will re-invent business models in the decade ahead. For example, imagine if fire insurance was used to prevent fires rather than paying you after your house burns down. Or if life insurance was to ensure you stay alive rather than pay your next of kin after you're dead.

As the late great Clayton Christensen illustrated in *The Innovator's Dilemma* (1997), disruption is mostly achieved when a startup offers a less expensive product using emerging technologies to meet a future or unmet customer need or niche. Christensen emphasized that it is not so much about the disruptive products themselves but more about new business models threatening incumbents. These days, we are finding that new business models typically include turning into platforms, then ecosystems, and finally, protocols. [In a conversation with Salim, Christensen acknowledged that his model didn't account for cross-industry disruptions like Uber.]

For example, Southwest Airlines treated its planes like buses and created an entire niche market for itself in low-cost, no-frill air travel. Google created the AdWords business model, which never existed before the advent of web pages.

How can you take an existing business and transform the delivery, pricing, personalization, and/or timing of the product or service so it is distinctly better? Think Netflix versus Blockbuster, both gave you access to movies, but Netflix brought the movies into your home, first as a mail order business sending DVDs and then streaming. Netflix flourished, and Blockbuster, which stuck to its old model of store-centric distribution, went bankrupt.

In his 2005 book, *Free: The Future of a Radical Price*, Chris Anderson expanded upon the lower cost positioning of the disruptor, noting that pretty much all business models—and certainly those that are information-based—will soon be offered to consumers for free. The popular "freemium" model is just such a case: many websites offer a basic level of service at no cost while also enabling users to pay a fee to upgrade to more storage, statistics, or extra features. Advertising, cross-subsidies, and subscription business models are other ways of layering profit-generating operations on top of what is essentially free baseline information.

Kevin Kelly expanded on this idea in a seminal post entitled "Better than Free," which appeared on his Technium blog in 2008. In digital networks, anything can be copied and is thus "abundant." So how do you add or extract value? What is valuable for customers? What is the new scarcity? What are the new value drivers? Kelly identified eight ways to build a business model when the underlying information is free:

1. **Immediacy**: Immediacy is the reason people order in advance on Amazon or attend the theater on opening night. Being the first to know about or experience something has intrinsic cultural, social, and even commercial value. In short: time confers privilege.

2. **Personalization**: Having a product or service customized just for you not only gives added value in terms of quality of experience and ease-of-use or functionality, but it also creates "stickiness," as both parties are invested in the process.

3. **Interpretation**: Even if the product or service is free, there is still considerable added value to any service that can help shorten the learning curve to using it— or using it better. Kelly often jokes: "Software: free; the manual: $10,000."

4. **Authenticity**: Added value comes from a guarantee that the product or service is real and safe. That it is, in Kelly's words, "bug-free, reliable, and warranted."

5. **Accessibility**: Ownership requires management and maintenance. In an era where we own hundreds of apps on multiple platforms, any service that helps us organize everything and improve our ability to find what we need quickly is of particular value.

6. **Embodiment**: Digital information has no "body," no physical form until we give it one—high definition, 3D, a movie screen, or a smartphone. We willingly pay more to have free software delivered to us in the physical format we prefer.

7. **Patronage**: "It is my belief that audiences *want* to pay creators," Kelly wrote. "Fans like to reward artists, musicians, authors, and the like with tokens of their appreciation because it allows them to connect. But they will only pay if it is very easy to do, the amount is reasonable, and they feel certain the money will directly benefit the creators." He adds that another benefit of a simple payment process is that it capitalizes on users' impulsiveness. Examples include iTunes songs and Spotify, as well as Netflix subscriptions. Customers choose to pay for each of these services even though the same content can be acquired through piracy.

8. **Findability**: A creative work has no value unless its potential audience can find it. Such "findability" only exists at the aggregator level, as individual creators typically get lost in the noise. Thus, attaching yourself to effective channels and digital platforms, such as app stores, social media sites, or online marketplaces where potential users can find you, has considerable value to creators (and, ultimately, to users).

We believe that Kevin has identified the business models of the 21st century. If you examine most information-based businesses, you'll find one or more of the eight embedded in them.

• • •

Let's return to the Business Model Canvas—and specifically *partnering*, which is one of its most productive features.

Fred Wilson of Union Square Ventures has shown that many incumbents in different industries are currently being disrupted—and not by just one startup but by many different startups all attacking one individual service within an industry. Wilson sees major disruption in business models as either "unbundling" or "re-bundling."

Here's what he means: a classic bank offers many services such as payment infrastructure, trust, mobile and social wallets, e-commerce and m-commerce solutions, lending, investments, stocks, etc. It is a consolidated or aggregated offering of different individual financial services. Those banks are now being disrupted by a variety of financial startups, including Square, Stripe, Wise, Lending Club, Robinhood, Kickstarter, eToro, Estimize, and more recently, DeFI (or Decentralized Finance). We consider this fragmentation of individual financial services a form of unbundling.

Now, what if all these startups decide to cooperate or merge within the next five years? What if they agreed to create alliances via open APIs? What if they partnered and re-bundled? You'd end up with a completely new bank with at least 10x less overhead than its predecessors, as the new entity would require less real estate and far fewer employees.

Let's note that most of the successful blockchains are protocols that have used gamification and token economics to attract, galvanize and activate a community. Basically, they are ExOs.

In sum, Step 6 is about creating new business models, which increasingly tend towards free and freemium models. These new business models have, potentially, eight new value drivers to generate revenues and differentiate them from competitors. It also allows for a long-term strategy to align with adjacent ExOs in a particular industry to fully disrupt incumbents rather than just one individual good or service. Talk about a powerful double-disruption scenario.

Step 7: Build the MVP (Minimal Viable Product)

Demystifying Customer Discovery

Correctly deciphering your customer's needs is a crucial cornerstone in shaping your business. This process, termed Customer Discovery, involves engaging in proactive dialogues and outreach to validate your customer assumptions with utmost confidence. The goal is to unearth a prevalent problem or need and design a solution that caters to the largest feasible customer base, in line with their specific requirements.

Engaging frequently with your prospective customers fosters a deeper understanding of their usage patterns. It empowers you to stratify your market based on the customer's profile, purchasing autonomy, and motivational triggers.

At its core, Customer Discovery is about perceiving and understanding the customer's pain points and their genuine need for a resolution.

Think of Customer Discovery as a laboratory for business Experimentation. Upon concluding this process, it's valuable to reflect on what you and your team have learned. Did you encounter any surprises? These unexpected revelations could signal the need for a business pivot, invalidate a previous assumption, or unveil an unexplored market niche.

Finally, pose this pivotal question to yourself and your team: Are you crafting vitamins or aspirin? This metaphor highlights the distinction between products or services that are "nice to have" (vitamins) and those that are "need to have" (aspirin). While vitamins may enhance well-being, they are not essential. On the other hand, aspirin-like solutions provide immediate relief from pain, making them indispensable to the user.

When Rohit Khare (along with Salim Ismail) built Angstro, an AI-based social graph, Rohit insisted on talking to as many people as possible about the idea. The risk in Salim's mind was that he might give the idea away; the reward, in Rohit's view, was that they got free feedback on the idea, plus get a sense of who was interested, who might already be working on the same idea, and who might be future partners. Rohit was right. (Angstro was sold to Google in 2010.)

Minimal Viable Product

A key output of the Business Model Canvas is the *Minimum Viable Product* (MVP). This is an applied experiment to determine the simplest product that will allow the team to go to market and see how users respond (as well as help find investors for the next round of development). Feedback loops can then rapidly iterate the product to optimize it and drive the feature roadmap of its development. Learning, testing assumptions, pivoting, and iterating are key to this step. The Build/Measure/Learn process in Lean Startup is invaluable for building the MVP.[50]

Notice the contrast. While Step 1 is about the MTP, or Purpose, this step is about Experimentation. This is not the whole story. As Peter Thiel has pointed out: "Not all start-ups thrive by Experimentation and purpose only" LinkedIn, Palantir, and SpaceX were fundamentally successful due to

---

[50]   The Lean Startup | Methodology, http://theleanstartup.com/principles.

a strong vision of the future. Similarly, Thiel's observation is further substantiated by Aileen Lee's Unicorns research (which we addressed earlier in the chapter).

A key reason for an MVP is that it is much, much easier to change a product early in the development process than later. It's also critical to discover what the customer does and doesn't want, what they're willing to pay for, and ultimately, what your team is actually able to deliver.

The notion of an MVP plus iteration has been key to the success of SpaceX and the new generation of space companies. In the case of SpaceX, the company began by building their Falcon-1 rocket using a single Merlin Engine on the first stage. The first three launch attempts failed, but each one got them closer, testing as many systems and assumptions as possible. Luckily, after scraping together enough funding for a fourth attempt, the rocket succeeded. The Falcon-1 was literally a "minimum viable product," the smallest rocket that could get to orbit and prove the Merlin rocket engine, as well as the team's engineering and operating ability. But what the market really needed was a much bigger rocket, the Falcon-9, which used nine of the Merlin engines in the first stage. This iterative approach worked, and Falcon-9 has become the most successful launch system ever built.

Step 8: Validate Marketing and Sales (Right side of the canvas)

Once the product is being used in its chosen market(s), a customer acquisition funnel needs to be established to help drive (or entice) new visitors to that product. Its role is to qualify potential customers, then convert them into users and paying customers.

A good starting point for this process is Dave McClure's AARRR, the onomatopoeically titled "Pirate" model for startup metrics. This model tracks the following steps and key metrics:

- *Acquisition*: How do users locate you? (Growth metric)
  o *Start with online advertising and a basic offer*
  o *Iterate the offer via A/B testing on multiple platforms*
  o *Keep iterating until you find a consistent stream of leads (and you never stop iterating)*

- *Activation*: Do users have a great first experience? (Value metric)
  o *Try multiple offers and collect feedback to make a great first impression*

- *Retention*: Do users come back? (Value metric)
  o *Measure NPS and find ways of adding more value or more offerings.*

- *Revenue*: How do you make money? (Value metric)
  o *Today, the most successful and sticky business models are subscription based.*

- *Referral*: Do users tell others? (Growth metric)
  o *Here again, the NPS approach is key to testing virality.*

The AARRR model is not easy to forget once you use it, and most successful Silicon Valley companies have used some variant of this approach.

At this point, the holy grail of product-market fit should have been achieved. That is, customers have become very excited by your product and are willing to pay for it.

In late 2004, at Amazon, a software developer, Charlie Ward, wrote up a half-page idea that suggested a premium subscription model might work. An internal finance guru shot down the idea, saying that the shipping costs would explode if everyone ordered small items. Jeff Bezos applied Amazon's MTP (is it better for the customer) and forecasted that the extra orders would allow them to build more logistics hubs. Thus was born Amazon Prime, a shift in the business model that was iterated aggressively. Today, Prime boasts more than 200 million subscribers globally.

Step 9: Implement SCALE and IDEAS

In the first edition of this book, we posited that a great MTP and four of the ten attributes from SCALE and IDEAS would enable you to achieve ExO status. Looking back, we are prepared to revise that claim, as it is now clear that you must be relentless about implementing MTP and *all ten* SCALE and IDEAS attributes where possible. Not least among the reasons for this is that if you're not using the full complement of these tools, someone else is.

Suman Sasmal puts it very well: "Entrepreneurs have aspirations that are disproportionate to the resources they have. The SCALE attributes take such aspirations miles ahead!"

Let's review the components of SCALE and IDEAS.

ExO Attribute	Startup Implementation
MTP	Formulate an MTP in a particular problem space, one that all founders feel passionate about.
Staff on Demand	Use contractors, SoD platforms wherever possible; keep FTEs to a minimum.
Community & Crowd	Validate the idea in MTP communities. — Get product feedback. — Find co-founders, contractors, and experts. — Use crowdfunding and crowdsourcing to validate market demand and as a marketing technique.
Algorithms	Identify data streams that can be automated and help with product development. Implement cloud-based and open-source machine and deep learning to increase insights.
Leveraged Assets	Do NOT acquire assets. — Use cloud computing, TechShop for product development. — Use incubators like Y Combinator and Techstars for office, funding, mentoring, and peer input. — Starbucks as office space

Engagement	Design product with engagement in mind. — Gather all user interactions. — Gamify where possible. — Use incentive prizes to engage crowd and create buzz.
Interfaces	Design custom processes for managing SCALE; do not automate until you're ready to scale.
Dashboards	Set up OKRs and value serendipity and growth metrics dashboards; do not implement value metrics until the product is finalized (see Step 10).
Experimentation	Establish a culture of Experimentation and constant iteration. Be willing to fail and pivot as needed.
Autonomy	Implement a 'lite' version of a Holacracy. Start with the General Company Circle as a first step, then move on to governance meetings. Implement the GitHub technical and organizational model with radical openness, transparency, and permission.
Social Technologies	Implement file sharing, cloud-based document management, collaboration, and activity streams internally and within your community.

The trick, of course, is to find the right sequence of implementing the attributes, which has been covered in the attribute chapters in the section titled 'Pre-requisites' (e.g., don't implement Autonomy without an MTP).

SmartGroup, a publicly listed HR benefits company in Australia, launched ten projects corresponding to the SCALE and IDEAS attributes. Every quarter, they relaunch ten new ones, so they're constantly applying the ExO model. How have they done? Over a four-year period (Oct 2014 to Oct 2018), the company stock price increased 10x.

Step 10: Establish the Culture

Perhaps the most critical and complex step in building an ExO involves establishing its culture. Think again about PayPal's culture of close friendship rather than formal work relationships. In a fast-scaling organization, culture, along with the MTP and Social Technologies, are the glue that keeps a team together through the quantum leaps of an ExO's growth. Needless to say, given that even defining the term 'culture' has proven enduringly difficult, this is a particularly challenging step.

According to noted hotelier Chip Conley, "Culture is what happens when the boss leaves." That pretty much sums it up. We would only add that culture is a company's greatest intangible asset. As many have observed, "Culture eats strategy for breakfast." From the "HP Way" and IBM's "Think" to Google's playrooms and Twitter's warehouse, it is hard to overstate culture's added value.

Establishing a corporate culture starts with learning how to effectively track, manage and reward performance. And that begins with designing the OKR system we outlined in Chapter 11 and then continues through the process of getting the team habituated to transparency, accountability, execution, and high performance.

Finally, and this has often proven the most difficult of all (especially when it conflicts with the personalities of the company's leadership), a great corporate culture is built on trust. Employees and customers need to believe that the company has their best interests at heart. And management needs to place its trust in employees to make the right choices, even to propose new products or a change in the direction of the company. Only with trust can an ExO move swiftly and assuredly at the pace the new economy will require.

Luckily, with the combination of an MTP and the IDEAS attributes, trust is built into an ExO, thus the culture is almost prescriptively assured.

Step 11: Ask Key Questions Periodically

There are eight key questions you need to think about throughout your journey towards building your ExO startup. Successfully answering each one will get you closer to becoming an ExO:

1. Who is your customer?
2. Which customer problem are you solving?
3. What is your solution, and does it improve the status quo by at least 10x?
4. How will you market the product or service?
5. How are you selling the product or service?
6. How do you turn customers into advocates using viral effects and Net Promoter Scores to drive down the marginal cost of demand?
7. How will you scale your customer segment?
8. How will you drive the marginal cost of supply toward zero?

Again, that final question on that list is the most critical for an ExO. To be truly disruptive to the status quo and achieve the 10x scalability, some combination of IDEAS and SCALE must drive down the cost of supply exponentially.

A final word on timing: For any startup to be successful, it must combine requisite skills, hard work, and great market timing (especially when it comes to technology). As Ray Kurzweil says: "An invention needs to make sense in the world in which it is finished, not the world in which it is started." This is a profound point, one often missed by founders. It is about understanding the evolutionary trajectory of technology. That is, what technology capacities will become feasible in two or three years, given the pace of Moore's Law? When you develop a product with the near future in mind instead of the present, it greatly increases your chances of success. Bill Gross, the founder of IdeaLab, analyzed hundreds of startups and found that timing accounted for 42 percent of the difference between success and failure.

In the founding days of Singularity University, Peter and Salim had the chance to meet with the founders of Siri before it was sold to Apple. During that meeting, the Siri team explained that in the earliest days of Siri, they designed the product based on where they expected the technology to be in three years' time. Put simply, if they had designed Siri based on the available technology, by the time it came to market three years later, it would have been out of date. They were skating to "where the puck would eventually be."

Futurist Paul Saffo has said that most transformative (technological) inventions fail the first few times when launched and generally take fifteen years to be fully realized. Why? Various reasons: too early, bad timing, unproven business models, and integration issues—all resulting in a poor customer experience in an even poorer marketplace. Michiel Muller adds: "It takes a 9x improvement to move people from incumbent products to new products from startups."

There is a certain threshold value that overcomes perceived risk, which is why we've set a minimum 10x requirement for starting Exponential Organizations.

Step 12: Building and Maintaining a Platform

Finally, we need to revisit the definition of *platforms*. It is a business model that creates value by facilitating exchanges between two or more interdependent groups, typically consumers and producers. Note that the most valuable companies in the world are platforms (Google, Amazon, etc.).

Leading platform expert Sangeet Paul Choudary identified the four steps needed to build a successful platform (as opposed to a successful product):

1. Identify a pain point or use case for a consumer.
2. Identify a core value unit or social object in any interaction between a producer and consumer. This could be anything. Pictures, jokes, advice, reviews, and information about sharing rooms, tools, and car rides are examples of things that have led to successful platforms. Remember that many people will be both producers and consumers; use this to your advantage.
3. Design a way to facilitate that interaction. Then see if you can build it as a small prototype you can curate yourself. If it works at that level, it will be worth taking to the next level and scaling.
4. Determine how to build a network around your interaction. Find a way to turn your platform user into an ambassador. Before you know it, you will be on a roll.

To implement platforms, ExOs normally follow four steps in terms of data and APIs:

1. **Gather:** The algorithmic process starts with harnessing data, which is gathered via sensors, people, or imported from public datasets.[51]
2. **Organize:** The next step is to organize the data. This is known as ETL (*extract, transform,* and *load*).
3. **Apply:** Once the data is accessible, use algorithms and artificial intelligence such as machine or deep learning to extract insights, identify trends, and tune new algorithms and artificial intelligence. These can be realized via tools such as Hadoop and Pivotal or even (open source) deep learning algorithms and artificial intelligence such as DeepMind or Skymind.
4. **Expose:** The final step is exposing the data in the form of an open platform. Open data and APIs can be used in such a way that an ExO's community develops valuable services, new functionalities, and innovations layered on top of the platform by remixing published data with their own. Examples of companies that have successfully exposed their data this way are the Ford Company, Uber, IBM Watson, Twitter, and Facebook.

---

[51] For more on how to create effective value propositions, we recommend reading Osterwalder's new book, *Value Proposition Design: How to Create Products and Services Customers Want.*

We can't emphasize the following strongly enough:

*"The world that is emerging is very different
from the one we've known"*

—George W. Bush

Power is becoming easier to acquire but harder to keep. Thanks to strong viral and social network effects that allow startups to scale rapidly, it is now easier than ever to start new companies and disrupt industries. But when it comes to social networks, the reverse is also true. Facebook, for example, is an incumbent, and its network effects and lock-in make it hard to usurp—underscoring the great advantage a platform has over a product or service.

In her book, *The End of Competitive Advantage: How to Keep Your Strategy Moving as Fast as Your Business*, Rita Gunther McGrath illustrates that we can only obtain what she calls Transient Competitive Advantages via platforms and purpose, community, and culture (i.e., an ExO).

Notes for Enterprise ExOs (EExOs):

Much of what we have covered in this chapter applies to pure startups, as well as to startups growing out of existing enterprises. However, there are some special considerations for Enterprise ExOs (EExOs).

According to Salim, the greatest danger when building an Enterprise ExO is that the "immune system" of the parent company will come and attack it. Thus, the following suggestions for budding EExOs:

- **Only go after new markets.** This is largely to avoid an immune system response from the company. If you want to transform an existing cash cow or leapfrog a current business unit, you need a stand-alone unit with a small team that is isolated and fully autonomous.

- **Establish direct support** from—and a direct formal link to—the CEO. Whatever you do, do not settle for any other reporting line below the CEO, and that goes triple for the CFO.
- **Spin out versus spin in.** If you are successful, spin everything out and create a new company; don't try to wedge the emerging business back into the mothership. If your startup is truly disruptive, it won't fit neatly anywhere, *and internal politics will only escalate, especially if you are cannibalizing an existing revenue stream. The only exception we've found is when individual EExOs are part of a larger platform play, as with Apple's products, which start out at the edge and are brought into the center.*
- *Invite* **the most disruptive change-makers** from within your existing organization to work on your EExO. Management expert Gary Hamel has said that young people, dissidents, and those working on the geographic and mental peripheries of your organization are the most interesting, free, and open thinkers. Look for rebels. The good news is that they won't be difficult to find.
- *Build* **your ExO completely independent** of existing systems and policies. That includes actual physical separation. Try hard not to use existing premises or infrastructure unless they deliver a huge strategic advantage. As with any new startup, it's critical for a new ExO to operate as a greenfield operation, relying on speed and iteration, both of which are hard in large organizations.

As Steve Jobs said, "We run Apple like a startup. We always let ideas win arguments, not hierarchies. Otherwise, your best employees won't stay. Collaboration, discipline, and trust are critical."[52]

WWED. This stands for "What Would Elon Do."

Possibly the most ambitious entrepreneur in the world today is Elon Musk. From one point of view, the way Elon Musk operates is actually very simple. After picking an MTP, he looks for a supporting technology that's growing exponentially (e.g., solar energy, brain computing interfaces, batteries). He then looks out ten years on that doubling pattern and asks, "What will the price performance be in ten years?" Elon refers to this as "first-principle thinking," meaning looking at the fundamentals.

For example, in the early days of Tesla when considering the cost of lithium-ion batteries, he looked at the spot price of the major components (lithium, graphite, cobalt, and manganese) and determined that, in volume, the price of these batteries could come down considerably. Then he starts building a company against that—because it takes about ten years to build a global company. As Peter is fond of saying, "If you build a product or service using today's technology, you're out of date by the time you launch." But it also goes without saying that Elon's success is also due to the fact that willing to take big, calculated risks.

---

[52] For those interested in a more thorough treatment of starting an ExO, Peter Diamandis and Steven Kotler's second book, BOLD (Simon & Schuster, Feb 2015), is written for the entrepreneur interested in going from an idea to running a billion-dollar company in record time.

Does the process work? Here are some case studies:

- Enter Rokk3r Labs out of Miami. They use the ExO model to build startups. Since 2015, they have built 40 companies using the methodology and took their company public as a result.
- Roger Hamilton read ExO in 2014 and used the model to build his EdTech startup. Genius Group went public on the New York Stock Exchange in 2022.
- Tens of thousands of entrepreneurs globally are using the model to build the next generation of ground-breaking startups

What's Next...

Now you have a sense of both the ExO Attributes and a process for building an ExO. There's one call to action to keep in mind as you finish the last couple of chapters in this book:

WHAT WILL YOU BUILD ??

17

Conclusion

M arco Vanossi is a Brazilian software developer who studied computer science at Unicamp. He proved to be a programming prodigy early in life: At just 15, Marco created Latin America's first search engine.

In the years since, he has founded multiple start-up companies, almost all with their own MTP. "I'm passionate about pushing the limits of what can currently be done with state-of-the-art technology." At the same time, he's created hundreds of apps and recently settled into the Snapchat ecosystem. As of this writing, Marco is the leading Snapchat 3rd party developer in the world. His Snapchat lenses have been viewed more than 30 billion times.

Think about that: a single human being has the leverage to impact the entire world. Marco's secret: an exponential mindset and an attitude to never surrender but instead to find the solution to every problem he encounters.

• • •

In this book, we have given you all the tools you need to start and successfully run an Exponential Organization. But there is one thing we can't give you: the key mindsets required for you to operate as an exponential entrepreneur. That is something you must generate and maintain within yourself.

Over the years, Peter has given a lot of thought to what constitutes the key ExO-related Mindset. He teaches these mindsets to his Abundance360 members and believes that in building an Exponential Organization, the right mindsets come before everything else—and it governs every step thereafter.

Peter asks the following question: What do you think made Elon Musk, Mahatma Gandhi, Jeff Bezos, Martin Luther King, Steve Jobs, Anousheh Ansari, or Martine Rothblatt so successful?

Was it their technology, their wealth, or was it their Mindset? I think almost everyone would agree that the right mindset is the most critical asset for ANY entrepreneur or leader. Take away all of their wealth, their technology, and their relationships, but leave them their mindset, and chances are they would succeed again.

But why is Mindset so important, especially during this era of global and rapid exponential change? Because your mindsets are the filter through which you see the world, they are the operating system of your brain.

Your mindset(s) determine how you spend your time, who you spend your time with, the decisions you make, where you invest your resources, and your vision of what is even possible for you in the future.

Mindset is everything!

The problem is that few of us ever pause to consider how our mindsets influence our lives, what mindsets we have, where we got them, or even what mindsets we want to develop.

Let me ask you another few questions: Do you know what your dominant Mindset is? Do you know where you got it from? What Mindset would you LIKE to have dominate your view of the world? Most of us don't realize that we can purposefully select and shape our mindsets.

As a way of expanding on this point and explaining how mindsets work, let me share a current and very relevant analogy. As we've discussed in detail earlier in the book, the entire field of artificial intelligence has been in hyper-rapid growth for the past decade. As it turns out, one branch of AI, called Neural Networks, has been designed based on the way our brain works. Today AI scientists train a neural net in the same way that we would train a dog, a child, or even ourselves. These neural nets are trained by being shown example after example, over and over again. For instance, if you want to train a neural net to recognize a cat, AI scientists would typically show the net thousands of pictures of various cats. In doing so, the net would learn to recognize that cats have ears, fur, a tail, and four legs. But if you then show the same neural net a picture of a dog, the algorithm will tell you that the dog is a cat.

It doesn't know any better. It's only been trained to see cats! The same is true for our brains: the conclusions we draw and the actions we take are only as good as the data we've used to shape our minds. Most of us don't realize that we are CONSTANTLY training our mindsets through the media we consume, the friends we hang out with, and the books we read. For example, if you watch CNN, what Peter calls the *"Crisis News Network,"* every day for hours on end, you'll be put on RED ALERT.

Today's network news bombards us with 10-to-1 negative to positive news stories that make us feel pessimistic and fearful and put us into a scarcity mindset. But it doesn't need to be that way. As an exponential entrepreneur, you can instead choose to have an "Abundance Mindset" powered by the unprecedented period of exponential change before us.

Peter's mission with his mindset-related work is to help teach entrepreneurs about six key Mindsets that he believes EVERY entrepreneur and leader should at least be familiar with—and, ideally, master—if they hope to surf atop this tsunami of change rather than get crushed by it.

#1: A Purpose-Driven Mindset

Let's begin this mindset journey by discussing a Purpose-Driven Mindset. The objective of a Purpose-Driven Mindset is perhaps best summed up by a quote I attribute to my friend Tom Bilyeu's father:

> Find something you would die for and live for it. Doing anything significant, big, and bold requires a TON of hard work. It also involves countless risks, setbacks, and restarts. While some people are lucky, most success stories require recovering one more time, facing the challenge, and beginning again. Over and over.

So how do you fuel that persistence, and where do you focus it?

My favorite analogy is that of an aircraft, where passion is the jet engine powering your plane, and purpose is the rudder directing your flight path. As we've also discussed in this book, a deeper dive here takes you into the realm of developing your Massive Transformative Purpose.

#2: A Curiosity Mindset

Next up is a brief dive into a Curiosity Mindset. Einstein famously said, "I have no special talent. I am only passionately curious." You could argue that curiosity is responsible for all major scientific and technological advances because it's rooted in the desire to seek the truth and explore the unknown. Having a Curiosity Mindset means always asking insightful questions and not taking things at face value.

Peter recently spoke with the brilliant writer Tim Urban, creator of the *Wait But Why* blog and one of the most curious people he's met. For Tim, a Curiosity Mindset is being actively interested in adding to the knowledge tower in your mind and being energized by the dopamine hits you get by going from confusion to clarity.

"When you begin with a curious mindset," Urban said, "you're both more interested in what you're learning, and you retain more of what you've learned." Because Google gives us all of us the power to know almost anything we're curious about, what matters more today than raw knowledge is the quality of the questions you ask.

Peter has often commented that whenever he drops off his 11-year-old twin boys at school, his parting comment to them is, "Ask great questions today." Funny enough, it's the same advice he gives entrepreneurs and executives. Further, as Peter's friend Tony Robbins says, "The quality of your questions determines the quality of your life." And, if you fashion yourself as an entrepreneur, being curious is especially important for you. As Peter and Salim have studied the most successful entrepreneurs and companies, from Amazon to Google and Uber to SpaceX, their success in the early days was due in large part to their relentless use of Experimentation to define their product-market fit.

#3: An Abundance Mindset

Next up is an Abundance Mindset. An Abundance Mindset is one that realizes that every year brings more and more opportunity and that technology is a force converting what was once scarce into greater and greater abundance. There are two key dimensions of this Mindset: Abundance vs. Scarcity and Optimism vs. Fear. Nothing is more fundamental to an abundance mindset than how you see the world in these two dimensions.

Mastering this will bring you greater fulfillment and less stress. It will change how and where you see opportunity. If you're an entrepreneur, an abundance mindset will inspire the best employees to work for you, while visionary brands, partners, and investors will want to work with you.

Just think of the sort of people whose company you enjoy. Would you rather spend your day with someone who thinks the world is falling apart and sees danger around every corner? Or with someone who believes that the passionate and determined human mind can overcome almost every challenge?

Today, technology is a force that converts scarcity into abundance, over and over again enabling a world with an abundance of capital, energy, communications, computation, food, water, shelter, healthcare, and knowledge.

Living in a world of ever-increasing opportunities and abundance means you should not fear the future or resent an opportunity you've missed. Next year will bring more.

Things that were once available only to the richest are now available to almost anyone—anywhere on the planet. A child in Zimbabwe can Google any information they want or even video conference with someone on the other side of the world for free! Many things we paid millions of dollars for just a few decades ago are now available on our smartphones for no cost.

Through his mindset work, Peter's mission is to liberate us from our unhealthy "Scarcity Mindset" by sharing example after example of growing abundance that will train our neural nets towards data-driven optimism.

In a world of scarcity, there's a limited pie. If your neighbor gets a slice, then you get a smaller slice. This is a world of limited resources and zero-sum competition. But when you have an Abundance Mindset, rather than slicing the pie into thinner and thinner slices, you simply bake more pies.

This is the future that exponential technologies enable.

Remember: Creating a world of abundance isn't about creating a world of luxury for everyone; it's about creating a world of possibility.

How do you feel about creating an Abundance Mindset in your life? Peter and Salim believe this is one of the critical mindsets all of us can have for the decades ahead.

#4: An Exponential Mindset

The challenge humans have in understanding an Exponential Mindset is that our brains evolved for a linear world. 200,000 years ago, during early hominid evolution, the rate at which things changed was so so sloooow.

Nothing changed from millennium to millennium, generation to generation... the life of your great-great-grandparents was the same as the life of their great-great-grandchildren.

As such, our minds and intuition became wired for a slow and linear world. What mattered to us back then was being able to track the game we hunted and our ability to escape the predators who hunted us. Linear projections were all we needed.

Today we live in an exponential world where technologies like computation, artificial intelligence, biotechnology, VR, robotics, blockchain, and Web3 are doubling in power every 18 to 24 months, riding on top of Moore's Law of exponential growth.

These are the technologies that allow us to transform scarcity into abundance, pursue Moonshots, and set new longevity goals for ourselves and those we love.

Understanding how fast the exponential world around us is changing is critical to all aspects of our lives. It impacts what we study, what career we pursue, where we invest our money, and if you're an entrepreneur, what company you should start.

For entrepreneurs, seeing around the corner of tomorrow and being agile enough to adapt to what's coming is more important than ever before.

If you master this Exponential Mindset, you will not fear the future but learn to anticipate it. You'll gather the clarity and confidence which will serve you so on many levels.

#5: A Moonshot Mindset

Exponential technologies enable our next mindset, known as Moonshot Thinking.

Most people and companies are happy with incremental progress in their lives. They are happy with 10% more revenue or salary or a 10% reduction in costs. The challenge is that if you're only aiming for 10%, then 10% is likely what you'll get. Why are many folks happy with 10%? Because 10% is anchored in an incremental and scarcity mindset.

But the world's most successful people don't act based on scarcity. They act based on their Abundance and Exponential Mindsets and pursue a 10x improvement in their lives. Put differently, they pursue a 1000% change, what we'll refer to as a Moonshot.

A Moonshot Mindset lets us set goals that are radically difficult. Billion-person challenges. Objectives that sound crazy until they are suddenly achieved and thereafter are called breakthroughs.

Moonshots are ventures that require a lot of risk, new ways of thinking, and data-driven Experimentation, but they are also ventures that ultimately pay exponential rewards.

A Moonshot Mindset allows us to ask: What is the 10X version of my product? My company? My industry? Or my life?

Perhaps you came to this book not being interested in a Moonshot, just figuring out your Purpose or MTP would be good enough. But don't discount the excitement of taking a Moonshot.

There are many benefits to having a Moonshot Mindset. Here are just a few to get you started:

1. When you shoot for 10X improvement and try to do something radically hard, you approach the problem you're solving in a completely different way.
2. You understand that "the day before something is a breakthrough; it's a crazy idea." Your Moonshot Mindset gives you permission to think about and try crazy ideas.
3. If you're a leader or an executive, an added benefit is that Moonshots focus and motivate your team, helping you to attract the best talent in the world.

#6: A Gratitude Mindset

Finally, but by no means least, is a Gratitude Mindset. Being grateful involves regularly making the shift from expectation to appreciation and from overwhelm to thankfulness. It means constantly recognizing that we're living in a world of increasing abundance—that today is better than yesterday and that tomorrow will be better still. Peter and Salim believe that being grateful is especially important for entrepreneurs. Here are five of our favorite reasons:

1. You feel better! Expressing gratitude causes our brain to release dopamine and serotonin: the two crucial neurotransmitters responsible for our emotions.
2. You make everyone else around you feel better as well! When you're in gratitude, and you're burning 20% brighter and 20% happier, your mood will influence everyone around you. You literally make the world a happier place.
3. As a leader, when you're grateful, it's much easier to encourage your team to be grateful—which improves the relational well-being both for individuals and the group.
4. When you're "in gratitude," you invest in relationships. Ultimately, "who you go through life with" is everything. Relationships bring joy, meaning, and love. Add in your leadership role, and you focus on the positive results you can create for others.
5. When you're grateful, you are more optimistic, more inspired, and healthier. And this attracts the most incredible talent and individuals into your orbit.

There is NO downside to gratitude.

Healing the World

Remember the data described at the beginning of this book regarding the Fortune 100 study between ExO and non-ExO companies? To summarize: The most ExO-friendly organizations delivered 40x the shareholder returns compared to the most inflexible, traditional enterprises.

As Raj Sisodia has written so compellingly in *The Healing Organization*, new organizational forms need not just to be sustainable but also lead the process of healing our planet, our communities, our people, and our institutions. We couldn't agree more: purpose-driven, scalable, adaptable organizations—ExOs—are natural candidates to heal the world and transition it from Scarcity to the Abundance that is our singular destiny.

What does that mean?

Up until recently, most of human products and services were based on a scarcity model. But as we have learned to digitize products and services—that is, turning them into 1's and 0's—it has allowed us to dematerialize physical things, duplicate them, and transmit them in a fashion that has effectively dropped the incremental cost of that production and transmission to zero.

The implications of this widespread virtualization are so profound as to be almost unbelievable. What it means is that, for the first time in human history, we may be on the brink of a *post-scarcity world*. One reason this is so unimaginable is that our minds, evolving over the past 300,000 years, were wired for scarcity, not abundance. So the notion of an end to endemic scarcity is not only earth-shattering, it is literally mind-boggling.

That said, there is no doubt that a post-scarcity world will require a very different form of organization to survive and succeed. This transformation is already well underway.

It is hard not to see these changes in nearly apocalyptic terms. In the 2000s, a figurative information asteroid, the Web, struck the Earth. In the 2010s, we experienced a Cambrian explosion of new organizational forms (e.g., DAOs) emerging and being tested. And, entering the 2020s, the data is clear that ExOs are now the dominant species of organization on Earth. The days of large, hierarchical dinosaur organizations are numbered.

Tania Hodgkinson, Founder and CoQuoptach at InnovThink Coaching, frames it as follows: "Exponential Organizations (ExOs) and a new social contract they embody form an integral part of this paradigm shift. In this transformative landscape, ExOs also bear a significant responsibility of addressing how we educate and empower the emerging intelligence, for these very intelligences will become our future teachers. It requires us, all those in or emerging into leadership to develop our mindset and capabilities to take up this existential responsibility. It has become a key leadership development area in my practice."

The 2020s: The Decade of the ExOs

Revisiting the Fortune 100 data, you'll remember, in terms of Revenues, between 2014 and 2021, ExOs enjoyed a 13.04 percent compounded growth rate compared to a meager 0.14 percent CAGR for their non-exponential counterparts.

Similarly, in terms of profitability, top ExOs enjoyed profit-to-sales ratios of 18.68 percent—making them 6.8 times more profitable than their non-exponential counterparts. Most tellingly, the profitability of the best ExOs stayed firm at 18 percent during the pandemic year—even as their non-exponential peers suffered a catastrophic negative 2.3 percent.

Regarding asset utilization, the best ExOs had a median asset ratio (revenues/assets) of 88.2. That was almost 11.7 *times* better performance leveraging assets compared to non-ExO companies. Such performance gaps can be firmly attributed to a median score on the specific exponential attribute of leveraged assets. The top 10 Exponential Organizations had scored 2.5 out of 4, compared to their bottom 10 non-exponential peer-group score of only 1.5.

And here's the most impressive discovery: the market cap for the top exponential firms grew at a median 13.6 percent CAGR between April 2014 and December 2021. By comparison, traditional companies during this period went backward, managing only a negative 2.4 percent CAGR in their valuations. Together during that eight-year interval, top ExOs achieved a combined 5.3X in their market valuations—a figure that wildly exceeded even the otherwise impressive S&P 500 Index of 2.5X.

Now, imagine what it will look like from the point of view of traditionally organized and run enterprises as the first of the new ExOs enter their marketplace. It will be like horse-drawn wagons encountering their first automobiles—the newcomers will seem so powerful, so fast-moving that they will be likely to create terror and despair. Entire industries will attempt to create barriers to the arrival of these alien companies—new laws, warning off customers, special taxes—but nothing will stop these ExOs because they are too quick, too adaptable, too efficient—and ultimately too popular with employees, suppliers and most of all, customers.

By the end of this decade, we can safely predict that almost all top-down, traditionally hierarchical businesses and nonprofits (even the biggest and most venerable ones) will have metamorphosed into Exponential Organizations—or they will be on the brink of oblivion. That's why you can be certain that in the boardrooms around the world, this inevitable fate is being discussed—and that radical changes are already in the works.

And that is a good thing. Because if we are to live in a world beyond scarcity, we will need ExOs to best take advantage of that new abundance.

We wrote this book to give you the best possible preparation to build your Exponential Organization—or use the latest information to fine-tune the one you already have—to best prepare yourself for success in the stunning world that awaits us just around the corner.

Now, set your mind to win. And good luck.

The ExO Library

Now that you've read deeply about the ExO Model and know how to build one, we're here to help. This book is just the first of what will be a series of books over the next few years that will look at the application of the ExO philosophy in every sector of the modern world.

In book 2, we will team up with one of the world's most successful turnaround experts to look at how to bring the ExO model to legacy organizations to give them new life (yes, it can be done).

In book 3, we'll see how the ExO model can make the public sector (government, cities, countries, and institutions) work at new levels of efficiency, flexibility, and, amazingly, high levels of productivity and quality.

And there is a whole lot more—newsletters, content updates, conferences, for a start—to come in the months ahead. So, if you are interested in continuing this conversation—and we expect that you are—grab the QR code below. You will get free entry into the ExO Ecosystem, and we will reward you with an NFT for doing so.

We'll see you in the Exponential future!

Salim Ismail
Peter H. Diamandis, MD
Michael S. Malone

June 2023

Glossary of Terms

Exponential Organization: An ExO is a purpose-driven, agile, and scalable organization that uses accelerating technologies to digitize, dematerialize, democratize, and demonetize its products and services, resulting in a 10x performance increase over its non-ExO peers.

OpenExO: OpenExO is the world's leading global ExO transformation ecosystem, made up of more than 25,000 clients, investors, consultants, coaches, collaborators, tech leaders, and innovation specialists. Together, we are committed to helping organizations, institutions, and people transform the world for an exponentially better future by implementing and evolving the ExO model and practices.

OpenExO Community: The OpenExO Community is a place where exponential transformation specialists collaborate and interact with the opportunities that exponential technologies make available. This involves mindset transformation, business model transformation, and knowledge of how to harness exponential technologies.

ExO Ecosystem: The ExO Ecosystem encompasses all organizations that are working towards creating Exponential Organizations. This includes the OpenExO Community and beyond the community, including organizations that traditionally would be considered competition.

ExO Model: ExO Model = ExO Attributes (ExO Attributes = MTP + 5 internal attributes + 5 external attributes). The ExO Model is comprised of 11 components or attributes. ExO attributes are the building blocks that allow you to create an Exponential Organisation with global reach and impact. They leverage existing and emerging technologies that enable an organization to access and manage abundance in the form of available resources, potential clients, or useful information. They are the practices that set industry leaders apart. An overarching Massive Transformative Purpose (MTP) defines the goal that the organization strives to achieve. The ExO Model was created by studying Exponential organizations.

ExO Attributes: ExO Attributes are the building blocks that allow you to create an Exponential Organization with global reach and impact. They leverage existing and emerging technologies that enable an organization to access and manage abundance in the form of available resources, potential clients, or useful information. The ExO Attributes are MTP + SCALE + IDEAS. (These are defined below.)

Massive Transformation Purpose (MTP): The MTP reflects an organization's aspiration—the core purpose of its existence. It describes the change in the world that you want to achieve while recognizing that it will not be accomplished in the short term. It inspires action, expresses your passions, and creates an emotional connection that drives you and others toward meaningful, positive change.

SCALE Attributes: These attributes help manage leverage abundance that exists outside of the organization. The attributes are Staff on Demand, Community and Crowd,

Algorithms & Artificial Intelligence, Leveraged Assets, and Engagement.

Staff on Demand: The Staff on Demand attribute relies on a pool of prequalified workers hired on an as-needed basis to conduct operational elements of your core business. Responsibilities range from simple tasks to complex work and may even include mission-critical processes.

Community and Crowd: Community, in the ExO context, is made up of a large global group of individuals who are passionate about your MTP and are directly involved in the main functions of your organization. They are loyal to a shared goal and devoted to solving the grand challenges surrounding your organization's purpose.

Artificial Intelligence and Algorithms: An Algorithm is a step-by-step set of instructions used to automate a task or solve a specific problem. Artificial Intelligence (AI) explores how algorithms can be made "intelligent," allowing digital systems to learn to solve problems without predetermined instructions and discover solutions to new problems without human intervention. AI enables computer systems to behave or "think" like humans by learning to improve performance over time.

Leveraged Assets: "Leveraged and shared assets" is the practice of renting or sharing assets—even those that are mission-critical—to allow an organization to stay nimble and unencumbered, to begin rapidly, and to scale with minimum friction. Ideally, LSA also lowers the marginal cost of supply—to virtually zero in the case of a highly scaled model. By not owning physical or digital property, an ExO can remove the costs associated with managing that property, along with all related infrastructure costs.

Engagement: Engagement is the use of techniques like gamification, incentive prizes, and—more recently—crypto economics to keep stakeholders interested, involved, and increasingly committed to an organization's MTP or shared purpose. Through Engagement, ExOs gain the loyalty of their customers and Community and convert Crowd into Community. Engagement helps to create virtuous, positive feedback loops—which in turn allows for faster growth through innovation and customer and community loyalty. Companies like Google, Airbnb, Uber, eBay, Yelp, GitHub, and Twitter all leverage different Engagement mechanisms.

IDEAS Attributes: The IDEAS Attributes are internally focused and enable organizations to manage abundance and drive culture, enabling them to grow exponentially. These attributes are Interfaces, Dashboards, Experimentation, Autonomy, and Social Technologies.

Interfaces: In an ExO context, "Interfaces" refers to the automation of one or more SCALE attributes. Interfaces are the matching and filtering processes—using Artificial Intelligence and Algorithms, as well as automated workflows—that allow an organization to translate an abundance of data into precise and meaningful information that can be acted upon. Interfaces are the bridge between the external, SCALE drivers of exponential growth (the internal, IDEAS drivers for stabilization. An early example of interfaces are APIs, or application programming interfaces.

Dashboards: Traditional business reports focus on past events, while dashboards provide real-time information and can even make predictions. Dashboards are crucial for Exponential Organizations (ExOs) as they enable rapid decision-making in a fast-changing environment.

There are two types of dashboards: external and internal. External dashboards, similar to an automobile dashboard, present engagement metrics for early-stage companies and financial metrics for mature ones. They utilize leaderboards to drive community behavior and engagement, such as Peloton's competitions. Internal dashboards, like OKRs (Objectives and Key Results), facilitate collaborative goal-setting and real-time progress tracking. Unlike traditional KPIs, OKRs provide continuous insights into performance, aligning the entire enterprise toward its goals.

Experimentation: Experimentation is the means by which EXOs make data-driven decisions. Each experiment creates a set of learnings that can be used to improve a product, service, and/or process or test a new product or service. Experimentation thrives inside a culture of imagination and risk-taking and enables significant breakthroughs and non-linear growth. Historically, most decisions inside an organization were made by experts and consultants based on their "experience" or "intuition." Often, such decisions were made while flying the banner of "slow and steady wins the race."

Moonshots are the ultimate form of Experimentation, wherein an ExO, directionally inspired by its MTP, converts a sequence of successful experiments into large, funded initiatives with an audacious endpoint. As the name suggests, Moonshots carry considerable expense and risk, but they also represent tremendous potential payoffs, propelling the company that much closer to realizing its MTP.

Autonomy: Autonomy is an organizational approach characterized by self-organized, multidisciplinary teams that operate with decentralized authority and, ideally, self-select their work—all in service of hitting OKRs and the company's MTP and Moonshot(s). This approach stands in stark contrast to the traditional hierarchical workplace. Autonomous ExOs are flatter, populated by highly motivated self-starters who are empowered to innovate.

Social Technologies: Social Technologies encourage and optimize peer-to-peer, collaborative interaction in an ExO. Social Technologies encompass communication tools (i.e., social messaging and discussion forums, like Zoom, Slack, Notion, Google Docs, etc.), collaboration tools (such as cloud-based document management for sharing and real-time editing), and workflow tools (to manage tasks and activity streams).

EXOS: EXOS is a cryptographic token that provides a way to access the resources and capabilities of the ExO Ecosystem required for transformation in the face of disruption. It's used in places like the OpenExO Platform to deliver transformational impact.

ExO profile: This is your profile on the OpenExO Platform. This profile is available publically and can be shared with people that are not in the OpenExO Community.

Immune System: Any time a large organization attempts to innovate or transform itself, the corporate immune system—certain employees and processes hard-wired to prevent organizational transformation—will always attack.

The corporate immune system does its job for a good reason: established organizations usually have a working business, which is important to maintain. The goal here isn't to kill the immune system. Instead, it is to manage it.

ExO Canvas: The ExO Canvas is a management template that helps visionaries, innovators, top executives, and entrepreneurs design agile organizations by leveraging exponentially accelerating technologies. Use the ExO Canvas to design a new ExO or to implement the ExO framework within an existing organization.

Abundance: Traditional business models are based on scarcity, where value comes from selling a product or service that is limited in supply. Exponential technologies, however, generate an abundance of everything.

Abundance360 (A360): A year-round mastermind run by Peter Diamandis. This is Singularity University's highest-level leadership program. More details are available at www.a360.com.

6Ds: Concept used to describe a chain reaction of technological progress that leads to both upheaval and opportunity.

6Ds: Digitized: Anything that becomes digitized—representable by ones and zeros—can be accessed, shared, and distributed by computer. It takes on the same exponential growth seen in computing.

6Ds: Deceptive: Exponential trends aren't easily spotted in the early days. Growth is deceptively slow until it begins to be measured in whole numbers.

6Ds: Disruptive: Digital Technologies outperform previous non-digital models in both effectiveness and cost, disrupting existing markets for a product or service.

6Ds: Dematerialized: The need for bulky or expensive single-use physical products—radio, camera, GPS, video, phone maps—disappears as these items are incorporated into smartphones.

6Ds: Demonetized: As technology becomes cheaper, sometimes to the point of being free, money is increasingly removed from the equation.

6Ds: Democratized: Once something is digitized, more people can have access to it. Everyone has access to powerful technologies, giving individuals and entities the opportunity to create the next big breakthrough.

Business Model Canvas: Business Model Canvas is a tool for developing new or documenting existing business models on one page. It is made up of nine elements or blocks: customer segments, value proposition, channel, customer relationship, revenue streams, key resources, key activities, key partners, and cost structures.

Design Thinking: A design methodology that provides a solution-based approach to solving problems. It's extremely useful in tackling complex problems that are ill-defined or unknown by understanding the human needs involved, re-framing the problem in human-centric ways, creating many ideas in brainstorming sessions, and adopting a hands-on approach in prototyping and testing.

An early adopter: An early adopter is an individual or business that uses a new product or technology before others, shares your vision, and is willing to try your MVP even though it may not yet have been perfected.

ExO Advisors: Provide micro-consulting sessions to clients and fellow ExO Ecosystem members about topics within their subject matter expertise.

ExO Workshop: An event designed to help participants understand the ExO framework and gain experience using it. It can be run for one organization or as an event featuring participants from different firms. Companies then have the option of running the complete ExO Sprint to achieve real transformation. Workshops serve as an introduction to the disruptive forces shaping our world and a new type of organization set to succeed in the rapidly changing marketplace—an "Exponential Organization"—ExO.

The ExO workshop can be run for various group sizes with a minimum of 10 participants. For groups of more than 50 people, paying an additional facilitator is recommended. The workshop is delivered by one in-person Certified ExO Trainer and may additionally include a number of virtual ExO Coaches and ExO Advisors as appropriate (to be specified in the final design).

ExO Sprint: The ExO Sprint provides a learn-by-doing approach to finding a business model that connects with abundance, overcomes the challenges organizations typically encounter when attempting transformation, and builds innovation capability into your teams. ExO Sprints result in actionable ExO projects that, once completed, transform an existing business into an Exponential Organization—or even a set of them. The ExO Sprint includes two streams of activity. The first, the Edge Stream, focuses on developing initiatives outside the existing organization and business lines. The second, the Core Stream, emphasizes developing initiatives to be implemented within the current organizations. The ExO Sprint takes place for 10 weeks.

ExO Sprint Methodology: The ExO Sprint Methodology is a 10-week process to allow organizations to transform both the core of the organization and to build exponential initiatives on the edge. The process comprises of the ExO Attributes + coaching + use of search-oriented innovation methodologies—i.e., design sprints, lean + consulting on exponential technology to become an Exponential Organization.

ExO Sprint Stream: Core: It is focused on innovation—adapting to external industry disruption without changing the existing business model (so as to avoid triggering an immune system reaction).

ExO Sprint Stream: Edge: It is focused on disruption—on creating the next generation of organizations (new businesses outside of the existing organization), which will eventually lead the industry.

Awake Session: A half-day in-person session for an extended audience (C-suite, management, and other employees) to learn about opportunities from exponential technologies, linear versus exponential thinking, and disruption risk. This session explains the strategies powering the world's fastest-growing companies—the ExO Attributes—and how they can be profitably implemented into an organization.

Align Workshop: An interactive two-day in-person session where Sprint teams work with their ExO Coaches to first evaluate the organization's status quo and then start using the ExO methodology to brainstorm and validate new business ideas. Equality within the teams allows members to unshackle their creativity and exercise skills they usually suppress in their jobs.

Disrupt Session: An intensive one-day session where teams pitch their initiatives to a panel of their own senior executives, along with ExO Ecosystem members who have extensive start-up experience. It's like a full day of Shark Tank to help your teams strengthen and rework their "half-baked" ideas.

Exponential Organizations 2014 (**Book**): First book in the ExO series, it outlines changes taking place in the world due to exponential technologies, the consequences of resisting disruptive innovation in the business environment, and discusses a new type of exponential organization, what makes them exponential. Authors: Salim Ismail, Michael S. Malone, Yuri van Geest

Exponential Transformation (**Book**): Second book in the ExO series. A how-to manual for those wanting practical advice on how to implement the ExO Sprint Methodology. Authors: Francisco Palao, Michelle Lapierre, Salim Ismail

Lean Startup: A methodology for developing businesses and products, which aims to shorten product development cycles and rapidly discover if a proposed business model is viable; this is achieved by adopting a combination of business-hypothesis-driven Experimentation, interactive product releases, and validated learning.

Minimum Viable Product (MVP): The MVP is a kind of applied experiment to determine the simplest product that will allow the team to go to market and see how users respond.

Moore's Law: Computing power continuously doubles in capacity and performance while decreasing in cost.

Appendix

Appendix A: Tools

https://openexo.com/exo-resources

At the link above, you'll find an extensive list of tools, resources, and guides developed by the OpenExO community. These include the following:

- **Community Calendar**
  - https://web.openexo.com/calendar/
- **MTP Tool via Peter Diamandis**
- **ExO Builder**
  - https://canou.openexo.com/
- **ExO Canvas**
  - https://platform.openexo.com/ecosystem/tools/canvas
- **ExO Database**
  - https://old.openexo.com/exo-global-database/
- **ExQ Dashboard**
  - https://platform.openexo.com/ecosystem/tools/exq
- **Event Toolkits**
  - https://platform.openexo.com/ecosystem/tools/toolkit
- **ExO Wallet**
  - https://github.com/exoeconomy/EXOS-Core/releases/

- Shared Google Drive Folder
  - https://drive.google.com/drive/folders/13T7-k5JJnyInbzxjEORk9WLsValV1s9S
- ExO Toolkit
  - https://github.com/exoeconomy/ExO-Tool-Kit
- Transformation Guide
  - https://web.openexo.com/exo-transformation-guide-download/?submissionGuid=6414d32c-17a5-49c6-a274-dbc69bae0922
- ExO Insight
  - https://insight.openexo.com/
- Books
  - https://platform.openexo.com/ecosystem/resources/books
- ExO Economy
  - https://economy.openexo.com/tools
- Community Case Studies
  - https://old.openexo.com/community-case-studies/
- ExO Solutions Case Studies
  - https://web.openexo.com/exo-solutions-case-studies/
- Fortune 100: The success imperative report
  - https://web.openexo.com/f100-report-download/
- Top100 report
  - https://web.openexo.com/top100-report/
- Subscription Pricing
  - https://web.openexo.com/platform-subscription/

Appendix B: Writing Your Enterprise MTP

Now that you've seen how it works at the personal level, it's time to create your enterprise's MTP.

There are several steps to consider when writing an enterprise MTP:

1. Identify the problem or challenge your organization is passionate about addressing. This should be a problem that resonates with your team and that they are committed to solving.
2. Develop a clear and compelling vision for the future that your organization wants to create. This vision should be inspiring and motivating and should inspire your team to take bold and innovative action.
3. Craft a simple and compelling statement that captures the essence of your MTP. This statement should be easy to remember and inspire your team to take action.
4. Develop a plan for how your organization will achieve its MTP. This plan should include specific goals, strategies, and tactics that will help you achieve your MTP
5. Communicate your MTP to your team and stakeholders. This will help to ensure that everyone is aligned and committed to achieving your MTP.
6. Monitor and evaluate your progress towards achieving your MTP. This will help you to identify areas where you may need to make adjustments or changes in order to achieve your goals.

Now you have the foundation on which to build—to compose—your company's MTP. The final challenge is to translate your answers above to a structure larger than yourself: a powerful, fast-moving enterprise filled with brilliant, hard-working people prepared to help you realize your dream and make it theirs.

As one of the strongest advocates of institutional MTPs (and keeping on track with his own MTP), Peter has developed the following tutorial to help you write your own company MTP. Recognizing that the process can seem intimidating, he offers it as a series of steps (you'll notice some similarities to your personal MTP).

STEP 1: Aspirations

List aspirational areas that fill you with excitement, wonder, and desire. Here are a few prompts to help you come up with "positive, aspirational areas for your MTP":

- What capabilities do you want to create for humanity?

- What did you want to do as a kid before anyone told you it was impossible?

- If we gave you $1 Billion to achieve an extraordinary goal, what would you do with the money?

(1)_____
(2)_____
(3)_____

STEP 2: Problem-solving

List a few big challenges or problems that you would love to solve or injustices that are painful or anger you?

- If we gave you $1 Billion to make the world a better place, what would you do with the money?

(1)_____
(2)_____
(3)_____

STEP 3: Ambition

Who do you want to be a HERO to? Who would be the beneficiary of your MTP-related efforts? Who do you want to focus on?

(1)_____
(2)_____
(3)_____

STEP 4: Service

Write down a few powerful action-verbs that describe specific actions you want to take related to those individuals you want to serve (Inspire, Transform, Impact, Create, Solve...).

(1)_____
(2)_____
(3)_____

STEP 5: Brainstorming

Write down a few potential MTPs. Keep your MTP short, definitely under 20 words. It should be something easy to remember and memorize.

Consider the following sentence structure:

The purpose of this enterprise is to (action/verb) and (action verb) to (Who do you want to be a hero to) (Your Aspirational purpose/Challenge you want solved)

Example: "The purpose of this enterprise is to **inspire** and **guide entrepreneurs** to **create a hopeful, compelling and abundant future.**"

STEP 6: Crowdsource

Show these MTPs to a small number of people you trust to give you the truth and wisdom to see the value of your ambitions. Ignore the advice of anyone who tries to get you to dial back those ambitions.

STEP 7: Incubate

Leave those MTP candidates alone for a while. Listen to your heart. It will tell you which one to pick.

STEP 8: Share

Share your new MTP with your employees, your stakeholders, and the world.

Appendix C: Sources and Inspirations

All the books below were extensively reviewed, analyzed, and cross-referenced with the ExO Model.

"(PDF) Co-evolution of platform architecture, platform services, and platform governance: Expanding the platform value of industrial digital platforms. https://www.researchgate.net/publication/349159621_ Co-evolution_of_platform_architecture_platform_ services_and_platform_governance_Expanding_the_ platform_value_of_industrial_digital_platforms" n.d. ResearchGate. Accessed May 10, 2023.

Abel, Katie. 2020. "What to Know About New Zappos CEO Kedar Deshpande. https://footwearnews.com/ 2020/business/executive-moves/kedar-deshpande-zappos-1203046074/ " footwearnews.com. .

Anderson, Chris. 2006. *The Long Tail: Why the Future of Business is Selling Less of More.* 1st edition ed. N.p.: Hyperion.

Anderson, Chris. 2009. *Free: The Future of a Radical Price.* 1st Edition ed. N.p.: Hyperion.

Anderson, Chris. 2012. *Makers: The New Industrial Revolution.* N.p.: Crown Business.

Antonopoulos, Andreas M. 2016. *The Internet of Money: Talks by Andreas M. Antonopoulos.* Edited by Sarah Zolt-Gilburne, S.H. E. Hariry, Maria Scothorn, and Pamela Morgan. N.p.: Merkle Bloom LLC.

Ashton, Kevin. 2016. *How To Fly A Horse: The Secret History of Creation, Invention, and Discovery*. 1st edition ed. N.p.: Windmill Books.

Atkin, Douglas J. 2019. "How Airbnb found its Purpose and why it's a good one. https://medium.com/@douglas.atkin/how-airbnb-found-its-purpose-and-why-its-a-good-one-b5c987c0c216 " Douglas John Atkin.

Azhar, Azeem. 2021. *The Exponential Age: How Accelerating Technology is Transforming Business, Politics and Society*. N.p.: Diversion Books.

Bacon, Jono. 2019. *People Powered: How Communities Can Supercharge Your Business, Brand, and Teams*. Illustrated edition ed. N.p.: HarperCollins Leadership. Foreword: Peter H. Diamandis.

Bacon, Jono. 2019. *People Powered: How Communities Can Supercharge Your Business, Brand, and Teams*. N.p.: HarperCollins Leadership.

Blablacar. 2021. "Culture. https://blog.blablacar.com/about-us/culture " blog.blablacar..

Blank, Steve, and Bob Dorf. 2012. *The Startup Owner's Manual: The Step-By-Step Guide for Building a Great Company*. 1st edition ed. N.p.: K & S Ranch.

Blank, Steven G. 2013. *The Four Steps to the Epiphany: Successful Strategies for Products that Win*. 2nd edition ed. N.p.: Cafepress.com.

Block, Peter. 2018. *Community: The Structure of Belonging*. N.p.: Berrett-Koehler Publishers.

Bonnet, Didier, Jerome Buvat, and Subrahmanyam KVJ. 2015. "When Digital Disruption Strikes: How Can Incumbents Respond? https://www.capgemini.com/consulting/wp-content/uploads/sites/30/2017/07/digital_disruption_1.pdf" *Capgemini Consulting*, 12.

Booth, Jeff. 2020. *The Price of Tomorrow: Why Deflation is the Key to an Abundant Future*. N.p.: Stanley Press.

Borders, Max. 2018. *The Social Singularity: How decentralization will allow us to transcend politics, create global prosperity, and avoid the robot apocalypse*. N.p.: Social Evolution.

Botsman, Rachel, and Roo Rogers. 2010. *What's Mine Is Yours: The Rise of Collaborative Consumption*. Illustrated edition ed. N.p.: Harper Business.

Brand, Stewart. 1999. *The Clock Of The Long Now: Time And Responsibility*. First ed. N.p.: Basic Books.

Brynjolfsson, Erik, and Andrew McAfee. 2012. *Race Against the Machine: How the Digital Revolution is Accelerating Innovation, Driving Productivity, and Irreversibly Transforming Employment and the Economy*. N.p.: Digital Frontier Press.

Brynjolfsson, Erik, and Andrew McAfee. 2014. *The Second Machine Age: Work, Progress, and Prosperity in a Time of Brilliant Technologies*. Illustrated edition ed. N.p.: W. W. Norton & Company.

Case, Steve. 2017. *The Third Wave: An Entrepreneur's Vision of the Future*. N.p.: Simon & Schuster.

Catmull, Ed, and Amy Wallace. 2014. *Creativity, Inc.: Overcoming the Unseen Forces That Stand in the Way of True Inspiration.* Illustrated edition ed. N.p.: Random House.

cbinsights.n/a."The Complete List Of Unicorn Companies https://www.cbinsights.com/research-unicorn-companies" cbinsights.com.

Chace, Calum. 2016. *The Economic Singularity: Artificial intelligence and the death of capitalism.* N.p.: Three Cs.

Cheng, Michelle. 2020. "Uber's market value has just reached an all-time high https://qz.com/1928990/ubers-market-cap-surpasses-its-ipo-valuation/" qz.com.

Chesbrough, Henry. 2019. *Open Innovation Results: Going Beyond the Hype and Getting Down to Business.* N.p.: OUP Oxford.

Chou, Yu-Kai. 2015. *Actionable Gamification: Beyond Points, Badges, and Leaderboards.* N.p.: Octalysis Media.

Choudary, Paul. 2020. "The State of the Platform Revolution 2021 https://platforms.substack.com/p/the-state-of-the-platform-revolution" Platforms, AI, and the Economics of BigTech.

Christensen, Clayton M. 2000. *The Innovator's Dilemma: The Revolutionary National Bestseller That Changed The Way We Do Business.* 1st HarperBusiness ed edition ed. N.p.: Harperbusiness.

Christensen, Clayton M. 2013. *The Innovator's Solution (Creating and Sustainability Successful Growth).* 1st edition ed. N.p.: Harvard Business Review Press.

Christensen, Clayton M. 2016. *The Clayton M. Christensen Reader*. N.p.: Harvard Business Review Press.

Christensen, Clayton M. 2016. *The Innovator's Dilemma: When New Technologies Cause Great Firms to Fail*. N.p.: Harvard Business Review Press.

Collins, Jim. 2001. *Good to Great: Why Some Companies Make the Leap and Others Don't*. 1st edition ed. N.p.: HarperBusiness.

Collins, Jim. 2009. *How The Mighty Fall: And Why Some Companies Never Give In (Good to Great, 4)*. 1st edition ed. N.p.: JimCollins.

Collins, Jim, and Morten T. Hansen. 2011. *Great by Choice: Uncertainty, Chaos, and Luck--Why Some Thrive Despite Them All (Good to Great, 5)*. 1st edition ed. N.p.: Harper Business.

Collins, Jim, and Jerry I. Porras. 2004. *Built to Last: Successful Habits of Visionary Companies (Good to Great, 2)*. 10th Revised ed. edition ed. N.p.: Harper Business.

Cooper, Brant, Patrick Vlaskovits, and Eric Ries. 2013. *The Lean Entrepreneur: How Visionaries Create Products, Innovate with New Ventures, and Disrupt Markets*. 1st edition ed. N.p.: Wiley.

Cowen, Tyler. 2013. *Average Is Over: Powering America Beyond the Age of the Great Stagnation*. 1st edition ed. N.p.: Dutton.

Craft. 2019. "How Old Are the $1B+ Tech Unicorn Companies? https://priceonomics.com/how-old-are-the-s1b-tech-unicorn-companies/" Priceonomic.com.

Cusumano, Michael. 2001. *Strategic Thinking for the Next Economy*. 1st edition ed. N.p.: Jossey-Bass.

Cusumano, Michael A., David B. Yoffie, and Annabelle Gawer. 2020. "The Future of Platforms https://sloan-review.mit.edu/article/the-future-of-platforms/" MIT Sloan Management Review.

Davidow, William H., and Michael S. Malone. 1992. *The Virtual Corporation: Structuring and Revitalizing the Corporation for the 21st Century*. 1st edition ed. N.p.: Harpercollins.

Dean, Sam. 2020. "Tony Hsieh is gone, but his Las Vegas vision is finding new life https://www.latimes.com/business/technology/story/2020-12-12/tony-hseih-change-vegas-legacy" thelatimes.com.

Deane, Steve. 2021. "2021 Airbnb Statistics: Usage, Demographics, and Revenue Growth https://www.stratosjets.com/blog/airbnb-statistics/" stratosjets.com.

Diamandis, Peter H., and Steven Kotler. 2012. *Abundance: The Future Is Better Than You Think (Exponential Technology Series)*. N.p.: Free Press.

Diamandis, Peter H., and Steven Kotler. 2020. *The Future Is Faster Than You Think: How Converging Technologies Are Transforming Business, Industries, and Our Lives (Exponential Technology Series)*. 1st edition ed. N.p.: Simon & Schuster.

Diaz, Ana. 2021. "What is Roblox? And how did it get so huge? https://www.polygon.com/22326123/what-is-roblox-explainer-public-offering" Polygon.

Doerr, John. 2018. *Measure what Matters: OKRs - the Simple Idea that Drives 10x Growth*. N.p.: Portfolio Penguin.

Dyer, Jeff, Clayton Christensen, and Hal Gregersen. 2011. *The Innovator's DNA: Mastering the Five Skills of Disruptive Innovators*. 1st edition ed. N.p.: Harvard Business Review Press.

Earth Overshoot Day. 2021. overshootday.org. https://www.overshootday.org/.

Eggers, William D., and Paul Macmillan. 2013. *The Solution Revolution: How Business, Government, and Social Enterprises Are Teaming Up to Solve Society's Toughest Problems*. N.p.: Harvard Business Review Press.

Epstein, David J. 2019. *Range: Why Generalists Triumph in a Specialized World*. N.p.: Riverhead Books.

Ertel, Chris, and Lisa K. Solomon. 2014. *Moments of Impact: How to Design Strategic Conversations That Accelerate Change*. N.p.: Simon & Schuster.

Ferriss, Timothy. 2009. *The 4-Hour Workweek: Escape 9-5, Live Anywhere, and Join the New Rich*. Expanded, Updated ed. edition ed. N.p.: Harmony.

Fischer, Bill, Umberto Lago, and Fang Liu. 2013. *Reinventing Giants: How Chinese Global Competitor Haier Has Changed the Way Big Companies Transform*. 1st edition ed. N.p.: Jossey-Bass.

"5 Platform Businesses For The Next 5 Years https://seekingalpha.com/article/4417382-5-platform-businesses-for-next-5-years" 2021. Seeking Alpha.

Furr, Nathan, and Jeff Dyer. 2014. *The Innovator's Method: Bringing the Lean Start-up into Your Organization.* N.p.: Harvard Business Review Press. Forward: Clayton M. Christensen.

Gartenberg, Claudine, Andrea Prat, and George Serafeim. 2016. "Corporate Purpose and Financial Performance https://dash.harvard.edu/handle/1/30903237" *Harvard Business School Working Paper* No. 17-023 (September).

Gassmann, Oliver, Karolin Frankenberger, Michaela Choudury, and Michaela Csik. 2020. *The Business Model Navigator ePub eBook: The strategies behind the most successful companies.* 2nd Edition ed. N.p.: FT Publishing International.

Grant, Adam. 2016. *Originals: How Non-Conformists Move the World.* N.p.: Penguin Books.

Hagel III, John, and John S. Brown. 2005. *The Only Sustainable Edge: Why Business Strategy Depends On Productive Friction And Dynamic Specialization.* N.p.: Harvard Business Review Press.

Hagel III, John, John S. Brown, and Lang Davison. 2010. *The Power of Pull: How Small Moves, Smartly Made, Can Set Big Things in Motion.* N.p.: Basic Books.

Hamel, Gary. 2007. *The Future of Management.* 1st edition ed. N.p.: Harvard Business Review Press.

Hamel, Gary. 2012. *What Matters Now: How to Win in a World of Relentless Change, Ferocious Competition, and Unstoppable Innovation.* 1st edition ed. N.p.: Jossey-Bass.

Hamel, Gary, and C. K. Prahalad. 1994. *Competing for the Future*. 1st edition ed. N.p.: Harvard Business Review Press.

Hartmans, Avery. 2017. "Quirky, the invention startup that burned through $200 million and went bankrupt, is back from the dead with a new business model https://www.businessinsider.com/quirky-reborn-new-ownership-business-model-2017-9" Businessinsider.com.

Hastings, Reed, and Erin Meyer. 2020. *No Rules Rules: Netflix and the Culture of Reinvention*. N.p.: Penguin Press.

Herrera, Ángel M., and Francisco Palao. 2021. *Massive Transformative Purpose: The guide to provide sense to your projects and your life*. N.p.: Editorial Bubok Publishing.

Hill, Dan. 2012. *Dark matter and trojan horses. A strategic design vocabulary*. 1st edition ed. N.p.: Strelka Press.

Hoffman, Reid, and Ben Casnocha. 2012. *The Start-up of You: Adapt to the Future, Invest in Yourself, and Transform Your Career*. 1st edition ed. N.p.: Currency.

Hoffman, Reid, Ben Casnocha, and Chris Yeh. 2014. *The Alliance: Managing Talent in the Networked Age*. N.p.: Harvard Business Review Press.

Hoffman, Reid, and Chris Yeh. 2018. *Blitzscaling: The Lightning-fast Path to Building Massively Valuable Companies*. N.p.: HarperCollinsPublishers.

Horowitz, Ben. 2014. *The Hard Thing About Hard Things: Building a Business When There Are No Easy Answers*. N.p.: Harper Business.

Hufford, Lisa. 2016. *Navigating the Talent Shift: How to Build On-Demand Teams that Drive Innovation, Control Costs, and Get Results*. N.p.: Palgrave Macmillan US.

Ian. 2019. "How Tesla Used A $0 Marketing Strategy To Dominate A Market https://www.mar-ketingstrategy.com/marketing-strategy-studies/how-tesla-used-a-0-marketing-strategy-to-dominate-a-market/" marketingstrategy.com.

Ismail, Salim. n/a. "11 Secrets You Need To Know For Exponential Growth https://blog.growthinstitute.com/exo/11-attributes" Growth Institute.

Jain, Naveen, and John Schroeter. 2018. *Moonshots : Creating a World of Abundance*. First Edition ed. N.p.: Moonshots Press.

Johansson, Frans. 2004. *The Medici Effect: Breakthrough Insights at the Intersection of Ideas, Concepts, and Cultures*. 1st edition ed. N.p.: Harvard Business Review Press.

Kahneman, Daniel. 2013. *Thinking, Fast and Slow*. 1st edition ed. N.p.: Farrar, Straus and Giroux.

Kanter, Rosabeth M. 1989. *When Giants Learn to Dance*. 1st edition ed. N.p.: Simon & Schuster.

Kaplan, Marcia. 2021. "Raising Funds Becomes Easier with New SEC Rules https://www.sec.gov/smallbusiness/exemptofferings/regcrowdfunding" prac-ticalecommerce.com.

Kapp, Karl M. 2013. *The Gamification of Learning and Instruction Fieldbook: Ideas into Practice*. 1st edition ed. N.p.: Wiley.

Kawasaki, Guy, and Guy Kawasaki. 2012. *APE: Author, Publisher, Entrepreneur-How to Publish a Book*. 1st edition ed. N.p.: Nononina Press.

Keeley, Larry, Helen Walters, Ryan Pikkel, and Brian Quinn. 2013. *Ten Types of Innovation: The Discipline of Building Breakthroughs*. 1st edition ed. N.p.: Wiley.

Kelly, Kevin. 2011. *What Technology Wants*. Illustrated edition ed. N.p.: Penguin Books.

Kelly, Kevin. 2016. *The Inevitable: Understanding the 12 Technological Forces That Will Shape Our Future*. 1st edition ed. N.p.: Viking.

Kelly, Kristin, and Nate Carter. 2019. "The Purpose Wheel by IDEO https://www.ideo.com/blog/design-an-organizations-purpose-statement-with-this-tool" Design an Organization's Purpose Statement With This Tool.

Kim, W. C., and Renee Mauborgne. 2005. *Blue Ocean Strategy: How to Create Uncontested Market Space and Make Competition Irrelevant*. 1st edition ed. N.p.: Harvard Business Review Press.

Kotler, Steven. 2021. *The Art of Impossible: A Peak Performance Primer*. N.p.: Harper Wave.

Kotler, Steven, and Jamie Wheal. 2017. *Stealing Fire: How Silicon Valley, the Navy SEALs, and Maverick Scientists Are Revolutionizing the Way We Live and Work*. N.p.: Dey Street Books.

Kurzweil, Ray. 2006. *The Singularity Is Near: When Humans Transcend Biology*. N.p.: Penguin Books.

Kurzweil, Ray. 2013. *How to Create a Mind: The Secret of Human Thought Revealed*. Illustrated edition ed. N.p.: Penguin Books.

Laloux, Frédéric. 2014. *Reinventing Organizations: A Guide to Creating Organizations Inspired by the Next Stage of Human Consciousness*. N.p.: Nelson Parker.

Lee, Kai-Fu. 2021. *Ai Superpowers: China, Silicon Valley, and the New World Order*. N.p.: HarperCollins Publishers.

Lencioni, Patrick M. 2012. *The Advantage: Why Organizational Health Trumps Everything Else In Business*. 1st edition ed. N.p.: Jossey-Bass.

Lock, S. 2021. "Leading hotel companies worldwide 2020, by number of properties https://www.statista.com/statistics/197869/us-hotel-companies-by-number-of-properties-worldwide/" Statista.com.

Lockhart, Mike. 2016. "Project 98 MQ-9 Predator RC Drone https://diydrones.com/forum/topics/project-98-mq-9-predator-rc-drone" diydrones.com.

Malnight, Thomas W., Ivy Buche, and Charles Dhanaraj. 2019. "Put Purpose at the Core of Your Strategy It's how successful companies redefine their businesses https://hbr.org/2019/09/put-purpose-at-the-core-of-your-strategy" *Harvard Business Review*, (September - October).

Malnight, Thomas W., Ivy Buche, and Charles Dhanaraj. n.d. "Put Purpose at the Core of Your Strategy https://hbr.org/2019/09/put-purpose-at-the-core-of-your-strategy" Harvard Business Review. Accessed May 18, 2023.

Malone, Michael. 2009. *The Future Arrived Yesterday: The Rise of the Protean Corporation and What It Means for You.* 1st edition ed. N.p.: Crown Business.

Malone, Michael S. 2007. *Bill & Dave: How Hewlett and Packard Built the World's Greatest Company.* 1st edition ed. N.p.: Portfolio Hardcover.

Maurya, Ash. 2012. *Running Lean: Iterate from Plan A to a Plan That Works.* 2nd edition ed. N.p.: O'Reilly Media.

Mazzucato, Mariana. 2021. *Mission Economy: A Moonshot Guide to Changing Capitalism.* N.p.: Harper Business.

McChrystal, Stanley, Tantum Collins, David Silverman, and Chris Fussell. 2015. *Team of Teams: New Rules of Engagement for a Complex World.* N.p.: Portfolio.

McGonigal, Jane. 2011. *Reality Is Broken: Why Games Make Us Better and How They Can Change the World.* Illustrated edition ed. N.p.: Penguin Books.

McGrath, Rita G. 2019. *Seeing Around Corners: How to Spot Inflection Points in Business Before They Happen.* N.p.: Houghton Mifflin Harcourt. Foreward: Clayton Christensen.

McGrath, Rita G., and Alex Gourlay. 2013. *The End of Competitive Advantage: How to Keep Your Strategy Moving as Fast as Your Business.* N.p.: Harvard Business Review Press.

McKinsey Quarterly. 2020. "Purpose: Shifting from why to how https://www.mckinsey.com/business-functions/organization/our-insights/purpose-shifting-from-why-to-how" McKinsey & Company.

McNamee, Roger. 2004. *The New Normal: Great Opportunities in a Time of Great Risk*. N.p.: Portfolio Hardcover.

Mele, Nicco. 2013. *The End of Big: How the Internet Makes David the New Goliath*. N.p.: St. Martin's Press.

Merchant, Nilofer. 2012. *11 Rules for Creating Value In #SocialEra*. N.p.: CreateSpace Independent Publishing Platform.

Microsoft. 2016. "Microsoft to acquire LinkedIn https://news.microsoft.com/2016/06/13/microsoft-to-acquire-linkedin/" Microsoft News Center.

Moazed, Alex. n.d. "Platform Types: What they are and how to design platforms by type https://www.applico-inc.com/blog/what-makes-uber-different-from-android-how-to-make-sense-of-platform-businesses/"Applico. Accessed May 10, 2023.

Moretti, Enrico. 2013. *The New Geography of Jobs*. Reprint edition ed. N.p.: Mariner Books.

Morree, Pim d., and Joost Minnaar. 2020. *Corporate Rebels: Make Work More Fun*. N.p.: Corporate Rebels Nederland B.V.

Muioi, Dave. 2020. "Healthy.io acquires fellow smart-phone urinalysis startup Inui Health https://www.

mobihealthnews.com/news/healthyio-acquires-fellow-smartphone-urinalysis-startup-inui-health" mobihealthnews.com.

Newport, Cal. 2016. *Deep Work: Rules for Focused Success in a Distracted World.* N.p.: Grand Central Publishing.

Nott, Brandon. 2020. "'A Robot for Every Person': The Next Wave of Personal Productivity https://www.uipath.com/blog/robot-for-every-person-next-wave-personal-productivity" UiPath.

O'Brien, M. E., and Eman Abdelhadi. 2022. *An Oral History of the New York Commune: 2052-2072.* N.p.: Common Notions.

O'Keefe, Brian. 2020. "100 Fastest-Growing Companies https://fortune.com/100-fastest-growing-companies/" Fortune.com.

OpenExO. 2020. "ExO-Tool-Kit https://github.com/exoeconomy/ExO-Tool-Kit/blob/master/MTP-Tool/GGI%20ExO%20Tools%20MTP%20-%202020-06-25%20R1-1-fillable.pdf " exoeconomy / ExO-Tool-Kit.

Osterwalder, Alexander, and Yves Pigneur. 2010. *Business Model Generation: A Handbook for Visionaries, Game Changers, and Challengers (The Strategyzer series).* 1st edition ed. N.p.: John Wiley and Sons.

Osterwalder, Alexander, Yves Pigneur, Gregory Bernarda, and Alan Smith. 2014. *Value Proposition Design: How to Create Products and Services Customers Want (The Strategyzer Series).* 1st edition ed. N.p.: Wiley.

Osterwalder, Alexander, Yves Pigneur, Alan Smith, and Frederic Etiemble. 2020. *The Invincible Company: How to Constantly Reinvent Your Organization with Inspiration From the World's Best Business Models.* 1st edition ed. N.p.: Wiley.

Osterwalder, Alexander, Alan Smith, Yves Pigneur, and Gregory Bernarda. 2014. *Value Proposition Design: How to Create Products and Services Customers Want.* N.p.: Wiley.

Owens, Trevor, and Obie Fernandez. 2014. *The Lean Enterprise: How Corporations Can Innovate Like Startups.* 1st edition ed. N.p.: Wiley.

Pentland, Alex. 2014. *Social Physics: How Good Ideas Spread? The Lessons from a New Science.* New Edition ed. N.p.: Scribe Publications.

"Pipelines, Platforms, and the New Rules of Strategy https://hbr.org/2016/04/pipelines-platforms-and-the-new-rules-of-strategy" n.d. Harvard Business Review. Accessed May 10, 2023.

Pistono, Federico. 2013. *Robots Will Steal Your Job, But That's OK: how to survive the economic collapse and be happy.* N.p.: CreateSpace Independent Publishing Platform.

Porter, Jon. 2019. "Reddit to double employees after raising $250 million https://www.theverge.com/2021/2/9/22274077/reddit-funding-round-250-million-double-employees-investment" Theverge.com.

Radjou, Navi, Jaideep Prabhu, and Simone Ahuja. 2012. *Jugaad Innovation: Think Frugal, Be Flexible, Generate Breakthrough Growth.* 1st edition ed. N.p.: Jossey-Bass.

Raworth, Kate. 2017. *Doughnut Economics: Seven Ways to Think Like a 21st-Century Economist.* Illustrated edition ed. N.p.: Chelsea Green Publishing.

Ries, Eric. 2001. *The Lean Startup: How Today's Entrepreneurs Use Continuous Innovation to Create Radically Successful Businesses.* N.p.: VIKIN.

Ries, Eric. 2017. *The Startup Way: How Modern Companies Use Entrepreneurial Management to Transform Culture and Drive Long-Term Growth.* N.p.: Currency.

Rifkin, Jeremy. 2014. *The Zero Marginal Cost Society: The Internet of Things, the Collaborative Commons, and the Eclipse of Capitalism.* N.p.: St. Martin's Press.

Rose, David S. 2014. *Angel Investing: The Gust Guide to Making Money and Having Fun Investing in Startups.* First Edition ed. N.p.: Wiley.

Rose, David S. 2016. *The Startup Checklist: 25 Steps to a Scalable, High-Growth Business.* First ed. N.p.: Wiley. Foreword: Bill Gross.

Saldanha, Tony. 2019. *Why Digital Transformations Fail: The Surprising Disciplines of How to Take Off and Stay Ahead.* 1st edition ed. N.p.: Berrett-Koehler Publishers.

Sanei, John. 2017. *What's Your Moonshot?: Future-proof yourself and your business in the age of exponential disruption.* N.p.: Mercury.

Sarazin, Benoit, Patrick Cohendet, Laurent Simon, Madanmohan Rao, and Ruiz Émilie, eds. 2021. *Communities of Innovation: How Organizations Harness*

Collective Creativity and Build Resilience. N.p.: World Scientific.

Savoia, Alberto. 2019. *The Right It: Why So Many Ideas Fail and How to Make Sure Yours Succeed*. Illustrated edition ed. N.p.: HarperOne.

Schwab, Professor Dr.-Ing. K. 2017. *The Fourth Industrial Revolution*. N.p.: Currency.

Scoble, Robert, and Shel Israel. 2013. *Age of Context: Mobile, Sensors, Data and the Future of Privacy*. 1st edition ed. N.p.: CreateSpace Independent Publishing Platform.

Searls, Doc. 2012. *The Intention Economy: When Customers Take Charge*. 1st edition ed. N.p.: Harvard Business Review Press.

Shen, Lucinda. 2016. "Here's Why These 29 Companies Fell Off the Fortune 500 https://fortune.com/2016/06/06/fortune-500-companies-departing/" Fortune.

Shirky, Clay. 2010. *Cognitive Surplus: Creativity and Generosity in a Connected Age*. 1st edition ed. N.p.: Penguin Press HC.

Sinek, Simon. 2011. *Start with Why: How Great Leaders Inspire Everyone to Take Action*. N.p.: Penguin Publishing Group.

Sinek, Simon, Peter Docker, and David Mead. 2017. *Find Your Why: A Practical Guide for Discovering Purpose for You and Your Team*. N.p.: Penguin Publishing Group.

Skelton, Matthew, and Manuel Pais. 2019. *Team Topologies: Organizing Business and Technology Teams for*

Fast Flow. Illustrated Edition ed. N.p.: IT Revolution Press.

Solis, Brian. 2013. *WTF?: What's the Future of Business?: Changing the Way Businesses Create Experiences*. 1st edition ed. N.p.: Wiley.

Spear, Steven J. 2010. *The High-Velocity Edge: How Market Leaders Leverage Operational Excellence to Beat the Competition*. 2nd edition ed. N.p.: McGraw-Hill Education.

"Spring 2021 TOC https://sloanreview.mit.edu/issue/2021-spring/" n.d. MIT Sloan Management Review. Accessed May 10, 2023.

Stone, Brad. 2018. *The Upstarts: Uber, Airbnb, and the Battle for the New Silicon Valley*. N.p.: Little, Brown.

Taleb, Nassim N. 2007. *The Black Swan: The Impact of the Highly Improbable (Incerto)*. Annotated edition ed. N.p.: Random House.

Taleb, Nassim N. 2012. *Antifragile: Things That Gain from Disorder (Incerto)*. 1st edition ed. N.p.: Random House.

Thakor, Anjan V., and Robert E. Quinn. 2013. "The Economics of Higher Purpose https://ecgi.global/sites/default/files/working_papers/documents/SSRN-id2362454.pdf" *European Corporate Governance Institute (ECGI)*, no. Finance Working Paper N° 395/2013 (December), 50.

Thomas, Andrew. 2018. "3 Big Reasons Why Purpose Leads to ProfitsWhy are Airbnb, Nike and Patagonia so successful? It starts with purpose https://www.inc.com/andrew-thomas/3-big-reasons-why-purpose-leads-to-profits.html" Inc.

Tinlin, Liz. 2014. "In pursuit of purpose http://www.bluebabel.co.uk/bb2017t/wp-content/uploads/2014/09/In-pursuit-of-purpose-Market-Leader-June-2014-Liz-Tinlin.pdf" *Market Leader magazine*, (June), 4.

Tracy, Brian. 2010. *How the Best Leaders Lead: Proven Secrets to Getting the Most Out of Yourself and Others*. N.p.: AMACOM.

U.S. Securities and Exchange Commission. 2021. "Regulation Crowdfunding https://www.sec.gov/small-business/exemptofferings/regcrowdfunding" www.sec.gov.

Van Alstyne, Marshall W., Sangeet P. Choudary, and Geoffrey G. Parker. 2017. *Platform Revolution: How Networked Markets are Trasnforming the Economy - and How to Make Them Work For You*. N.p.: WW Norton.

Van Doren, Paul. 2021. *Authentic: A Memoir by the Founder of Vans*. N.p.: Nextone Incorporated.

Vigna, Paul, and Michael J. Casey. 2016. *The Age of Cryptocurrency: How Bitcoin and the Blockchain Are Challenging the Global Economic Order*. N.p.: Macmillan USA.

Voshmgir, Shermin. 2020. *Token Economy: How the Web3 reinvents the Internet*. 2nd edition ed. N.p.: Token Kitchen.

Wadhwa, Vivek, and Farai Chideya. 2014. *Innovating Women: The Changing Face of Technology*. N.p.: Diversion Books.

Westerman, George, Didier Bonnet, and Andrew McAfee. 2014. *Leading Digital: Turning Technology into Business Transformation*. N.p.: Harvard Business Review Press.

"Why the platform economy can unlock prosperity for billions of workers https://www.weforum.org/agenda/2020/11/digitalization-platform-economy-covid-recovery" 2020. World Economic Forum.

Wiggers, Kyle. 2020. "Major pharma companies, including Novartis and Merck, build federated learning platform for drug discovery https://venturebeat.com/2020/09/17/major-pharma-companies-including-novartis-and-merck-build-federated-learning-platform-for-drug-discovery/" Venture Beat.

Wood, Betty. N/A. "Airbnb is now bigger than the world's top five hotel brands put together https://thespaces.com/airbnb-now-bigger-worlds-top-five-hotel-brands-put-together/" thespaces.com.

Zeratsky, John, Braden Kowitz, and Jake Knapp. 2016. *Sprint: How to Solve Big Problems and Test New Ideas in Just Five Days*. N.p.: Bantam Press.

Zook, Chris, and James Allen. 2012. *Repeatability: Build Enduring Businesses for a World of Constant Change*. N.p.: Harvard Business Review Press.

Zutavern, Angela, and Josh Sullivan. 2017. *The Mathematical Corporation: Where Machine Intelligence and Human Ingenuity Achieve the Impossible*. N.p.: PublicAffairs.

Acknowledgments

We'd like to express our deepest gratitude to the following collaborators, without whom this book would absolutely not have been finished.

First and foremost, Lisa Pereira, who has endured almost four years of rewrites, gathered and curated ideas and submissions from hundreds of community members and tracked and chased and cajoled Peter and Salim over the duration.

Second, to Joe DiNucci and Atiya Dwyer of Silicon Valley Press and to our editor, Susan Goldberg, who have stuck it out through so many rewrites we've lost count.

Third, to Mike Malone, whose ideas stemming from the 1980s are seeing their fruition and success in this new breed of organization.

And finally, the following members of the ExO community who have given their time and ideas and have discussed and distilled these topics for over a decade now. Out of hundreds of people who participated, these members were relentless in their participation. Thank you !!

Aaron Bare

Alex Jeong

Ajlan Nihat Gun

Alina Gratschner

Angela Barnard

Angie Carrillo

Anuj Kulkarni (Anuj2)

Azim Pawanchik

Carlos Carvajal

Cesar Castro

Chander Nagpal

Charlotte Wieder

Crystal To

Daniel Plotrino

Devin Carlos Irizarry Voorsanger

Diego Soroa

Duane Fernandes

Eduardo Neves

Eric Patel

Erik Dam

Fabián Noyola

Fernando De los Rios

Francesco Derchi

Francisco Milagres

Gary Ralston

Gustavo Dougherty

Henrik Bo Larsen

Jamal Thorne

Jaroslav Dokoupil

Jose Tam

Juan Jose Dougherty

Julia Hitzbleck

Kamales Lardi

Karina Besprosvan

Kelley Rowe

Kent Langley

Kevin Allen

KristinaMaría Troiano-Gutierrez

Laércio Loureiro

Larry Camejo

Law Zhi Xiong

Len Nanjad

Luciana Ledesma

Majid Salehi

Matthias Schneider

Marc Bonavia

Marcio Chaer

Marianne Wyne

Michael Friebe

Michael Jonsson

Miguel Angel Rojas

Miguel Angel Sainz Gongora

Mynor Schult

Nader Benmessaoud

Narasimha Raju Nagubhai

Natalia Castía

Niki Faldemolaei

Nino Baraka

Nishan Degnarain

Oliver Morbach

Olga Calvache

Oscar Schmitz

Ozioma Egwuonwu

Pablo Angel

Paco Briseño

Patrik Sandin

Paul Epping

Pedro LÓPEZ SELA

Peter Kristof

Raju Narasimha

Ramon Salvador Fernandez Orozco

Roberto Alvarez

Sanjay RG Bhana

Satomi Yoshida

Silvia Tzenkova

Steven A. Rodríguez

Suman Sasmal

Suraya Sulaiman

Syakira Shahrul

Tania Hodgkinson

Trevor Harding

Werner Smit

Wolfgang Merkt

Younis Hijazi

About Salim Ismail

Salim Ismail is a sought-after business strategist who presents globally to the leaders of many of the world's largest companies and Heads of State. His book *Exponential Organizations* is considered by many to be the go-to guide for 21st-century organizations. The data shows that corporations that follow the ExO attributes deliver 40x shareholder returns compared to those that don't.

He has been featured across a vast array of media outlets, including *The New York Times*, CNBC, Bloomberg, *BusinessWeek*, *Fortune*, *Forbes*, *WIRED*, *Vogue*, Fox Business, and the BBC.

He is the Founder and Chairman of OpenExO, which helps companies implement the lessons from Exponential

Organizations by emulating the world's fastest-growing companies. They inspire innovators to replace incremental innovation with 10X improvements, implement groundbreaking technologies, and profitably achieve large-scale social impact. They have created billions of dollars of return on investment over the past 4 years for clients, including Procter & Gamble, HP, Visa, BHP, and Stanley Black & Decker.

Salim is the author of *Exponential Organizations*, published originally in 2014, and now the much anticipated second edition, *Exponential Organizations 2.0*, released in 2023. Both are global best-sellers.

Salim is a serial entrepreneur, having founded several technology companies, including Ångströ, which was acquired by Google. As a VP at Yahoo, he led Brickhouse, Yahoo!'s internal incubator. He was the Founding Executive Director of Singularity University and serves on the Board of the XPRIZE Foundation. These associations give him extraordinary access to the most influential innovators of our time, plus technologies and business ideas while they are in stealth mode.

Salim's breadth of work experience combined with his global outlook (he has lived in eight countries for at least a year each) gives him a uniquely macro vision of how the institutions that underpin our society and economy are broken and should be fixed. His epiphany-inducing presentations are known for impressing even the most skeptical listeners.is a sought-after strategist and a renowned technology entrepreneur who built and sold his company to Google. He was the founding Executive Director at Singularity University. As a prolific speaker, Salim gives more than 150 talks a year to audiences of all sizes around the world. He has been profiled across a vast array of media outlets, including *The New York Times*, *Bloomberg BusinessWeek*, *Fortune*, *Forbes*, *WIRED*, *Vogue*, and the BBC. Salim is the founder of OpenExO, where he serves as Chairman.

About Peter H. Diamandis, M.D.

Named by Fortune as one of the "World's 50 Greatest Leaders," Peter Diamandis is the Founder and Executive Chairman of the XPRIZE Foundation, which leads the world in designing and operating large-scale incentive competitions. He is also the Executive Founder of Singularity University.

As an entrepreneur, Diamandis has started over 25 companies in the areas of health-tech, space, venture capital, and education. He is Co-founder and Vice-Chairman of two public companies, Celularity and Vaxxinity. Dr. Diamandis is Co-founder and Chairman of Fountain Life, a fully integrated platform delivering predictive, preventative, personalized, and data-driven health. Finally, he also serves as Co-founder of BOLD Capital Partners, a venture fund with a half-billion dollars under management being invested in exponential technologies and longevity companies.

Diamandis is a *New York Times* Bestselling author of four books: *Abundance – The Future Is Better Than You Think*, *BOLD – How to Go Big, Create Wealth & Impact the World*, and *The Future is Faster Than You Think*. Most recently, he co-authored the #1 best seller *LIFE FORCE* with Tony Robbins, which chronicles the extraordinary healthcare and biotech revolution unfolding before our eyes.

He earned degrees in molecular genetics and aerospace engineering from MIT and holds an M.D. from Harvard Medical School. Diamandis' favorite saying is "The best way to predict the future is to create it yourself," a topic he explores in his podcast called *MOONSHOTS*.

About Michael S. Malone

Author Michael S. Malone is one of the world's best-known technology writers. He has covered Silicon Valley and high-tech for more than 25 years, beginning with the *San Jose Mercury News* as the nation's first daily high-tech reporter, where he was twice nominated for the Pulitzer Prize for investigative reporting. His articles and editorials have appeared in such publications as *The Wall Street Journal*, *The Economist*, and *Fortune*, and for two years, he was a columnist for *The New York Times*. He was editor of *Forbes ASAP*, the world's largest-circulation business-tech magazine, at the height of the dot-com boom.

Michael is the author or co-author of nearly twenty award-winning books, notably the best-selling *The Virtual Corporation*, *Bill and Dave*, and *The Future Arrived Yesterday*. He has also hosted three nationally syndicated public television interview series and co-produced the Emmy-nominated primetime PBS miniseries on social entrepreneurs, *The New Heroes*. Michael holds an MBA from Santa Clara University, where he is currently an adjunct professor. He is also an associate fellow of the Said Business School at the University of Oxford and is a Distinguished Friend of Oxford.

ARE YOU AN EXPONENTIAL ORGANIZATION?

LET SALIM ISMAIL SHOW YOU THE WAY

KEYNOTE SPEAKER

START THE CONVERSATION TODAY

SalimIsmail.com

Our Community Can Take Any Organization

10X

Are you Ready?

 openexo

OpenExO.com

READY TO IMPLEMENT EXPONENTIAL ORGANIZATIONS?

MOONSHOTS & MINDSETS PODCAST
by Peter H. Diamandis, MD

Dive into the world of innovation and big ideas with Peter Diamandis on his podcast, 'Moonshots & Mindsets.' Every week Peter interviews an Exponential Entrepreneur pursuing a major Moonshot.

Each episode features trailblazers who are daring to dream big, solving complex problems with their Moonshot projects.

Tune in to fuel your ambition and reshape your thinking. You'll learn how to design your Moonshot, how to fund it and how to overcome challenges. It's time to rethink the impossible.

Scan the QR code below to start listening.

SUBSCRIBE TO PETER DIAMANDIS' WEEKLY "TECH BLOG"

Twice-per week, my Tech Blog delivers you data-driven optimism about the incredible world exponential technologies are enabling. My mission is to take you from "fear and scarcity" to "optimism and abundance".

Curious about the technologies shaping an abundant future?

Curious about which technologies are adding decades to your healthspan?

The Tech Blog is a treasure trove of insights and data-driven optimism.

Subscribe by scanning the QR code below.

Made in United States
Orlando, FL
09 July 2024

48778545R00261